Enfield Libraries

Branch:	S			
1/16				
19ᵗʰ July	.			

To renew this ite
hotline on 0333 3
https://arena.your

E

Worthless

BY ROBYN HENNESSY

BROWN
DOG
BOOKS

Published under licence by Brown Dog Books and
The Self-Publishing Partnership,
7 Green Park Station, Bath BA1 1JB

www.selfpublishingpartnership.co.uk

ISBN printed book: 978-1-78545-058-7
ISBN e-book: 978-1-78545-059-4

Cover image by Banksy, who has been my favourite artist since
I was 10 years old
Cover design by Kevin Rylands

Printed and bound by CPI Group (UK) Ltd, Croydon CR0 4YY

CHAPTER 1

I Remember

I remember how it all started. The torment, the pain, the betrayal and the madness... My slow descent into hell. The day I realized my family could not protect me from the vicious world outside. My first needle, my first overdose, my first night restrained in a padded police cell. All the things I try to forget that I am today. How it feels to be truly lost and alone in a life so worthless... How, somewhere buried deep within the darkness, I became the evil that surrounds me in this meaningless existence... In a world that gives not a shadow of hope, my innocence was swept away like the ground beneath my feet, in an act of rage so brutal, its ashes would bury me with the scars it left behind, haunting every waking moment until the day I die... Today is September 2003 and I am eight years old.

It was a quiet area we lived in after moving away from the busy city of London. My dad had spent his entire life working on building sites to become a property developer and the only reason we were able to afford a house in the peaceful town of Frimley was his continuous career progression and hard work. This was a chance for a better life for all of us. Education in Surrey rather than London offered far better career prospects and higher chances of going to university, which was something my parents wanted for all of us, although at the time I was too young to understand and was just excited to be in a new place with a different school and new people. Although the area we lived in had many benefits, there was little work for builders, so my dad continued to work in London. Because of the hour's drive each way, he'd have to leave for work before 6am every morning and would struggle to make it home in time for dinner at 6pm. Mum would take care of us during the day when we weren't at school, and I'd say she did a pretty good job handling all five of us on her own whilst dad wasn't home.

My older sister, Callie, had just finished college. She only did the first year before we moved out of London and she wanted to continue her education in our new home, but all the hassle of moving simply put up too many obstacles. The local colleges did not offer the course she had started in London, which meant she would have had to catch up on an entire year's worth of work, so she went straight into full-time work aged seventeen. My two brothers were Jake, who was six years old, and Jed, who had just turned three. Then there was my identical twin sister, Ashleigh. We were extremely close and did everything together. We argued a lot and nothing has changed in that respect even now that we are both adults, but we remain soul mates to this very day and share a bond only twins can relate to. After all, how many people can you have known since before you were born?

When we started junior school in September our parents had asked for us to be in separate classes so that we could develop better as individuals, but we still met each other on breaks and would walk to and from school together every day. It was around this time that we started Judo. We had always been interested in sport and Mum had taken us as toddlers to the gymnastics play centre at Heathrow gym where we'd spend hours jumping on the trampolines, balancing on the beam and hanging upside down on the uneven bars. We had always been chubby kids but at the age of five it hadn't bothered me. It was only when I turned six and another kid asked me if I was going to be fat when I grew up because my mum was, that it had an effect on me and made me wonder if my body was bigger than all my friends'.

I didn't know much about body image and weight back then, just that losing weight was good and gaining weight was bad. Now, at eight years old, I had just completed my six-week beginner's Judo course and was ready to train for my first competition, which meant being weighed. My sister stood on the scale first. It read 41.2kg (90lb). Then it was my turn and to my coach's disapproval, it read 43.6kg (96lb). He told Mum in front of everybody, 'Well! They'll have to lose a few kilos if they want to compete, they won't stand a chance in those weight categories!'

I was so embarrassed and ashamed that I decided from that very moment I would try as hard as I could to lose 3kg, which would put me in the under-40kg category. Ashleigh and I both started eating healthily, cutting out snacks and replacing them with fruit and only drinking water, instead of juice or fizzy drinks. We started training three times a week, for one hour on Tuesdays and Thursdays and two hours on Saturdays. After only a few weeks, the weight was already starting to drop off. I didn't know much about calories back then, just not to have too many, so I still ate what I was given at home and after just under a month I was down to 40.2kg (88lb) in time for my next weigh-in. Ashleigh had also lost weight and was now 39kg (86lb), which was disheartening for me because although I had lost more weight than her, she still weighed less than me, and that made me extremely jealous. I hated being the fatter twin and I suppose that's when the competition really started… Between me and Ashleigh it was no longer about being the best in Judo alone; we were now engaging in a full-on war against each other in a bid to lose the most weight.

Mum had always been big. I remember watching her eat her way through gigantic portions at every meal, alongside countless sugary treats and carb-filled snacks, washed down with litres and litres of diet cola every single day. I'd never thought any less of her for being that way because everyone uses different coping mechanisms to deal with emotions and food was hers. Dad had always turned to alcohol as his very last resort if he couldn't cope, and I would discover later in life the most destructive methods of all, and how I would fall under their spells. I suppose in some ways Mum's size encouraged me to stay fit because she had always told everyone how proud she was of me and Ashleigh for our dedication to Judo and how happy it made her feel, knowing that we wouldn't go through the bullying she suffered at school for being overweight... But we all know how kids are, and if they can't bully you for one reason, they'll always find another. First was my accent. Because we had lived in London up until a few months previously, we still spoke with very strong South London accents, unlike most people living in Frimley who were middle-class and very well spoken. This meant that Ashleigh and I didn't really fit in at school because we spoke differently to all the other kids, who started bullying us because of it. I didn't take much notice of it back then because we had made friends outside of school with the children who lived by the local park, and if either one of us was ever really struggling, at least we still had each other. That's one of the great things about being a twin- there's always someone to look out for you and you'll always have their back, because you know they've got yours too.

When we weren't at Judo we would spend most of our time at the park, playing on the swings and messing around with other kids. We had only just been given the freedom of going out by ourselves and it was a great sense of maturity as we got our first taste of independence, even if it was just to the local park down the road. We met a girl named Beth who had fallen off the slide one day and Ashleigh had gone to ask if she was OK. We immediately became friends with her, and although she was a few years younger than us we got along well, and we would knock on her door if she wasn't already out, to ask if she was coming out to play. Then around Christmas that year we met two brothers named Charlie and Drew, during a snowball fight at the park. Charlie was two years younger than us and Drew was five years older than us, which meant he immediately became the leader of our group. He was usually nice to us and seemed cool, which I suppose drew us to him, but we would soon find out what evil he was actually capable of and just how cruel kids really can be. They were also new to the area which was something we had in common, but the fact that my twin sister and I were both tomboys meant we'd inevitably play the same games together in the park, such as football and manhunt. They'd occasionally invite themselves over to our house to play and we'd often go round theirs too.

Ashleigh eventually found quite a few friends at school but I was still struggling, so I'd usually sit quietly in class and simply focus on my school-work, which kept me happy because I enjoyed learning. I had friends at Judo and that made up for only having Ashleigh at school. Judo became a lot more serious after Christmas and there was even more pressure to lose weight and keep it off, as we had both been selected to compete in the Surrey Youth Games that Easter. We had been moved up from the intermediate to the advanced junior class, which was longer than the one-hour training session we were used to, but we'd still do both training sessions to help us lose weight and improve in the sport. This added up to five hours' training in the week, three hours on a Saturday and all day Sunday if we were competing. We started to make secret diets too; the first was called '321'. This diet consisted of three litres of water, two hours' exercise and only one meal per day. It was hard to stick to, but when we weren't at Judo we would run laps around the park, play high-intensity sports at school, or do floor exercises and jump rope in the back garden to make up the two hours of exercise. We'd eat breakfast or lunch at school before lying to our parents later by telling them we were eating dinner at a friend's house. This meant we could stay out an hour later as well as lose weight for Judo, so it was win-win situation.

I was almost nine years old now and had just started learning about calories. I'd watch my mum read the back of packaged food items when I asked her if I could have it, then she'd tell me either 'yes' or 'no' based on what she had read on the packaging. I had heard her talking about calories and diets with her mum, who was also overweight, so one day I innocently asked her, "Why do you read the food label before you let me eat it?'

She replied "I'm checking the calories. If it's under a hundred you can eat it, but if it's more it will make you fat for Judo'.

I then made her show me how to read the calorie content on food packaging and from that moment onwards I read the label of everything I ate, refusing to eat anything that was more than one hundred calories. By this time the kids at the park had started calling us 'the calorie freaks' as we'd refuse any sweets over one hundred calories from the local shop and would refuse to eat altogether if we were competing the next day, but we didn't care so long as we lost weight for Judo.

When the Sunday of the Surrey Youth Games finally arrived, I was woken up at 6:30am by Mum telling me to get dressed as it was time to leave for the competition. Weigh-in was at eight o'clock and my hands were shaking with nerves as they took me to stand on the scales. I was dehydrated because I had not eaten since Friday evening and had not drunk anything since 5pm the night before, but I forced myself to stand strong as I had a competition to win. I weighed 36.3kg (79lbs) and felt the biggest sense of achievement as my parents read the scale in disbelief whilst the coaches told them I would have to be moved down to fight in the under-37kg category, as I was now too light for the under-40kg. Mum had to pay five pounds for me to move weight category because the judges would have to re-arrange all my fights, but my parents were proud of my hard work and so was I. I now felt as though all those hungry, sleepless nights and extra training sessions had been worth the pain.

Ashleigh weighed 37.6kg (82lb), which meant she stayed in the under-40kg category, proving even more satisfying for me because not only had I lost the weight I wanted to, but I was no longer the fat twin. I had now lost 7.3kg (16lb) since I started Judo and was in the best physical shape I had ever been in, although all the commitment and self-discipline I'd developed had started to take a toll on my mental stability.

After waiting around for a few hours after weigh-in, my weight category was called and it was almost time for my first fight. I remember feeling nervous as I stood at the side of the mat, ready to make my way to the centre where the referee stood, feet away from my opponent. The timer started and I grabbed the collar and sleeve of the girl I was fighting, who also had a firm grip of me seconds after the fight began. She was shaking me, pulling me around all over the floor space, when suddenly I heard my coach shout "Pull her back! Don't let her scare you, just throw her!'

I turned in for the throw, pulling all my body weight forwards as I wedged my back into the front of her torso. Using all my strength, I attempted to pull us both forwards and onto the ground. She was pulling backwards as hard as she could to resist me throwing her, but I continued to pull forwards before suddenly changing direction to push all my weight towards her. I then swept her leg off the ground with my foot, keeping hold of her jacket so as to land on top of her with as little of my body touching the ground for maximum points. I felt the impact as we landed, but before I hit the floor the timer stopped, as the referee raised his right arm in the air and shouted "Ipon!'

'Ipon' scores ten points for throwing your opponent onto their back from standing, resulting in an automatic knock-out win... I was ecstatic! Seeing my parents applauding me in the crowd with my coaches and other parents made me feel so proud, like I had achieved something really great.

I had two more fights over the next twenty minutes, losing one two points and winning the other with a hold-down after missing being thrown by inches. Afterwards, all the girls in my weight category were called up to the judges' panel whilst the referees called out the names of the three top-scoring competitors out of all ten girls in each weight group. The names they called out were the competitors who had won their place in the next round, which would give them a chance to win a medal. They called my name out first and I couldn't believe my ears- I had made it to the next round! When I walked back to Mum, who was standing by the side of the mat, she hugged me and told me how proud she was of me whilst we waited for Dad to return with Ashleigh. Her weight category had been called shortly after mine to a different mat so I didn't get to watch her fight, but I could tell she was happy when she returned with Dad. She had a huge smile on her face as she told us that although she had not made it to the next round, she had still won one of her two fights and was extremely happy about it. I felt bad for her because she had not made it to the medal round, but I said nothing about that and simply congratulated her on how well she had fought.

By the time I was called for the second round I was already shattered from my other fights and from waking up at 6:30am, but I fought as hard as I could and came out with a bronze medal. I saw the envious look on Ashleigh's face when I stood on the podium to collect my medal and although it sounds incredibly cruel looking back now, it added to my sense of accomplishment to know that I had fought better than her that day. It's awful to have to compete and be compared to someone your entire life, but as long as you're winning it's a great feeling.

I brought my medal with me the next day to show off to everyone at school. I stood at the front of the room whilst the teacher announced my achievement to the whole class and I wore that medal around my neck all day, feeling as though nothing could bring me down. When I walked past the park with Ash on the way home from school, Charlie and Drew were sitting on the swings with Beth so we walked through the steel gate and into the park to join them. Drew had a water bottle and they were playing truth or dare, so we asked to join in and they spun the bottle. It landed on Charlie. Before anyone else could speak, Drew immediately said to Charlie, "I dare you to kiss Beth.'

Charlie was only seven years old and Beth was barely six. All of us laughed as they kissed each other before Charlie bounced straight off Beth's lips, stating that it was the most disgusting thing he had ever done. He said that she kissed all slobbery like an old lady, and then he and Drew both started chanting "Granny kiss! Granny kiss!' as they pointed at Beth, laughing.

She was so upset that she ran all the way home. She only lived yards away from the park but I felt really bad for her, not only because of how young she was, but because Charlie and Drew were teasing her about something they'd made her do in the first place. It was now Charlie's turn to spin the bottle and it landed on me. Charlie said to me, still laughing "I dare you to shag Drew."

I didn't know what the word meant and neither did Ashleigh when I looked at her to check if she knew. Before I knew it, Drew had already pushed me onto my back and pulled my legs apart, lifting up my school dress, which left only my underwear and his unzipped trousers separating our private parts as he humped me and groped my chest, pinning me to the ground with his other hand for around ten seconds. I tried to roll out of it but was getting nowhere, so I gave up and just tried not to cry. I felt disgusted and ashamed and wanted to leave right away, but both boys refused to let us leave the park. We ignored them as we removed ourselves from the situation, heading straight for the exit gate.

Drew started chanting "Pussyole! Pussyole!" which was a disgusting word used by some teenagers for a coward. I wanted to cry because I felt so embarrassed and ashamed at what had just happened, but I sucked it up and walked home with Ashleigh whilst I tried not to cry. We went about our evening routine just as if it were any other day, watching TV and eating dinner before exercising until it was time for bed. The next morning I didn't discuss with anyone what had happened in the park that afternoon and subconsciously agreed with Ashleigh, without saying a word, that we would never repeat this to anyone. We didn't really know what was going on, just that it was wrong and made us dirty, so for those reasons I think we just felt we'd be in trouble if we told anyone, or they'd think it was our fault.

...And that was how it all started.

CHAPTER 2

Something's Wrong

I became a lot quieter and more withdrawn in school after that day and didn't bother trying to make friends for a while. I still went to Judo training and as the year progressed, Ashleigh and I both entered more advanced competitions, meaning we continued starving ourselves to stay under the weight limit. It was worth it, however, because by the age of nine we were competing internationally and our faces were appearing in the newspapers almost every other week. I struggled keeping my weight down as I was growing taller, but felt ever so guilty if I gained weight, so I stayed under 40kg (88lb) until I left Judo, aged twelve.

The constant dieting had an impact on my mood because I was not eating enough most of the time, so I became easily irritated and on occasions would burst into tears unprovoked in the middle of school. I think that was when teachers started to realize something was wrong, but no one ever questioned it, so I continued to cry alone right through to my teens. The crying and low mood were also because of the bullying, and as time went on and the Judo got better, the bullying got worse. The children at school had started to refer to me and Ashleigh as 'the Judo freaks', a name that would stick to me like glue until I reached high school.

I was also bullied about my height because I was taller than average, which was due to my genes but was also the result of excessive exercising, which stimulates growth hormones; and then there was the issue of my muscular physique. I had large biceps and shoulders, extremely muscular legs, a line down the middle of my chest and six-pack abs. The kids would shout 'Man!' at me when I walked through school and all it took was for one person to call me 'ugly' in an argument and before I could blink, the whole school were calling me 'ugly' too. I hated it. I would go home and cry every single day after school and it seemed my only escape was Judo. At Judo everyone included me in games, I wasn't the last person to be picked for teams and no one made me feel like I was the dead flowers on a forgotten grave, which is how the bullies at school made me feel. When I was at Judo I was somebody, and no one could take that away from me. At home I had discovered another talent besides Judo. Dad had bought an electric keyboard for Mum before I was born, because she was going to learn to play it, but she gave up after a few failed attempts, so it had been stored in a box under their bed ever since. She must have been clearing out her room because she was sitting with the keyboard lying on her bed, along with numerous other random things she had found. When I walked into her room and sat beside her to ask if it worked, she wired it up and asked if I wanted to have a go. A song was playing on the radio, I don't remember which one, but as soon as I heard the song I started copying it and within a few minutes I could play the track exactly how it sounded on the radio. Mum let me keep that keyboard and whenever I was feeling strong emotions- happy or sad- I would make up songs about how I was feeling. I would also listen to any song I liked in the charts and teach myself to play it. Ashleigh started picking up Dad's guitars and learnt to play a few of the songs he played, then went on to singing and writing her own music as well as playing by ear like me.

Ashleigh and I continued to go to the park down our road to play with Beth and Charlie more often than not, but would avoid Drew if he came out with Charlie. If Drew was at the park and there were no adults there he would bully me into being his little 'sex body' and would repeat what he did that day we played dares, except it would go on for much longer and he would try to take my clothes off in the process. He became more and more abusive as time went on and would throw stones and mud at me if I walked past the park alone, trying to get the other kids to join in and gang up on me whilst he physically assaulted me, bruising my body as well as my self-esteem. I often came up in bruises from Judo, however, so anyone who noticed marks on my skin would simply assume they were from training.

I was still only nine years old but by now Drew would regularly pull me behind the bushes at the back of the park, put his hands down the front of my trousers and make me perform sexual favours. Some days were worse than others, so it was a relief when he only wanted sex with clothes on. He was abusing Ashleigh too, but I would try and take the punches so she didn't have to as much, because even though she was less than a minute younger than me, she was still my baby sister and I had to protect her.

The bullying at school was becoming worse too. One morning I showed up to school and there were a group of around ten kids from my class waiting at the front gates for more of their friends. I sped up past the gates in an attempt to hurry through without being noticed, but one of the boys put his foot out and tripped me over, landing me flat on my face. The rest of the group surrounded me, laughing and pointing at me as I tried to stand up. One of the girls grabbed my school bag and threw it to the others, who then refused to give it back until the same boy who had tripped me unzipped my bag completely, throwing it up into the air and causing all of my things to fall out. I was so angry I wanted to punch the lot of them in the face or throw them into the air and onto the ground with a Judo throw, but I had not even made it back up off the ground yet because every time I tried to stand up, one of the other kids would push me back down.

This continued until the bell rang for the beginning of class, at which point the entire group of kids rushed past me, trampling over my things and kicking me as they ran past. I cried the tears I'd been choking back and carefully picked up all my things before slowly making my way to the toilets, where I cried again before entering my classroom, where I was shouted at for being late.

That little series of events was repeated almost every day at school and the kids would call me ugly and fat, and say that I smelled. In theory I probably did smell bad because I was starving myself so much that I would have been in ketosis, which means that instead of burning carbohydrates for energy, your body starts breaking down its own fat stores to get through the day, because it is not receiving adequate nutrition from your diet. Side effects of ketosis include bad breath and oily skin that produces the smell of sweat because as well as burning its own fat, the body also starts a detoxification process in which it cleans out the internal organs and purges waste toxins through the skin and tongue.

I was never bullied for being fat until I was spotted by other children in the lunch hall, drinking a meal replacement shake for my lunch that I had stolen from Mum to help me lose weight. It was only then that they saw it bothered me, so I guess that's why they started calling me fat. As for ugly, I don't know... Maybe I was, or maybe kids just used it as another reason to pick on me. Then there was Judo. Every time I won a medal I would bring it in to show and tell and would feel great about myself for a few minutes, but that soon stopped. At the next break the name-calling would start again and it was back to being 'the Judo freak'. I stopped bringing medals and trophies altogether and would pray on my life that no one had seen my face in the papers that week for representing the country in a Judo tournament. That way I thought just maybe, no one would bully me. No one would resent me for doing well, which could make the bullying even worse. I had to make it stop. All of the bullying, along with the sexual abuse, was too much for me and so I was trying everything in my power to make myself invisible. Then, just as I thought it could not get any worse, I was introduced to probably the biggest bully I'd ever meet in my life, James.

I was sitting on the swings with Ashleigh and we had the whole park to ourselves. It was the Saturday after our tenth birthday and we were only in the park in the first place because Drew was not there, but he soon showed up and walked straight over to us with a friend of his who we had not yet met. Maybe it was just random gut instinct, but I felt a bad vibe around him from the moment he set foot in that park and didn't like him one bit. We stopped swinging on the swings and stood still, wondering who this boy was and what he wanted with us. They walked up to the swings until they were just a few feet away from us and then started laughing, looking at each other as though they had just been talking about us. Drew suddenly pointed at us and shouted "Eeew look! It's the ugly twins" as he turned to face James, who was still laughing. "…Fucking Judo freaks."

I turned to face Ashleigh, who by now had tears welling up in her eyes and said to her, "Come on Ash, let's go. We don't have to listen to this."

Seconds later, Charlie entered the park with Beth. They had a football and asked us if we wanted to play. No one ever asked me to join in with anything, so Ashleigh and I agreed to play as long as James and Drew stayed away from us. However, they soon wormed their way back in and had us playing another one of Drew's sick games. This one was called 'Kings and Queens'.

A few more kids from the houses nearby had entered the park and joined in with our game by this point, which actually started off pretty fun. There were two climbing frames at opposite ends of the park so we split up into two teams and built forts around the climbing frames, which we pretended were castles from opposing kingdoms. Drew, Charlie, Ashleigh and three other kids were on one team at one side of the park, which left James, Beth and me on the other team with the two remaining kids who had come out to play. We made swords out of sticks and bombs out of rocks which we then threw at each other in the middle of the park, pretending it was our battle ground. Drew nominated himself to be king in his team and one of the kids who had joined us in the park became king of our team. Drew's team had already trashed our fort so I went with James to gather more sticks to rebuild our castle. He led me to some bushes behind a tree at the back of the park, situated on a hill, where I started to realize this game was no longer about swords or castles. He cornered me by the fence at the bottom of the hill where no one could see us.

"Do you have a boyfriend?" he asked, placing his hand on the fence behind my head with his arm over my shoulder, blocking any chance of escaping. I was feeling uncomfortable by this point so I tried to step away as I replied with "Get lost. I know what you want, I'm not interested".

He was a lot taller than me and a year older than Drew, which made him five years older than me, and his stocky tall build made him very threatening to a ten-year-old girl. He looked down at me and started laughing before giving me a look of disgust and saying "Why the fuck would I want you? No one would ever want you. You're disgusting".

But shortly after saying that, still standing over me so I couldn't walk away, he grabbed my arm and put my hand down his trousers. He was now facing me whilst he made me masturbate him, telling me I was not going anywhere until I'd done it. I thought if I did what I was told he would let me go, so I rubbed my hand up and down and I tried not to cry. Beth and Charlie came over, which is when I stopped, at which point James let me go, as they had almost seen what we were doing. Beth laughed and said "Have you seen your sister? It's gross! She's getting fingered by Drew!'

I cautiously walked over to where Ashleigh was sitting on Drew's lap and just like Beth had said, Drew had his hands down the front of Ashleigh's trousers. He was molesting her. She looked so scared and embarrassed, but all I could do was walk closer to them in the hope that he would stop in the same way that James had stopped when we were spotted. It didn't work, however. James went and sat beside them, ordering me to sit on his lap beside Ashleigh and Drew. He then unzipped my jeans, put his hands through my underwear and put his fingers inside my vagina. I was so scared, and Ashleigh was too... We were unable to speak, too scared to say a word, so we simply hoped and prayed in our minds that it would be over soon and we could just go home. The boys were looking at each other, laughing as they pulled their hands out from our private parts and said to each other "What the fuck? They're not even wet".

Then they both looked at Ashleigh and me as Drew said "You're both fucking disgusting. You're obviously boys, not girls! Girls like this stuff… You're both pathetic!' Then Drew threw Ashleigh off his lap and onto the ground from the high climbing frame they were sitting on, telling her to go away. I leapt up off James to follow Ashleigh, but he shouted "Where the fuck do you think you're going? You haven't finished what you started yet".

He grabbed my hips and pulled me back towards him, before turning around so he was on top of me, then he pulled his penis out of his trousers and put my hand back around it. I cried as I did what I was told, rubbing up and down until a white discharge came out. It was all over my hand, and I felt so filthy and ashamed at what I had just done.

Ashleigh was still at the other side of the park waiting for me on her own, away from the other kids. My heart, which had been pounding, suddenly felt shallow and weak as if it had stopped beating, whilst my head started to hurt as everything went blurry. I ran across the park to Ashleigh who was staring at the ground, sobbing quietly. Her voice was shaky as she whispered to me "Why didn't you help me? Why didn't you make it stop?"

I put my arm around her as we both cried and made our slow walk home. "I'm sorry Ash", I said, "I'm so sorry…"

The other kids had thrown mud at her whilst I'd been with James and they and Drew continued to throw rocks at us until we had walked out of the park, down the road and out of sight. When we arrived home it was almost time to go to Judo. Obviously neither of us really felt like going, but we wanted to appear as normal as possible so Mum and Dad wouldn't know what their filthy little daughters had been up to.

We got changed into our Judo suits in our bedroom and as I pulled my tight training top over my head, I caught a glimpse of my reflection in a mirror. I remembered what the bullies had said at school, how they called me ugly and fat. I also remembered how James had said that no one would ever want me and I thought maybe it was because I was fat. I looked at Ashleigh and asked her, "Do you think I'm fat?"

She replied, "Not as fat as me, I'm disgusting. At least you're tall so it doesn't look so bad on you."

She then sat down, lifting up her top to point at the thin layer of skin that covered her incredibly defined abs. She pinched the skin and said "Look, I'm so fat I have fucking rolls"… I looked at my stomach to see if it was the same and then told Ashleigh, "Well we won't get rid of it by staring at it. I guess we just have train even harder and eat even less, because whatever we're doing now's not good enough."

She replied with, "We're never fucking good enough. Don't you get it?"

We got into the car and neither of us spoke a word for the entire journey. I watched the rain fall from the sky and as it dripped down the windows of the car, I imagined the rain-drops were tears, each cried from a different pair of eyes. I wondered how many people cried today or was I the only one, alone in this pain? The drive felt longer than usual. Ashleigh and I were both upset but we were good at hiding emotions and Mum must have assumed we were simply tired, so instead of questioning our moods she simply dropped us off at Judo like any other Saturday.

When we got there it honestly did start to feel like any other Saturday. All of our worries were left outside the doors as we walked through the entrance, made our way onto the mat and got on with the training session. We ran for ten minutes or so then moved onto jump rope and stretching, followed by a game of football in which the losing team had to do one hundred push-ups. I liked losing because it meant I burned more calories, which meant I lost more weight. After warming up for thirty minutes we spent one hour practising technique, forty-five minutes circuit training and forty-five minutes of fighting to end the session. After cooling down and stretching out, all club members who were competing the following week in the internationals were told to weigh themselves before they left, so that the coaches knew exactly how

21

much they weighed.

They needed to know how much weight each fighter had to lose, gain or maintain, so they could coach each fighter to their specific needs. All this really meant for us, however, was being shouted at for gaining weight or not losing it fast enough. If you lost weight you didn't lose enough, and if you gained weight you totally failed. Ashleigh and I were both competing next week, so we went to weigh in with everybody else. I stepped onto the scales in front of all my coaches, my sister and the rest of the kids who were competing. It read 39.2kg (86lb) which meant I was over my weight limit and would have to compete in the next weight category if I didn't lose at least 2kg. Mum had also arrived now to pick us up and had been waiting beside the coach in charge of the Judo club. He said to her 'Your girls have real talent… Olympic talent I'd say, both of them. They just need to keep their weight in check and they'll be sorted.'

Mum looked so proud of us. Anyone would have thought hearing those comments would have made me happy at the least, but all I heard were the words 'need to lose weight'. As we drove home I kept thinking… What am I missing, what else? There must be something else… Something I'm not already doing that will help me lose weight. There's got to be another way… And that's when I remembered Charlie. He had been talking about his medication, which was prescribed for his ADHD, and I remembered him saying how much he hated taking the pills because the side effect stopped him from eating. I remembered how he said he just doesn't feel hungry and hates food completely when he's taken his pills, which he doesn't like because he usually enjoys eating sweets with the rest of us when we hang out. I had to get those pills… The thought of rapidly losing weight without being hungry consumed me; the pressure to take Judo to the next level and be the best I could be was overwhelming, so now all I could think about was how to get those pills from Charlie and how much they would help me. I had to find a way… There must be a way.

CHAPTER 3

Ritalin

When we arrived home from training it was almost 4pm. Ashleigh didn't want to go out after what had happened that morning, so I went to knock for Charlie on my own. His mum answered the door and looked me up and down. She was wearing grey tracksuit bottoms and an oversized pyjama top, with big gold hooped earrings and a silver chain around her neck. She was smoking when she answered the door and said calmly, in a welcoming voice, 'You must be Robyn or Ashleigh, Charlie never stops talking about you! Come inside, don't worry about taking your shoes off.'

She smiled as I walked up the stairs to Charlie's room where he was playing video games in his bed. His bed was nothing more than two mattresses stacked on top of each other with just a plain blanket, no sheets. Next to his bed lay two more beds, the same except with only one mattress for each, which I assumed belonged to his younger brother and sister who were downstairs. I closed his bedroom door behind me as I asked about the pills. 'So what are those pills you take? Do they really stop you feeling hungry?'

He was still playing his video game with his eyes glued to the screen when he replied, 'Yeah, I fucking hate them. My mum makes me take them to stop me being naughty apparently… But they don't work, I'll never stop being a little shit!' He then paused his game, dropping the controller onto his bed as we both started laughing. I sat next to him and asked, 'What if I did you a favour? You could sneak the pills out with you and pretend you're taking them, but I'll take them instead. I don't want to get hungry, I need to lose two kilos for my Judo competition next weekend. Would you do that for me, mate?'

He looked a bit surprised that anyone would want to take those horrible pills, but agreed to it and said, "Yeah fair enough, thanks actually! Just be careful, because we'll both get in trouble if you get caught.'

He then handed me a box of pills from the kitchen as soon as his mum went out, before instructing me to take one in the morning and one at lunch-time. I read the box, which said 'Ritalin Capsules 100mg'. I knew you couldn't just buy these from any shop or chemist as you had to have a prescription from the doctor to get them, so I'd have to rely on Charlie's friendship if I wanted to take Judo seriously and get my weight down even lower. Despite being advised not to take the Ritalin in the evening, I wanted to try it as soon as I could so I took one in Charlie's room shortly after being given them. I'd never taken any pill except paracetamol before now and I remembered how it had started dissolving in my mouth before I could swallow it, so I prepared myself psychologically before taking the Ritalin as I knew exactly how foul it would taste. I didn't want to take any chances so I filled my mouth with water from the bathroom tap, shoved the pill to the back of my throat and swallowed right away. I gagged and started choking because I couldn't keep it down, but Charlie held my mouth shut with both hands, pushing my head up towards the ceiling as he helped me swallow it with my second attempt. We both knew it would have been a complete waste if I'd spat it out, so he held his hands tight over my face until the pill was gone. My face was now red and my eyes were watering from gagging, but I still wanted to make sure I had swallowed the Ritalin. I felt around my mouth with my tongue to make sure the pill was completely gone and it was, so I thanked Charlie for helping me and we soon went back to being kids.

We continued to play video games whilst we talked for hours and although we were probably a bad influence on each other, it felt nice to have a friend. Sure enough, the pill started to kick in and I felt energetic, happy and not hungry at all. I asked Charlie if he wanted to go to the park and he told me he had a brand new football downstairs, so we took it with us and kicked it to each other in the middle of the road as we jogged to the park. We played football and practised jumping fences and flipping off climbing frames, before walking back to his house so I could use the phone. It was almost 7pm now and I was supposed to be home by then, so I decided to tell Mum I was eating dinner at Charlie's house. The Ritalin had taken away my appetite, and Mum would have to let me stay out until at least 8pm if I told her Charlie's family weren't eating until 7:30, so I got to stay out an extra hour later as well as losing weight in the process... Result!

Charlie and I went back to the park to play football until it was time for me to go home. When I got home, Ash was downstairs watching TV with my mum, dad and brothers. Mum shouted, 'You all right Rob?" as I walked through the living room to sit on the sofa beside Ashleigh. I replied to her, 'Yeah, we had pizza for dinner. It was lovely!'

She replied, 'You best not eat any more pizza this week as you still have that two kilos to lose.' She smiled and didn't mean anything by it but it was a reminder of just how close next weekend was. She then turned to face Ashleigh as well as me and said, 'I told your dad what your coaches said about you girls today. We're so proud you both!' To which my dad replied, 'You never know, the 2012 Olympic Games isn't too far away and they're holding it in London... You'll be sixteen by then and your coaches think you have a chance, so go for it!'

Mum and Dad then joked about what it would be like if Ashleigh and I had to fight each other in the Olympics, who would be disqualified for pulling the other one's hair and who would make it to the Olympics in the first place. Ashleigh and I both laughed, but when we went upstairs to our bedroom, she confronted me.

'You're hiding something. I'm not stupid, so don't lie to me. I know you didn't eat that pizza, I can tell by how happy you are.'

I smirked at her and could see the jealousy filling her eyes because I had done something that would make me lose more weight than her. I looked her straight in the eyes and said, 'I don't know what you mean. I love eating pizza! Why on earth would it make me sad?'

She said, 'Because the coaches told us to lose weight today so I know for a fact you would not be stuffing your face with pizza less than a week before Internationals!'

'OK' I muttered, 'I only ate two slices... OK, one slice. But you can't stop me losing weight, we're in this together. If you tell Mum and Dad I skipped dinner then I'll tell them what you were doing at 3am this morning. Does the word "exercise" sound familiar?'

And with that, neither of us said a word for the rest of the evening, until we were lying in our bunk beds about to fall asleep. I knew she was mad at me and it was immature of me to black-mail her, but we were still merely kids and as twins we had to compete against each other, meaning we couldn't both be the best. I eventually broke the silence by saying, 'Night Ash, love you.' To which she replied, 'Night Robs, love you too.'

We said that every night for as long as I can remember. Even if we were sleeping far apart in different houses, towns, or even countries, regardless of how angry we were at each other we would still both say those words or we were unable to sleep. I guess that's just one reminder of how close we are.

The next morning I took one Ritalin pill as soon as I woke up, followed by another one around midday, which is when Ashleigh and I went out to knock for Charlie. We'd been exercising that morning doing push-ups and sit-ups in our bedroom, followed by jump rope and spot jogging in the back garden. I skipped breakfast and only ate an apple for lunch as the Ritalin was stopping me feeling hungry, so I decided not to eat again until dinner, unless I 'ate round Charlie's house' again. The park was on the way to Charlie's house and we had planned to knock for him first, but we spotted Drew and James riding their bikes in that direction so we decided to head straight to the park instead to avoid them. Charlie eventually came out to the park after a few hours, by which point Beth was sitting with us too.

'I'm bored,' Beth whined to Charlie, who was lying on the floor ripping up tarmac by the swings. Ashleigh and I were also sitting on the floor by the swings and for the past hour, it seemed we had found nothing to do except sit and talk.

'Why don't we build a base?' Charlie asked. 'We can't build it here, though, people will see us in the park. We should go to the woods, my brother knows a good place.'

I didn't want to go to the woods. I'd been there a few times with Drew and he was an un-predictable bully. Sometimes he would be nice for a couple of hours and everything would seem fine, but he'd soon switch like a lightbulb for no reason and start hassling me for sex. I couldn't run away from him in the woods because he was the only person who knew the way out, and with no one else around I felt extremely unsafe because not a soul would be able to hear me if I called for help. Worse still, my parents would never allow us to go to the woods unsupervised, so if things did turn out badly, there was no way of confiding in them when I got home. This was firstly because of how much trouble I'd be in for lying to them and going to the woods in the first place, but also because I would have been the only one to blame, so as well as feeling upset at what had happened, I'd have no one to comfort me, since I'd brought it on myself.

Ashleigh asked, 'What's a base? Do you mean like building a den?' Charlie then told us it was exactly like building a den or fort except we would spend days or even weeks making it, and we could use it as a place to hang out when it was finished. I shook my head at the idea of going to the woods and said to everyone, 'I don't want to go to the woods. Why don't we build a base by those flats over there?'

I pointed to a block of flats opposite the park. It was fairly tall with six floors and there was a disused washing line area beside it, which appeared to have been empty for a very long time. Then we noticed some garages by the car park beside the flats.

'Do you mean over there?' Charlie asked as he pointed to the garages. There were more than twenty garages built next to each other, stretching in a long line beside the flats. It was an ideal place to build a secret base because unless you were standing right beside it, you couldn't see anything on top of it, and if we were to lie flat on the roof, no one could see us at all. Beth didn't want to climb up because she was scared and had to be home soon anyway as it was starting to get dark, but I wandered over there anyway with Ashleigh and Charlie.

It seemed a lot bigger when we were right up close and it was too high for any one of us to climb on our own, so we helped each other up using all our strength. Ashleigh and I stood side by side against the garages and as Charlie stepped onto our hands, we pushed him up over our heads and onto the roof. I then gave Ashleigh a foot up but could only lift her high enough to hang off the side, so Charlie grabbed hold of her arms and pulled her up whilst I pushed from the ground. Then it was my turn. I took a run-up of around ten feet then jumped as high as I could to touch the ledge of the roof, which I held onto and was then hanging from. I pulled myself up, pretending it was just like doing pull-ups at Judo, until eventually I was high enough that Charlie and Ashleigh could reach the top of my arms, which they held from either side as they pulled me up.

The roof seemed a lot higher up than when we had initially been gazing upon it from the ground and it didn't scare me too much, but I still felt safer if I kept my distance from the edge once I was up. The ground beneath was nothing but cold, hard concrete and a fifteen-foot drop from the roof, but I suppose we were all taken aback by how different our surroundings seemed from up there. Usually we could only see the small collection of houses beside the park or the occasional car driving further up the road, because any gaps beyond the foot-paths and roads were filled with trees. From the roof we could see past the park, beyond the schools and busy road behind it and way off into the distance where the woods separated our town from another. There were gardens leading onto the back of the roof that belonged to the houses from a different road, but all of them were at least fifty feet away from us, which meant we would have no trouble running or hiding if anyone saw us from their garden.

There were more than twenty of these gardens, but one right in the middle caught our eye. The rear end of this garden had been fenced off by the owners of the house, leaving an enormous square plot of land abandoned and hidden from sight. Whoever owned this plot of land was clearly using it for nothing more than gardening waste disposal, so surely they wouldn't mind or even notice if we made a mess there. This made the garage base idea even greater because as well as having twenty garage roofs, we now had half a garden too!

The abandoned land was filled sky-high with broken wood and mud, piled up with dead bushes and leaves that had been cleared from the rest of the garden. There was a beautiful oak tree in one corner of the garden, standing almost as tall as the flats, with a long, frayed rope dangling from one of the branches. It was hanging from too far up to try and reach by climbing, but the frayed end hung low enough for one of us to grab and pull down from the tree. We'd have to jump off the back of the roof to get to it, but if we were able to pull that rope down we could change it for a new one and build a rope swing.

After discussing with Ashleigh and Charlie what to build for our base and how to build it, we noticed there was a broken broom in the back of the garden. It still had most of its handle so Ashleigh got to work and started sweeping all of the sticks and leaves from the roof into a pile so we had somewhere to sit, as Charlie watched me jump in an attempt to grab the rope from the tree. When I ran and jumped I was solely focused on grabbing the rope and not where I was landing, so I failed to notice the flooded trench beneath my feet. As I jumped up high in the air I grabbed the rope and pulled it down, only to land in a four-foot ditch filled with filthy, muddy water. When I landed I was knocked over by the rope landing on top of me along with bits of oak tree which had fallen down with it, but aside from a few scratches and feeling a little embarrassed I was perfectly fine.

Ash and Charlie started laughing at me the second they knew I was OK, so I dug my hands deep into the trench and pulled out two handfuls of wet mud, which I threw at Charlie. Ashleigh and I were now both laughing at him, so he tried to throw some mud back at me as he took hold of Ashleigh's shoulders tightly, trying to hide behind her... He then pushed Ashleigh off the back of the roof and into the trench with me, but she managed to keep hold of his arms, leaving both of them screaming as she pulled him in with her. A huge splash replaced their screams for a moment as they fell into the water; by now our clothes were so wet we hadn't even noticed it was raining. The rain started to pour down as we stood up in the trench, the three of us now laughing hysterically as we threw muddy water at each other whilst screaming at the top of our lungs. It was the best laugh I'd had in a long time and I genuinely felt happy, but just like all good times it was soon cut short.

Our laughter suddenly fell silent when we heard an angry voice shout from the other side of the garage roof. 'Charlie? Charlie! You up there?!'

It was a woman's voice, one I recognized. She had just pulled up in a car, which we would have ignored any other time we'd been up there, but from the sound of the brakes slamming on and screeching, we knew something was wrong. There was a man's voice too... It was Drew. Charlie held his finger to his lips as a sign to be quiet, but Ashleigh and I had already felt the same bad vibe so we knew to be silent. I closed my eyes and felt a cold shiver run down my spine, bringing all the hairs to stand up on the back of my neck. I felt the same way any time Drew was around after what had happened, so for whatever reason he was here, I did not want to be seen. The three of us were now sitting in this deep, cold trench against the wall, fearfully cautious not to make a sound as we shivered in the water.

Charlie whispered quietly, 'It's my mum... Hide!' He turned to face

Ashleigh, who was holding my hand, still shivering. I looked at both of them and whispered, 'We need to get out of here.' Then, without a sound, we slowly stood up one by one and climbed back onto the roof, crawling on the floor using our arms to stay as low as possible so we would not be seen. Ashleigh and Charlie stayed behind me as I crawled as close to the edge of the roof as I could without being spotted, trying to look for a way out so they wouldn't find us. As I crawled close to the edge, I gave a hand signal to Ashleigh and Charlie for them to stay put, as I could now see Charlie's mum. She was still shouting, but not in our direction.

She was shouting to a window on the third floor of the flats, until a man in his thirties opened the window and shouted back to her, 'He's not in here! My kids are with their mum tonight. I think I saw Charlie in the park a few hours ago, he was with the twins. If he comes round here I'll tell him to go home!'

I then saw Drew come out from the stairwell to another flat and I watched him as he walked along the pathway, back to their car. He must have knocked for another friend of Charlie's because I listened from the roof as he told his mum they hadn't seen him, then I heard them arguing and calling Charlie every name under the sun. I sighed in relief as they got back into the car and drove off, before sitting up again as I said to Charlie and Ashleigh, 'It's OK, they don't know we were up here… We best keep this a secret from now on though. This can be our hide-out base!'

I smiled at Ashleigh as she asked Charlie, 'What was all that about? Why was your mum looking for you? She sounded pretty pissed off!'

He laughed and said, 'Fuck knows! I was supposed to be home for dinner an hour ago but I don't care, she can't tell me what to do!'

We all laughed as I checked my watch and realized it was also time for Ashleigh and me to go home. It would have been nice to stay out a little longer, but Ashleigh and I did listen to our parents, unlike Charlie, as we wanted to make them proud in every single way possible. We said goodbye to Charlie and agreed that no one would go up to the base without telling the others they were going first, but if any one of us did go on our own we could not tell anybody else. We also decided to bring some extra things to build the base with the next time we went, such as a sheet of tarpaulin to make a shelter against the roof and some rope to make a swing.

When Ashleigh and I arrived home it was almost 8pm and dark outside. We were soaked right through and covered in mud from the trench behind the garages, so we snuck straight upstairs and threw our filthy clothes in the bath where we washed the mud off before drying them with a hair dryer in our room. When our clothes were finally dry we put them in our wash basket like we usually would. Mum asked why they were damp, but we told her it was only because we'd been in the rain when it was pouring outside. She had left dinner for us on the kitchen side and my hunger pains had started to kick in as the Ritalin had worn off, but I had no intention of eating, since I'd done so well getting through the entire day on a single apple. Mum asked if we were hungry but Ashleigh told her we had eaten dinner at Charlie's house and had forgotten to phone her. She didn't like the fact that we hadn't told her before she cooked because the food would go to waste, but she believed us and said goodnight as we went to bed without having eaten.

The next morning I woke up and weighed myself, to realize I'd already lost the 2kg and more, which felt amazing. Now all I'd have to do was maintain it until Sunday, but I knew from experience that this was easier said than done. I kept my Ritalin close by and rationed my pills until Friday, when Charlie was getting his next prescription, which I needed desperately to maintain the progress I was making. School was hard because I felt weak and dizzy from not eating, but felt guilty and sick after eating lunch. However, I could not tell anyone I felt sick in case they sent me home and Mum would not let me go to Judo training that night, and I needed to be thinner than Ashleigh. On the plus side, my growing obsession with Ritalin and losing weight was steering my thoughts away from being bullied, so for the entire day I hardly took notice of the name-calling. Although my body was struggling physically, I stuck it out until 4pm each day when I would walk home from school with Ash. I hadn't been able to sneak a Ritalin pill at school that day because there were too many teachers monitoring lunch and classes, but I took one as soon as I got home and felt a huge stress relieved from my head. I failed to notice Ashleigh behind me, however… She walked straight into our bedroom as I took the pill and before I had time to hide the box, she snatched it out of my hands and read the label out loud.

'Are you fucking serious? You're taking drugs and you didn't even tell me?! I'm telling Mum!'

She turned to walk out of the bedroom but I pulled her back inside before she could shout for Mum or Dad. I was frantic with worry, trying to think of anything that would calm her down so she wouldn't tell on me. I looked her straight in the face and pleaded, 'Wait! They're only Charlie's tablets, not even real drugs… They're helping me lose weight by stopping me getting hungry. I only want to lose weight for Judo and everyone thinks I'm doing great now. Why would you mess that up for me?'

She snapped back at me, 'So that's why you were so happy that night you came home from Charlie's! You didn't eat pizza at all, did you? You lying sneaky cow! I can't believe you'd cheat to lose weight and not share with me. You just want me to stay fat because you're jealous that no one tells me to lose weight like they tell you, because the truth is that you are fatter than me and you will always be the fat twin!'

I almost burst into tears as I started to wonder if her words were true and if I really was the only fat one of the two of us. I pushed her and swore at her, telling her to shut up and that it wasn't true. She pushed me away and we continued arguing until we were both exhausted. She was angry at me because I'd been losing more weight than her and going behind her back to do so. However, her tone of voice changed dramatically as we sat down on the side of the bed and she now sounded quiet, calm and almost threatening. Her eyes were staring straight through mine as I looked up to see what she had to say… 'Give me some or I'm telling Mum.'

I was so angry by this point that I was almost crying. I resented Ashleigh and her threat. I was still mad at her for calling me fat, but now I had an even bigger problem; if I had to share my Ritalin with Ashleigh I'd have even less for myself, but what choice did I have? It was both or neither of us and these pills were the best shot we had at reaching our goals, so there was no way I was going to let it slip through my fingers like sand. I was used to Ashleigh throwing tantrums to get her own way just like I did when I wanted something. There was always tension and resentment between us from fighting, but it kept us closer together because it meant we shared secrets only we could ever know. The love between us was a strong bond which allowed me to forgive her instantly, and no matter how angry I was at her, the fight would always blow over eventually. I'd grown accustomed to being best friends with my twin, which effectively kept me best friends with my worst enemy.

I needed to lose weight and if it meant helping Ashleigh too, so be it. If Mum and Dad found out about the Ritalin, I'd be banned from seeing Charlie for sure and maybe even forced to stop Judo. There was no way in hell I could let that happen so I agreed to share it with Ashleigh, on the agreement that she didn't tell Mum. There was nothing anyone could have said to stop us taking the pills and nothing anyone could have done to make us change our minds. We were in this together now.

CHAPTER 4

Secrets

After taking the Ritalin, we searched the house for items we could take to the garages to build our base. I found a long blue rope in the garden that belonged to Dad and I asked him if Ashleigh and I could use it to build a rope swing. We told him we were building it in the park so he let us take it, but said he wanted us home for dinner at six. We had missed dinner the past two days running and both Mum and Dad wanted to make sure we were eating healthily, as we had our Judo competition coming up that weekend. We wore dark clothes so it would be easier to blend into the trench behind the garages if we had to hide again, along with black gloves which would be easier to grip the roof with when we climbed up. We walked to the park, where we met Charlie, before heading straight towards the garages. He had brought a knife so we could carve sticks to make daggers, but also to scare his brother off if he came by with James. Charlie had also brought a sheet of tarpaulin which he had stolen from a building site near his house, to use for a tent-like shelter for our base.

When we arrived at the garages we noticed a sofa bed, dumped by the bins beside the flats. It had a silver metal frame and a soft foam mattress, with two large red cushions dumped beside it. Ashleigh and I helped Charlie up onto the roof before lifting the sofa bed between us and passing it up to him. We then threw the rope we had brought, followed by the mattress and cushions, before climbing up ourselves. We steadily walked to the back of the roof where the trench had been filled with water the previous day, but to our surprise it had dried up with the rain and was now nothing more than an empty ditch. The three of us stood side by side as we examined it and discussed how we would build our base. Ashleigh pointed to the ditch behind the roof and said, 'We should put the sofa bed there and hang the tarpaulin over it for a shelter. That can be our seating area.'

Charlie and I agreed and soon got to work, wedging the sofa bed inside the ditch against the back wall of the garages. We placed the top two corners of the tarpaulin sheet on the back of the roof, holding it in place with bricks before burying the bottom corners with mud at the end of the garden. We'd created a tent-like shelter that sloped down from the back of the garages to the bottom of the garden, acting as a roof over the sofa bed inside the ditch to keep it dry. We knew the mattress would get damp whether it was under the shelter or not, so we used it as a third wall and placed it upright in the ditch against the tarpaulin.

The cushions were the perfect size to cover the sofa bed frame so we placed them neatly on top of it and had now finished making our shelter. Over the next few hours we swept dirt and leaves from the roof into a pile, which we then moulded with our hands to create a knee-high wall on the roof. This mud wall encircled the entire section of the garage roofs we were using and as we lay behind it so no one could see us from the ground, we pretended we were armed guards protecting our base. As for the rope swing, we didn't have enough time to build it before going home at six so we hid the rope underneath the shelter and left it for the next day.

When we arrived home, Mum and Dad were moving furniture around in the living room to create an empty space. There was a large box in the hallway which had been delivered whilst we'd been out and

Ashleigh and I were both curious as to what it could be. It couldn't have been a gift for any of us because it was no one's birthday and Christmas wasn't for months, so I asked Dad, 'What's in that box?' To which he replied in a proud voice, 'It's a treadmill for your mum.'

Mum had always been overweight and had applied for gastric surgery numerous times to help her lose it, but until today had been turned away by every doctor. They had now told her that if she lost some weight on her own to prove she was serious about it, they would give her a gastric band as soon as she was deemed fit enough to operate on. Mum was sitting on the sofa smiling next to my brothers as she said to all of us, 'Well, this is it. Time to get healthy! The doctors have said they can help me but only if I do my bit too, so here goes!'

I didn't understand much about gastric surgery or that being fat could ever become a life-threatening problem, but what I saw in front of me was a calorie-burning machine which I could use to lose even more weight for Judo. I could exercise whenever I wanted for however long I wanted, in front of the TV and in the comfort of my own home. This was fantastic!

As soon as Dad finished setting up the treadmill, I asked him, 'Can I have a go after Mum? Please! Please! Please?!" He laughed at how excited I was then turned to both Ashleigh and me as he replied, 'I've barely finished setting it up yet! Let me help your mum go first. You can both have a turn after dinner.'

We both ate dinner whilst we watched Dad help Mum walk on the treadmill. She had the speed set at 3mph and struggled keeping that pace going for ten minutes, but she had to start somewhere and I was proud of her for trying. I let Ashleigh run first because I wanted to make sure I did more than her, so it didn't matter how many calories she burned or how far she ran because I could simply run more after her. She ended up running 5km, which took her forty-five minutes, so I ran 6km in forty minutes to make sure I was better than her. I wanted to stop so many times but all I could think about was how hopeless my Olympic dreams would seem if I gave up and how weak quitting would make me, so I carried on running until I couldn't run any further. I felt great afterwards and an even greater sense of achievement when I weighed myself before bed that night. The weight was dropping off me and I owed it all to those pills, which were allowing me to train without poisoning my body with disgusting, calorific food. All I had left to do now was keep it a secret from anyone other than my twin, most importantly from Mum and Dad.

The next day after school, Ashleigh and I headed straight to the garages, where we met Charlie. We told him we didn't have long as we had Judo training in a couple of hours, so we made use of the time we had and carried on building the base. Our tarpaulin shelter had stayed in place and kept the rain out all night, so we got straight to work on making the rope swing. Behind the trench in the garden was a huge mud hill piled up high with broken bits of wood, so we rummaged through it on our hands and knees to look for a seat for our rope swing. We found a rusty old saw among the dirt in the pile, along with a plank of wood just thick enough to use for our swing. It was far too long to use when we found it, so Charlie spent the next two hours sawing through it with the rusted, blunt saw. He had blisters on his hands from working so hard but it was all worth it when we tied the piece of wood to the bottom of the rope. It fitted perfectly and looked amazing when we attached it to the oak tree.

Ashleigh was first to test it out, so she climbed back up onto the roof and turned back to face Charlie, who was standing with me down in the garden. As she approached the edge of the roof just above our shelter, I passed her the rope and she placed her legs either side of it, leaning back against the wooden seat we had made. She was incredibly excited to be the first person to test the swing, but through her shining smile I could see the fear creeping in as she took a deep breath and stepped towards the edge of the roof.

Charlie shouted, 'Are you scared?'

I caught Ashleigh's eye as she turned to face me and told her, 'Go on, Ash! You can do it.'

She took a firm grip of the rope with both hands and leapt forwards off the roof, before flying up metres into the air in front of us as she screamed in amazement and shouted through her laughter, 'This is the greatest thing we've ever built! I feel like I'm flying!'

Charlie and I both cheered at the fact the swing hadn't snapped and how brave Ash had been for trying it first, then together Charlie and I both shouted, 'I want to try! Let me have a go!'

We all took it in turns for what felt like hours on the swing, before neatly hiding it behind the oak tree when it was time to go home. As we climbed down from the roof Charlie said to us, 'This is going to be the best base ever! You're my best friends.'

No one had ever considered me a friend before, let alone a best friend! All the rejection from kids at school who only ever bullied me was suddenly non-existent and at that moment in time, nothing else in the whole world seemed to matter. We smiled and hugged each other as we said goodbye and walked our separate ways home.

As soon as we walked through the door, Ashleigh and I started getting changed for Judo, taking it in turns to keep watch whilst we took a Ritalin pill each. I smiled at her as we took a good look at both our bodies, which no longer seemed so bad since we'd lost some extra weight. As I stared into the mirror with my hands around my waist, I asked Ash if she thought I needed to lose much more. She pinched some of the skin on my stomach and said, 'Nah, you're good.'

I shook my head and pulled my training top over my face as I went on to say, 'I'm going to run on the treadmill again tonight.'

Ashleigh replied, 'But we have Judo. Do you mean you're going to run after training?!'

I smiled and told her that we needed to if we were going to do well at the weekend, so from that night onwards we both ran for an hour or longer after every training session. When we eventually arrived at Judo, some of the older kids walked in together wearing blue wrist bands. They were all carrying extra bags and it soon became obvious that they'd been swimming. One of the coaches greeted them by asking in a surprised voice, 'Since when did you lot swim? You'll need to get back in that pool if you haven't made the weight today, I'm serious! No calories can survive that workout!'

I didn't understand what he meant at first, but I soon got the message. I asked the coach, 'Does that mean swimming's good for losing weight?' To which he replied, 'Most definitely! Swimming burns more calories than any other physical activity and it works your entire body too!'

I smiled at him before heading over to the mat to train with everybody else, making sure I trained harder than all of them. I wanted the coaches to see me as different from the other fighters, I wanted to stand out. I wanted to be better than all of them.

After our two strenuous hours of training, Mum came to pick us up and take us home. We talked in the car about the international competition coming up at the weekend and Mum asked Ashleigh and me, 'Do you think you'll make the weight at the weekend?' To which Ashleigh replied, 'Oh, I think we will, Mum. I'm not worried!'

Of course she had no idea we meant anything by it, so she simply smiled and reminded us how proud she and Dad were of our success in Judo as she drove us home. I stepped out the car first and shouted, 'Shotgun! I'm on the treadmill first.'

Ashleigh argued and tried to run to the machine before me, but I got there first and was running on it before Mum had barely made it inside the house. Dad said, 'Come on girls, you don't need to be on that. You've trained already tonight, why don't you run tomorrow instead?'

I wasn't having any of it. I needed to burn more calories than Ashleigh and I needed to make my weight at the weekend, so I simply pleaded with my dad rather than arguing, and explained that I wouldn't take it too far, insisting I was only doing it to make the weight category on Sunday. He eventually agreed and let me run for an hour after training. Ashleigh had been doing push-ups and sit-ups whilst I'd been running, so I asked her how many she did so I could force myself to do more than her before I went to bed. She told me she had done one hundred of each and I knew she was lying and would probably have done two or three hundred, so I did five hundred push-ups, five hundred sit-ups and five hundred squats to be safe.

When Ashleigh and I eventually did go to bed, we stayed up and talked about how to burn more calories and how to hide it from Mum and Dad. I remembered what the coaches had said at Judo about swimming, so I asked Ashleigh what she thought about it and we decided we would get Mum to take us on Saturday. Dad was working that weekend and Mum was petrified of water, but we were ten years old, which was old enough to go by ourselves. Ashleigh asked me which pool we should go to and we soon both agreed on a swimming pool a couple of miles from our house, which didn't have much for children but had a 25m pool for lane swimming. This was great because we could swim up and down and race each other to burn as many calories as possible before Sunday, and it would be exciting to go by ourselves as we rarely went swimming without Dad or the rest of the family.

The rest of that week we spent all our free time exercising and building our base on top of the garages. School didn't seem to bother me so much because as the week went on, I became more and more focused on the competition on Sunday and that stopped me feeling so upset by the bullying from other kids at school. I felt superior to them because who else could honestly say that they were competing internationally with the chance of getting into the South of England Judo squad, which was the first step to fighting in the Olympics?

The Ritalin was keeping my mood up high, too, not only because of the effects of the amphetamines it contained, but also because of the weight it was causing me to lose. I no longer cared if anyone called me fat in school because aside from the fact that I was evidently doing something about it, the name-calling about my size motivated me to continue starving myself. I still felt upset about being called ugly and being excluded from interactional games with other children, but apart from only one lunch-time spent crying in the toilets, I found my sister Ashleigh when I wasn't in lessons and hung out with her group of friends.

When school finished on Friday afternoon, I walked home with Ashleigh as we shared our excitement for the weekend. We were picking up Ritalin and building our base today, swimming tomorrow and then competing on Sunday. This was going to be such a great weekend, because we'd be getting more Ritalin, which would make swimming lengths easier on Saturday, and we'd finally get some reward for all our hard work when we fought in the Internationals. As soon as we arrived home we changed out of our school uniforms, into our jeans and hoodies and started walking to the park, where we were meeting Charlie to go to the garages.

Charlie took longer than usual getting out as he was bringing his repeat prescription of Ritalin, which meant he had to sneak past his mum first. We waited for him for almost twenty minutes at the back of the park by the climbing frame. Ashleigh sat on her favourite swing and I sat on mine next to her. None of which compared to our rope swing of course, but the swings had always been our favourite place to sit in the park and so we sat happily and talked whilst we waited for Charlie. When Charlie arrived, he was riding a brand new bike, which he had been given as a gift from his dad a few days earlier. Any other kid would have been excited to be riding a new bike, but Charlie's face looked panicked and almost scared as he sped through the entrance gates of the park. Without even having time to take a breath, he looked behind him as Ashleigh and I asked what was wrong. The situation spoke for itself as we soon realized who Charlie was running from.

Drew entered the park with James following behind him; he took hold of Charlie by the scruff of his neck and shouted, 'That's my bike now, I said so. You can fight me if you've got a problem! Stupid little cunt.'

Charlie cried as his brother threw him off the bike and onto the ground, ripping Charlie's hoodie off in the process. Charlie shouted back through his tears, 'Dad bought me that! Give it back or I'll tell him you broke it!'

Drew laughed as he replied in the hate-ridden voice I despised, 'Dad's not coming back, ever. He's gone to prison because of you and your big mouth! Now we're never allowed to see him again and whose fault is that?' Drew then took one big step forwards as he hit Charlie in the face and ordered him to stand up, telling him to stop crying like a pathetic baby. 'Never could take a punch, could you?'

Charlie wiped the blood off his face and the mud off his clothes, whilst slowly limping over to the climbing frame Ashleigh and I had sheltered under for the duration of their fight. Drew followed shortly with James and I felt my heartbeat increasing because inside I knew that with every step they took, they were getting closer and closer to hurting us in the way they had before. Ashleigh and I were sitting completely under the climbing frame by this point and this particular climbing frame had two floors, the bottom of which had a play wall that meant no one could see what went on behind it. We were trapped and we knew it, and no one outside the park would be able to see what was about to happen. Ashleigh didn't say a word; I think she was too scared to speak or even cry. As Drew placed his arm around her and pulled her onto his lap, James unzipped my jeans and put his hands inside my underwear. I felt sick with helplessness as I felt his big cold hands touching me in every way he could. Drew then pushed Ashleigh down to the ground and onto her back, pulling her legs apart as he humped her through their clothes.

As Charlie watched from the swings, unable to help or even recognize that this was wrong, James pulled me away from Ashleigh as he took his hands away from my vagina and forced mine around his penis. It was just like the first time he'd made me do it, except by now I knew not to call for help or try to run away because it would only make things worse. I rubbed my hand up and down his private parts as he ordered me to go faster, whilst he kissed my numb lips, which were silenced in fear as I did what I was told. He pulled my jeans and underwear down to my knees as he pushed me onto my back and climbed on top of me, keeping my hands on his private parts as he pinned me down with his legs. He repeatedly touched my private parts and aggressively pushed my hands away if I tried to pull my clothes back up, then finally climbed off me when he heard the gate open from the other side of the park.

Drew had finished with Ashleigh a few minutes before we heard the gate squeak and as I stood up to walk beside her, we noticed Charlie was no longer inside the park. Ashleigh and I walked towards the entrance gates, where we saw Charlie standing at the side of the road, and since both Drew and James had stopped what they were doing for just a second, we took our chances and ran for it. Drew was shouting verbal abuse at us as well as throwing rocks, but we ignored him and walked towards Charlie as I comforted Ashleigh and told her to forget about what had just happened. Neither of us really understood the gravity of what was going on, we only knew it was something we could not tell Mum and Dad. After all, we barely even knew what sex was, so how could we tell if we were being sexually abused? For now it just seemed like it was something we had to put up with and I was OK with that, because I was distracted by the role of playing big sister to Ashleigh. She'd always fall down before me and I had to protect her as best as I could because she was still my baby sister.

When we reached Charlie outside the park, he handed me a bottle of pills. 'Here's your Ritalin, I guess we can't go to the garages today.'

I took the Ritalin out of his hand and popped two pills straight into my mouth. I thought I deserved to feel a bit of a buzz after what had just happened, so I gave Ashleigh two as well before thanking Charlie for staying out to give us the Ritalin. He asked, 'What are you doing tomorrow? It's Saturday, which means we have the whole day to work on our base.'

His offer sounded promising, but Ashleigh and I had already decided we were going swimming. Ashleigh choked back the tears and the lump in her throat as she replied, 'We're going swimming... Do you want to come?'

I didn't want anyone else to come swimming because it was supposed to be my day with Ashleigh, but Charlie was our best friend and I felt a little sorry for him after how his brother had treated him in the park, so I smiled with Ashleigh as we waited for his reaction. Charlie looked surprised but excited as he jumped to the offer and replied with, 'I'd love to! Are we going to Coral Reef?'

Coral Reef was a big indoor swimming pool, different to the pool we had planned. There was a pirate ship with water-shooting cannons, a volcano that erupted water and loads of other fun swimming entertainments. There was nothing for lane swimmers or people who swam to burn calories, but after discussing with Charlie which pool would be more fun to go to, our original plan was outnumbered with reasons to swim at Coral Reef instead. The three of us knew there was no way we could go to the garage roof today because Drew and James would see us from the park, but I had got my Ritalin, which was all I came out for. It didn't bother me too much that we couldn't build the base today, as I was happy enough to be going home and getting away from Drew and James.

Feeling drained from the events in the park, Ashleigh and I walked home to be away from everything. Tomorrow's a new day, I thought, as I comforted Ashleigh by telling her how fun tomorrow would be and that we could forget about Drew and James. She soon cheered up and we took it in turns on the treadmill as we shared a light workout to end the week. We told Mum about our change of plan for swimming and she agreed to drive us to Coral Reef with Charlie the next day, asking if we wanted any more friends to come with us. Of course she didn't know what had been going on with James and Drew, so when she asked us if Drew wanted to come swimming with Charlie we simply told her he wouldn't and we'd be fine without him. What we didn't realize, however, was that when Charlie asked his mum if he could go swimming with us alone, Drew would overhear the conversation and have other ideas.

CHAPTER 5

Coral Reef

When we woke up early Saturday morning, the house phone was ringing downstairs so I leapt up off my bed to go and answer it. It was Charlie's mum... I passed the phone to Mum as I waited for her to tell us Charlie was allowed to come swimming without his brother, but the conversation seemed to drag on for ages. When my mum finally passed the phone back to me, I spoke to Charlie, who told me he was only allowed to go on the condition that Drew and James came too. I took the phone up to my bedroom where I argued with him in the politest possible way, but he was adamant it would be OK. I told him I didn't want to go if Drew and James were going because they'd probably try and pull my bikini off in the pool or try to drown me, but I heard Drew's voice in the background saying he didn't like Ashleigh or me 'like that' anyway. Charlie reassured me that everything would be fine and we wouldn't even have to swim with them or anywhere near them. They just had to come with us in the car, so I had a long think about it with Ashleigh. She asked me quietly so Mum and Dad wouldn't hear us, 'What if Charlie's telling the truth? Do you think they'll leave us alone?'

I told her I didn't know for sure, but since their mum knew they were going swimming I thought they'd at least have to be nice to us to some degree. I knew they'd be nice in the car because my mum was taking us, and I thought all the excitement of swimming would distract them from us and maybe even deter them from hurting us. There was no way Ashleigh and I could be certain about it, but it seemed we now had no way out. We'd have to admit to Mum that we'd been arguing with James and Drew if we didn't want them to come with us or suddenly didn't want to go at all, so we got dressed and waited downstairs for Charlie to show up with Drew and James.

Ashleigh and I took longer than the average ten-year-olds getting ready as we stood in front of a mirror examining every swimming costume we tried on, judging our bodies by how fat we looked. We eventually gave up on finding a swimsuit that made either of us feel good about ourselves because although we both had six-pack abs and ribs showing, we still felt fat and self-conscious in everything we owned. We eventually opted for the bikinis Mum had bought us earlier in the week, when we first told her we wanted to go swimming. Mine was blue with silver dolphins on the bra piece and Ashleigh's was the same in pink. It was sparkly and made me feel grown up because it looked like an adult's bikini set and I knew it would make me feel more confident about practising my swimming, as I was still learning.

Almost an hour after Charlie had phones, all three of the boys turned up outside our house. Ashleigh answered the door and let them in. Drew smiled at my mum and brothers then nodded politely, before walking to the bottom of the stairs to see if I was nearly ready. Charlie and James walked into the front room where Ash was sitting on the sofa as I slid down the handrail of the stairs, throwing my swimming bag down before me. When I reached the bottom, Mum asked, 'Have you got everything, girls? Towels? Bikinis? Hairbrush?'

We answered, 'Yes Mum, can we go now?'

We then walked out of the front door and got in the car. Ash sat in the front as Drew and James took the middle seats, leaving Charlie and me in the back. Mum put the radio on and turned our favourite channel up loud, so we sang along to the songs we knew and talked for the entire forty-minute journey. The closer we got to Coral Reef, the less anxious I was of Drew and James, because this was now turning out to be not such a bad idea. As we drove closer to the swimming pool, I felt more and more excited until eventually, excitement was all I felt. This had actually turned out pretty well and Drew was being so nice to us, I thought this might even become a permanent change…

Ashleigh didn't seem so sure, however. Although there was little I could do to communicate privately with her from the back seat of the car, I sensed something was wrong and she didn't seem so excited to go swimming. She still didn't trust Drew, and knew he and James were only behaving this way because our mum was there, and it wouldn't take long for me to realize she was right.

When we arrived at Coral Reef, Mum pulled up outside the entrance doors, which were jammed open with people queuing to get in. Mum slowed the car down as she searched for a safe place to drop us off. Through my window I could see three sky-high water slides which looped around each other before disappearing back inside the building. I remembered swimming here years ago when Dad had taken us before we moved out of London. I was too small to ride any of the slides then, but I was tall enough now and as we sat in the car, I imagined the faces of thrilled swimmers being thrown from the slides, back into the pool.

Mum pulled over and Ashleigh was first to step out of the car, followed by the boys and then me. 'Stay together!' Mum shouted, as the five of us headed towards the main entrance. I suddenly felt unsure of what was going to happen after Mum had gone. She waved as she drove off, telling us to phone her later when we wanted to be picked up. As I stepped to walk beside Ashleigh, who still looked unsure, I told her everything was going to be fine and we'd have great fun whilst burning calories. However, my hopes of a change soon vanished and I began to feel the anxiety Ash had been feeling all along. James had seen the treadmill in our living room when he had stopped by our house that morning and had also noticed that our mum was overweight. He laughed at me and Ash as he said, 'Your mum's fucking fat! Does she force you to starve your bodies so she doesn't feel so bad about hers?'

I shouted back at him, 'Fuck off! At least my mum can take me swimming on a Saturday because she's not hungover or pregnant like yours!'

Ashleigh and Charlie both looked at me, stunned... I had finally gained the confidence to fight back a little. I was too angry to find it funny there and then but Ashleigh and Charlie could not stop laughing. Drew even joined in for a minute but I was soon put back in my place when James pushed me over, smashing my head against the metal bollard I landed on. My head began to hurt but I felt safe because there were so many people all around me I knew James and Drew could not touch me in front of all these adults.

We walked through the entrance to pay for our swim and James and Drew continued with their usual verbal abuse. It seemed like the only time Ashleigh and I were free from their bullying was when they were tormenting Charlie instead. They bullied him all the way through the changing rooms and into the pool because he couldn't swim, which meant he'd have to wear arm bands. Ashleigh was upset, but at a level she could just about tolerate, so she comforted Charlie and told him it didn't matter if he wore arm bands when we swam. We promised him we wouldn't laugh at him for wearing them and we didn't, not once. I knew how it felt to be laughed at, from the bullying I'd suffered since I was eight, so there was no way I'd let myself be the cause of that for anyone else.

Ashleigh and I changed into our bikinis and put our clothes in a locker, then walked to the pool where we sat on the edge and waited for the boys. Charlie joined us in the shallow end wearing his arm bands whilst Drew and James ran past us, splashing in the water as they shouted and tried to push us under. There were two small Jacuzzis at one side of the pool with rapids twisting around them in the shape of a number eight, joined to the rest of the pool by deep water where Ashleigh and I could not touch the bottom. There was a large waterfall entrance to a gigantic volcano which was surrounded by water, accompanied by a smaller waterfall that dropped from a larger Jacuzzi. Drew and James swam straight over to the volcano and Ashleigh and I decided to stay as far away from them as possible, so we pulled ourselves across the edge of the pool using the wall to move as we were weak swimmers. Charlie stayed with us as we entered one of the small Jacuzzis, which was empty by the time we reached it. We heard Drew shout as he swam away from the volcano and towards us, 'Eeew! Look at those skanky twins! And they've got a baby!'

James started laughing with him as they continued to make their way towards us. He was taunting Charlie for wearing arm bands in the hope that he could bully him into taking them off, so he could pull Charlie under the water, knowing full well he couldn't fight back. I had grown used to being called names because it happened so often at school now, but Ashleigh had only recently been bullied by anyone other than Drew and James. As a result, she found it more upsetting and harder to deal with than me, but it still hurt me never the less.

Ashleigh had been watching James and Drew as they made their way towards us but as they swam closer, she turned her eyes to face the pool floor and did not say a word. Charlie was looking up as his brother ran up the steps with James to join us in the Jacuzzi. Drew stopped running and immediately jumped into the middle of the Jacuzzi, followed by James, who was laughing as they splashed gallons of water over us. As Drew dived down to the bottom of the Jacuzzi, James grabbed my hair and pulled my head under water where he held it until I stopped moving. I must have only been under water for sixty seconds at most, but I was panicking because I couldn't breathe. Eventually I stopped struggling when I was so scared of what was happening that I thought this was how I would die. I was drowning and as I cried under the water, I accepted the fact that my final moments would be anything but peaceful.

After becoming too exhausted to move, I felt another hand take a firm grip under my arm whilst lifting me to the surface in one movement. It was Ashleigh, who was screaming at me as she cried, asking if I was OK whilst she pulled my face towards hers to see the colour of my lips. They had gone from a healthy pink to a terrifying blue within a matter of seconds. As James momentarily left us alone on one side of the Jacuzzi, I tried to make out what Ashleigh was saying whilst I concentrated on breathing. I felt dizzy and weak but soon snapped out of it as I had no other choice. I glanced at Ash to make sure she was not hurt but her eyes slammed shut like doors and her voice suddenly fell silent... Drew had been under water most of this time but was now staying above the surface whilst he crawled closer and closer to Ashleigh, until he was eventually cornering her as she tried to back away. He had ripped her bikini bottoms off after failing to remove her bra and was now forcing his hands inside her vagina, whilst groping her chest as he refused to give her bikini bottoms back.

I tried to push him away from her but I was not strong enough and as I sat beside Ash to try and comfort her instead, I felt James breathing heavily down my neck from behind me. He grabbed my hips and forced me onto his lap, laughing with Drew whilst he did it. He had taken his penis out of his swim shorts and was now trying to force it into my vagina from behind, whilst pulling my bikini bottoms off with one hand. His other hand was holding my wrists so I could not fight to keep my bikini bottoms on and as soon as he'd ripped them off, he placed both arms around my waist to stop me from scaping. Both boys knew Ashleigh and I would not run far as we were half naked, but they still dug their nails deep into our skin as they locked their arms around us to prevent any chance of escape. I felt so scared, so ashamed.

James pushed me back and forth on his lap as he rubbed my half-naked body up and down his, whilst continuing to breathe heavily down my neck. I turned my eyes away from Ashleigh as I could not bear to watch her being abused, feeling so helpless. I felt so guilty for not being able to protect her and I was crying myself, but when I looked at my twin, it was like watching myself in a mirror. When I watched Drew attacking Ashleigh, all I could see through her terrified eyes were the words she had said to me the first time this happened... Why didn't you help me? Why didn't you make it stop? It felt like I was having a nightmare where I was watching myself being raped, whilst asking guilt-ridden questions that would make anyone wish they were dead.

Ashleigh was still crying but had stopped struggling and was now staring blankly with her mouth closed, whilst cold tears rolled down her face. As I looked away from her, I noticed Charlie was still in the Jacuzzi. He wasn't helping them, but he wasn't helping us either. He was simply sitting on the side like nothing was happening. I couldn't work out whether he was deliberately cowering from the situation, or if he was just trying to ignore it because it was hurting him too. James finally threw me off his lap and pushed my head back under, but I was so relieved to be off of him that I didn't care if I choked on a mouthful of water. Drew shouted to him as he let go of Ashleigh and pushed her towards me, 'Eeew! You dirty cunt!'

Both boys laughed as Drew pointed to a disgusting white liquid which was now floating along the surface of the water. I knew exactly what it was and how it got there, so no matter how scared I was, I knew I had to make an escape as fast as I could. I quickly grabbed my bikini bottoms, which were now at the bottom of the Jacuzzi, before passing Ashleigh hers and expecting her to put them back on straight away, but what she did next frightened me beyond any fear I had ever imagined. She was still staring blankly, unable to move, and she was too terrified and exhausted to even stand up, as I put her bikini bottoms back on for her. I had never seen her like this and it was hard to watch, let alone help her on my own. I didn't know what to do.

As I pulled her bikini bottoms up past her knees and towards her hips, I accidently touched her private parts with the side of my hand. 'Sorry,' I said, expecting her to push my hand away and pull them up herself.

'It's OK' she replied, 'Everyone touches me there.' Her voice was so quiet she sounded like an empty soul, whispering after all life had been sucked out of it by an angel of death. I knew we had to get out of there and I'd either have to carry her out myself or wake her up from semi-consciousness if we had any chance of getting away, so I grabbed her hand and told her it was over now... We just had to get out of that

Jacuzzi, so we waited for the boys to walk ahead before escaping behind them, keep as much of a distance as possible.

As Ashleigh and I walked down the steps, Drew ran back to push me over the hand rail and sideways off the steps, causing me to fall into the pool below the Jacuzzi. I could just about touch the bottom if I stood on my tiptoe, but the rapids were pulling me in and I was finding it increasingly difficult to keep my head above the water. I screamed as I went under and felt myself being pulled around the rapids like a rag doll… There had been a lifeguard standing where I was now drowning, but he had seen Drew push me in and so instead of noticing, let alone rescuing me, he simply stood at the other side of the pool talking to Drew. Ashleigh jumped in after me but could not swim either, so she kept hold of the wall, which she could use to pull us both out when she grabbed me. This plan would have worked at any other part of the pool but the rapids were too strong and Ashleigh soon lost her grip, which left us both panicking as we sank deeper and deeper under water.

I remember holding her hand as tightly as I could, thinking everything would somehow be OK if we held onto each other. I didn't want to let go of Ashleigh because it was my fault she had jumped in in the first place, so I tried pushing her up to the surface as much as I could. We were both drowning when Charlie ran to our rescue at the side of the pool, holding a long float which he had taken from a stranger. He threw it as close to me as he could whilst keeping firm grip of one end, so that I could grab hold of the other end to pull Ashleigh and me to safety. With his help, I managed to pull myself to the side with one arm whilst holding onto Ashleigh with the other. When I reached the side of the pool, Charlie let go of the float and took hold of my arms with both his hands, supporting my weight whilst I lifted Ash to the surface and placed her on the side of the pool. She coughed as she lifted me up and out the water afterwards, by which point both of us were choking and struggling to catch our breath. We didn't even bother trying to talk as we were concentrating on breathing instead, but we still threw our arms around each other as Charlie asked if we were OK.

Drew and James were laughing and chanting 'Cry-babies! Cry-babies!' as they swam towards us with Charlie's armbands, which they had taken from him. There were now lifeguards crowding around us and Charlie soon realized his brother had got us all thrown out for swearing at them, but Drew had jumped straight back into the pool with James and they were refusing to get out. A family had also complained to the lifeguards about Charlie taking their float, barely even recognizing that he had used it to save our lives. All they saw was a bunch of rude-mouthed kids who were obviously thieves. I felt angry at this but relieved at the fact we now had an easy way out, so Ashleigh and I made our way to the changing rooms where we took our towels out from our lockers, ready to shower before getting changed and going home.

After showering with Ashleigh in the female changing room, we walked to a family cubicle to get dressed, but as soon as we opened the door, Drew and James followed us in with their bags full of clothes. Charlie was banging the door from outside as they locked us in, refusing to give him his clothes. Charlie was desperate, shouting, "Let me in, Drew! Give me my fucking clothes!'

Drew ignored him and started laughing with James as they pulled his towel under the changing-room door, leaving him standing naked outside the locked cubicle we were in. After a few minutes of continuous shouting and crying from Charlie, James unlocked the door and pulled Charlie in with us. He slipped on the wet floor and I threw his towel back to him so he could cover himself up as he was still completely naked. Drew took hold of Ashleigh and placed her on his lap whilst James did the same with me. I felt extremely uncomfortable but not scared as such, because I thought they were still wearing their swim shorts under their towels. I was wrong however, as I would soon realize when James grabbed my hand and pulled it behind my back and under his towel. He wrapped my hand around his penis as he ordered me to masturbate him, holding me close with his other hand. I reluctantly did what I was told until he said I could stop, which was the only thing I knew. When he eventually allowed me to stop, he still forced me to stay on his lap and as he put both his hands down my bikini bottoms, I turned to face Ashleigh, who was crying.

Drew had pulled her legs apart and was facing her as he rubbed his body up and down against hers. He was standing up and had her back against the wall whilst he ignored her tears and tried to kiss her. 'Kiss back!' he whispered with his teeth gritted, as he carried on humping her through her tears. Both Drew and James laughed any time Ash or I tried to stop them, and Charlie simply curled up in the corner of the changing cubicle. His eyes were closed, and with his hands covering his ears, he rocked back and forth trying not to cry. James was still forcing his hands inside my vagina and it hurt so much, I kept on struggling to try and fight him off. I screamed as loud as I could before he placed his hand over my mouth and said, 'No one's going to hear you so you might as well stop.'

He kissed the back of my neck and my entire body was shaking by this point. I thought to myself about what he had just said, and he was right. This changing area was full of screaming children, laughing and playing loudly. Who's going to notice the difference between someone screaming in laughter and someone screaming for help?

I stopped struggling until I heard a man walking past our changing cubicle and as I carefully watched the gap underneath the door, I waited until I could see his feet then shouted for help. 'Help! Someone fucking help!' James and Drew immediately started laughing as loud as they could, trying to make it sound as though we were simply playing with them. As they concentrated on getting rid of the stranger who walked past, I quickly made a break for it and grabbed Ashleigh's hand whilst unlocking the cubicle door. We ran out to the other side of the changing room and tried to hide from the boys. The man who had walked past was gone, but we were free from James and Drew so we concentrated on finding a single cubicle each to get dressed in. Drew and James followed us out and soon took hold of Charlie to keep him from telling on them, but as usual Charlie would keep his mouth shut. He never called for help but I never resented him for that, even to this day. He was only eight years old himself so I suppose he didn't understand what was going and even if he did, he would have been too scared of his brother to tell the secret.

After a few minutes of searching for a free changing cubicle, Ashleigh and I found two single ones side by side. I locked the door behind me as soon as I'd made sure Ash was safe in her cubicle beside mine, then started drying myself with my towel. I could still hear the boys running up and down the changing area and it didn't take long for them to suss out which cubicles Ashleigh and I were in. Before I knew it, both James and Drew had reached their arms under our changing cubicles and pulled the towels out from under our feet. James took Ashleigh's and Drew took mine, leaving us both standing cold and naked, debating whether or not to open the door to chase after them. After taking my towel and refusing to give it back, Drew then climbed the side of my changing cubicle and poked his head over. He spat down at me as I screamed because I was completely naked, then he tried to reach down and take my clothes. I eventually decided to get dressed whilst I was still wet in the hope that my clothes would dry me out a little, but the main reason for doing so was because I knew there was no way in hell I was getting my towel back without running around the main changing area naked. That's what Drew and James wanted, and I was safe from them as long as I had my clothes on whilst staying inside my locked changing cubicle.

Drew had also taken Ashleigh's towel but by the time I had got dressed, he had dumped both our towels on the floor by an empty locker. I picked up the towels and noticed that Drew and James were no longer around, so I made as little noise as I possibly could to prevent them coming back to aggravate us. I knocked on Ashleigh's changing room and as I peeped through a hole in the side of the door, I could see she was still standing naked without a towel. The gap was merely inches separating her cubicle door from the floor, but I was small enough to fit under it. I startled her when I crawled under but I quickly whispered, 'It's OK! It's only me.'

She helped me under and pulled me up, then hugged me tightly. Her face was bright red from crying and her body had been shivering for so long that her lips and finger tips were turning blue. 'Here...' I said, as I wrapped a towel around her. I used the other towel to dry her feet and help her get dressed, as she was too cold to move herself. She thanked me and then said, 'I want to go home. I hate this.' She had stopped crying but was still visibly upset by everything that had happened. I told her we were only minutes away from calling Mum and she would pick us up soon to take us home, so we finished getting dressed before walking to the hairdryers to check our faces in the mirrors. We then made our way out of the main exit doors as we looked around to make sure James and Drew weren't following us. We didn't talk a lot to each other; I think Ash was still upset... I didn't feel quite as upset as her, but I still felt extremely dirty and ashamed by what had happened with James and Drew. Although I knew he had forced me, I still felt I should have done more to stop it. I felt extremely guilty too, because this was all my fault. If I hadn't suggested going swimming for exercise in the first place, we wouldn't be in this mess. If I hadn't waited for Charlie to get my Ritalin yesterday, none of this would have happened. Ashleigh was hurting and it was all my fault... I couldn't protect her. I got her into a mess I could not get her out of and I felt so guilty and tortured by it, that I think that's when my depression started.

When we walked out of those doors, for the first time in my life I truly wished I was dead. For all the pain I had caused Ashleigh, I did not deserve to carry on living. This world would be a much better place without me, and I owed it to my family to ensure they weren't burdened by my pathetic life any longer.

CHAPTER 6

I'll Never Tell

As we walked out of the exit doors and into the car park, I searched through my phone for Mum's number. Merely seconds into calling her, I felt a fist hit me from behind, knocking my phone out of my hand and onto the floor. It was James, accompanied by Drew and Charlie who had been waiting for us outside. I turned around to face James before backing away and picking up my phone, but he aggressively picked it up before I could and shouted, 'What the fuck do you think you're doing? You can't call your mum yet, it's too early! If you call her now, she'll know we were all kicked out and you'll be in just as much trouble as us.'

He was right. What was I thinking? No adults had helped me before, so what good would my mum be able to do now? I didn't want to get Ash in trouble or be banned from seeing Charlie as a consequence of being kicked out, because I relied on Charlie's friendship to supply me with Ritalin, so I kept my mouth shut and did as I was told.

'OK', I answered. "Can I have my phone back please? I won't call anyone, I swear.'

He threw my phone to Drew, who then teased me with it for a while but eventually gave it back, so I agreed not to call anyone for a lift for at least an hour. I turned to Ashleigh whilst Drew and James became preoccupied with teasing Charlie, and I sat down beside her as I tried to comfort her. I told her we were safe now because we were in a public place with cameras and people surrounding us, which meant James and Drew could not hurt us anymore. I told her we only had to wait for an hour until we could call Mum, and we would tell her we were swimming for the entire time and that we had fun. We knew we couldn't tell anyone about what had happened because we felt so dirty and to blame, but at ten years old we hardly understood the seriousness of our abuse, so it didn't hurt so much because we still thought it was just like bullying... But who tells on a bully? Everyone would think we were weak and our family thought we were so strong because of the Judo, so we couldn't tell them about anything that was happening as then we would no longer be their perfect little girls. We'd always tried so hard to make Mum and Dad proud. I wasn't going to let Drew and James ruin that for us.

After sitting at the side of the road for around twenty minutes, the boys were all whining about how bored they were as they tried to think of something to do to pass the time. Charlie asked Drew, 'Do you want to build a base? We could make one at the side of the car park.' Drew answered, 'Well that's stupid, everyone will see you there! I'm going to the woods. Who's coming?' James jumped to the offer and Charlie started following behind, but Ashleigh and I stayed put and refused to follow them. Ash told me she did not want to go to the woods because she was tired and just wanted to go home. I didn't want to go either because I knew what the boys were like and after what had happened in the pool, there was no way in hell I would go with them into a forest where they could do whatever they wanted to us. We told them we were happy sitting at the side of the car park and didn't mind waiting there instead, but Drew quickly said, 'You have to come with us. Your mum said we have to stay together, and I'm not getting in shit because you won't do as you've been told.'

Charlie told them to fuck off and leave Ash and me alone, but Drew and James simply laughed in his face and pushed him down to the ground beside Ashleigh and me. Just as they were about to leave us behind, a man in blue uniform walked out of the building accompanied by two lifeguards. He was smartly dressed and I assumed he was the manager. I started to feel something was wrong as he approached us with the two lifeguards, who began pointing at us, telling him, 'That's them!'

He addressed all of us when he said, 'Hello, I'm the manager of Coral Reef. We've had complaints about you five all day and you've been asked to leave, so you need to leave the premises now or we'll be calling the police.' I didn't know what to do. Drew started shouting and swearing at him, which only seemed to make the situation worse. Charlie pleaded with the manager, 'But we've left the pool. Can't we even sit outside in the car park? We're not doing anything wrong.'

The manager disagreed and made it very clear that we had to leave the entire area surrounding the building, so it seemed Ashleigh and I had no other choice but to go to the woods with the boys.

James followed Drew in front whilst Charlie walked behind with Ashleigh and me. I noticed the worried look on Ashleigh's face as we walked towards the woods but I was too afraid to turn back because the Coral Reef staff had threatened to call the police, so I walked alongside her as we followed Drew into the woods. At first glimpse it was beautiful. The trees were so high that for a moment I believed they touched the sky and each one was surrounded by a thriving bed of brightly coloured flowers, which stood out from the black paths of dirt. All the beauty of the scenery was soon swept away, however, by a sickening sense of fear as though all the bright colours were about to turn to dust the second Drew and James proved their actual intentions for luring us into the woods.

James and Drew walked ahead as Ashleigh and I followed behind with Charlie. I wanted to hold Ashleigh's hand to show her that everything would be fine because I was right next to her to make sure no one touched her. However, I also knew the boys would bully us for holding hands, which would only make things worse, so I carried on walking as close to Ashleigh as possible to reassure her as best as I could. I never truly believed I could protect her of course, but if I was able to assure her that she was safe then maybe I wouldn't feel so scared myself. It felt like we had walked for hours because every step we took felt like we were treading on egg shells around James and Drew. Their abuse had always been considerably worse when there were no adults around and it seemed as though with every second that passed, the danger was becoming greater.

The further we walked into the woods, the less Drew and James bothered to talk to each other. They simply took hold of large sticks which they used to knock down flowers and tall patches of grass, whilst shouting loudly as though they had taken over the forest and were now destroying it. We walked a little further before stopping at a hut-like base that somebody had already built, before Drew ripped apart every little detail as he tore the whole thing down. Charlie said it would be a good idea to use the wood from their base to build ours, but it seemed Drew had other ideas. He grabbed Ashleigh's hand and pulled her away from me, before putting his hands down her trousers and through her underwear whilst ordering her to do the same to him. She complied with Drew in fear of being beaten with no adults around to protect us.

James grabbed my hips from behind and pulled me towards him as he put his hands between my legs and ripped through my underwear, forcing his hands inside my vagina yet again. I was so scared I could barely breathe but the fear did not bother me anywhere near as much as the sense of defeat I felt, which made me feel utterly hopeless and worthless. After everything that had happened inside the swimming pool, I had walked out of Coral Reef thinking it was all over, when in reality that was far from the case. James groped me from behind as he pulled one of my hands behind my back, forcing it down his trousers. 'Rub it!' he ordered, as he held my hips tighter until his grip became painful. I hated this and felt so dirty and ashamed, but I preferred facing away from him as I could not bear to look at his face, which scared me beyond any stretch of the imagination.

After groping my body and holding me close for a considerable amount of time, James suddenly threw me onto the floor whilst pulling down his trousers and taking out his penis out of his underwear completely. I knew the drill by now; I thought I would just have to lie on my back with my legs apart and soon this would be over. I didn't even bother resisting as I knew this would only make things worse, so I closed my eyes and waited for the worst. He shouted at me for doing so, however, and I was unsure as to how I had made him mad, but I didn't dare argue as he grabbed me by the scruff of the neck whilst pulling me onto my knees to face him. He told me to suck it, which I refused and so he hit the side of my face, which knocked me back onto the cold ground. I turned my head to look up to where Ashleigh was still being held by Drew, who was waving his penis around in her face whilst ordering her to suck it. She was crying and covering her face with her hands and I felt so ashamed at the fact that I could not stop it. I hated having to watch her being hurt, but there was nothing I could do so I turned my head the other way to face James.

To my surprise he had turned his back by this point and I saw this as a chance to escape, so I quickly crawled forwards until I was back up on my feet and running towards Ashleigh. I took a firm grip of her hoodie and pulled her up towards me whilst telling both boys to fuck off, then I pulled her close by my side and ran as fast as I could with her. She eventually caught up with me as I had been supporting most of her weight whilst running, leaving her stumbling next to me for most of our escape. The boys didn't bother to chase after us for very long as they both smoked heavily and were very unfit, but we carried on running as fast as we could until we were completely out of the woods. I felt bad for leaving Charlie behind with his brother and James as they were so aggressively abusive towards him, but I had to put my sister and me first, as we were in the most danger around them.

We ran until we were on the main road which lead back to the swimming pool and we didn't stop until we were certain we could be seen by adults and other members of the public. We walked back to the car park of Coral Reef and decided to sit outside the entrance doors where Mum had first dropped us off. We were very cautious of the Coral Reef staff coming out to speak to us again as we had returned after they'd told us to leave, but the manager only walked outside briefly and could see the pair of us were upset so he nodded at us before walking back inside. I sat down against a wall with Ashleigh and stroked her hair as I held my arm around her shoulders, trying to make her feel safe because I was there to protect her. She cried for what felt like hours, but I told her in the nicest possible way that she had to stop crying or else Mum would know we had done something bad.

I was freezing cold because my hair was still wet from swimming and by this point I just wanted to go home, so I reached into my pocket for my phone, which I then used to dial Mum's number. She didn't answer for a while and as the phone continued to ring, I felt more and more agitated and scared of the conversation that was about to take place. My voice was quiet and shaky and I could feel a lump swelling up inside my throat as tears started to fill my eyes, but I took a deep breath and faced the ground as I told myself to man up and hide all my feelings from my mum. I had to appear normal or else she would know something had happened, and how disgusted would she be if she found out what her filthy daughters had really been up to? Let alone if she found out we'd been kicked out of Coral Reef. I didn't want to let anything slip when I spoke to her, although I knew I'd have to tell her something as she'd want an explanation for why we were no longer with the boys, asking to be picked up alone. I had to think of something fast…

When Mum eventually answered the phone, I took a deep breath and tried to focus on sounding normal. She answered in a calm voice, 'Hi girls, how was swimming?' I automatically started my lies about how much fun we had and how exciting it was, although a strong part of me desperately wanted to scream and shout the truth about what had really happened. Despite being extremely upset, I maintained my front as I calmly told Mum, 'Swimming was good, thanks. We're ready to be picked up now.' To which she replied, 'OK, I'll leave now, so make sure you stay with the boys until I get there.'

My head started pounding... What do I tell her? It was then that I decided I would say something, I finally had the courage... 'We're not with the boys, Mum, we fell out, so I'm just with Ashleigh now.'

She then began to sound less calm as she went on to ask why we had fallen out, to which I replied almost without thinking, 'They were being horrible, Mum... They said we had to stay with them and they tried to make us suck their dicks...'

Mum quickly snapped back in a shocked and confused voice, 'What?! What do you mean?'... My voice suddenly fell silent. I opened my mouth but failed to make any words come out... Mum stuttered a little when she questioned me, as if she was disgusted at what I had said and I knew from then that there was no way on earth that I could tell her what had happened... I decided there and then that I would never tell her, as my fears of how she would react had been proved true. I felt at fault for what had happened and now I knew it had to be kept secret. My decision never to tell was not Mum's fault and I have never blamed her because I had most likely misinterpreted the way her words sounded through the phone, but I felt from that moment that I could never tell anyone about what was going on as it would make me a bad person, because it was somehow all my fault. I managed to compose myself before answering and telling Mum, 'Never mind, just come and pick us up.'

I continued to comfort Ashleigh whilst we waited for Mum and after almost forty minutes I felt a huge sigh of relief as I saw her pull up next to us in the car park. She rolled down the window and asked if the boys were coming as she didn't feel completely comfortable leaving them there with no way home, but I tried as hard as I could to convince her they would find their own way back and we could leave without them. She wasn't buying it, however, and insisted we waited for a few minutes. Sure enough, all three boys turned up and began to run as they approached our car. Drew and James returned to playing innocent as they shouted, trying to appear as scared as possible, 'Wait!! Stop!! Were you really just going to leave us?'

Worthless

I couldn't believe it. After running away from them all day, they still caught up with us and all my escape efforts had been for nothing. Mum shouted out of the window, 'Get in then, quickly. All of you.'

Charlie got in first, sitting behind Ashleigh in the middle row of seats. Drew followed behind and sat next to him, leaving James with the option of sitting either with them or me. Sure enough, he chose to sit next to me in the back of the car and I felt my body turn completely numb as I felt the greatest sense of defeat, ever. This was still not over... This day was never going to end, and every time I came close to escaping, Drew or James would always find another way to get me.

James grabbed the top of my thigh as Mum began to drive, though she could not see us properly in the mirror from the driver's seat, so after flinching, I simply stared blankly out the window and tried to focus my attention outside instead. James soon let go of my leg and I still felt extremely uncomfortable and scared, but I knew it would soon be over as we would be home and away from them. As Ashleigh and I tried not to cry, Mum asked the boys where they wanted to be dropped off. They agreed on being dropped off at Charlie and Drew's house, then kept up their innocent act by being polite and thanking my mum for the lift. This angered me severely because I wished that someone, just someone, would see through their lies and realize what was actually going on. I hated how blind adults could be and how easy it was for James and Drew to bully us, but I suppose in some ways it made me stronger, because I learnt at a very young age that no one would be there to protect me, and that I could only ever count on myself. I grew up fast in that sense because I lost the emotional need to be cared for, which meant no one could take it away from me as it was already gone.

We soon arrived at the boys' house, where Mum pulled up to let them out. They casually made their way inside and towards a window, before sticking their middle fingers up at us the moment Mum's back was turned. I turned my head to ignore it, which also meant I failed to see the note Charlie was holding up for me and Ashleigh, which read 'Meet at garages tonight'. This meant I let Charlie down later that night when he snuck out to our garage base, only to wait and wait as Ashleigh and I failed to arrive. However, even if I had noticed that note I was in no fit state to go back out after all that had happened at Coral Reef, so it was probably for the best that Mum simply drove off and took us home. When we finally arrived home, Dad was sitting downstairs with our brothers, Jake and Jed, who were watching TV as they greeted us when we walked through the door. Dad asked us, 'Did you have fun, girls?' To which we replied, 'Yes thanks. We ate a lot when we were out though, so we don't want dinner tonight, thanks.'

Dad then agreed with Mum that we didn't have to eat dinner if we didn't want to, as we had our Judo competition the next day and would have to weigh in early, so Ashleigh and I went straight upstairs to our room where we spent most of that afternoon. Ashleigh eventually went downstairs at around 7pm, which was the first time I'd found myself completely alone that day, meaning I could finally think without having to hide how I was feeling. At first it scared me because as I lay in my bed staring blankly at the ceiling, I found I could not stop crying. After a few minutes of silent tears rolling down my cheeks, I looked to the left side of my bed and put my hand down the side to reach for my secret stash of Ritalin. I don't know what I was thinking and maybe it was the pain thinking for me, but I immediately opened the entire packet and shoved the remaining eight pills into my mouth. I felt a sudden heaving response from my stomach and thought I was going to vomit as they tasted so foul without water, so I ran to the bathroom and placed my mouth around the tap above the sink. I managed to keep all eight pills down as I rinsed my mouth out with water, but as I turned back to face my bedroom door I also noticed a packet of paracetamol lying on the floor. I remembered asking Mum what they were for one day when she took them for a headache, and she said they were for taking pain away. I was in a lot of pain, mentally rather than physically, but at ten years old I did not understand the difference so I picked up the packet and swallowed twelve pills.

That should do it, I thought to myself, as I gulped down even more water from the tap before returning to my bedroom, where I collapsed onto my bed face down. As I rolled over onto my back, I suddenly started to feel sick and dizzy as though the room was spinning around me in circles. I was out of breath and breathing really fast, but felt too weak to move, so I simply lay in my bed staring into space until Ashleigh returned almost two hours later.

'Night Robs, love you,' she whispered as she switched the light off. I mumbled back to her, 'Night Ash, love you too,' and with that she went to sleep. I was too weak to move from my bed but at the same time I was feeling increasingly energetic as the Ritalin had kicked in and was keeping me awake. It was a strange sensation, because although the amount of Ritalin I'd taken was more than enough to give me a buzz, I was still physically drained and emotionally upset about the day's events. I strongly recall this as one of my first experiences with depression, something I would endure countless times again throughout the rest of my life. It left me with a sense of disconnection from reality which came as a comfort, but also with a feeling of complete emptiness. I felt as though I was nothing more than a spiritless body, shadowing the living as I grew closer to death.

I tried to ignore how I was feeling by blocking out the depressive thoughts and focussing only on the buzz I was feeling from the Ritalin, but it still did not take the pain away. 'Those stupid paracetamol didn't work,' I thought to myself, since I was still in so much pain. I had also started to feel extremely sick and thought I would vomit on more than one occasion throughout the night, but nothing ever made it from my stomach up to my mouth. I suspect this was because I had hardly eaten all day, but I still kept a bucket close to my bedside just in case. I remained awake enjoying the buzz and lying in the exact same position until 4:30am, which was when I finally fell asleep, only to be woken less

than two hours later to get ready for Sunday's Judo competition.

CHAPTER 7

Destroyed

Mum woke me by tugging on my duvet and softly saying 'Wake up, girls, it's time to get ready now.' I was so tired I wanted to stay put in my bed, but I knew that was no option. As I opened my eyes and sat up, I turned to face Ashleigh, who was already dressed and was packing her bag for the competition.

'We're leaving in 10 minutes!' Dad shouted from the bottom of the stairs, in an attempt to hurry us up. I quickly put my Judo trousers on with a white t-shirt and dragged myself downstairs, leaving Ash to pack both our bags.

"I don't feel well," I said to Mum, who told me to stop being silly and that I was just nervous for such a big competition. At ten years old I wouldn't have known what a 'comedown' was as I had not yet been taught about drugs, so I was easily convinced that what Mum said was true and that I was simply feeling sick with nerves. I walked downstairs, grabbing my hoodie from the hallway as I made my way to the car, where my brothers were waiting. Ash followed shortly with both Mum and Dad, who told us not to eat or drink anything as it could jeopardize our weigh-ins. As we pulled out of the driveway and onto the road, Mum told us to remember how proud they were of us and that they just wanted us to try our best today, because winning medals is only a plus and not a necessity as long as we gave our all. Ashleigh and I were still upset from Coral Reef the previous day, but we both pushed it aside in our minds as it was now time to focus on the competition. I struggled with that more than Ashleigh because from the moment I woke up, I felt as if I would vomit. I tried to put on a brave face for Mum and Dad so they would not suspect anything with regards to my overdose the night before, but this was proving harder than I thought the closer we came to arriving at the competition.

After sleeping through almost the entire fourty-five-minute journey, we arrived at Crystal Palace for the London Internationals. It was a privilege to be here, as the building and surroundings were so beautiful, but all I could think about was how sick I felt and how to get out of fighting. Weigh-In time came along and both Ash and I made the weight no problem, but were both feeling too sick to fight. Ashleigh eventually went on to win a silver medal but I had managed to vomit all over the seating area by the Judo mats, so had to sit out and was not allowed to fight. I distinctly remember Mum and Dad being annoyed and slightly angry that they had committed so much to paying for all my Judo training on top of the entry costs for the competition, but I didn't care because I felt so dead inside about what was going on that it didn't matter to me what they thought. All I cared about was that they never found out the truth.

After hanging round all day to collect Ashleigh's medal, we drove home and I was finally able to catch up on the sleep I'd missed last night. I was knocked out by 5pm and apart from popping into my room once to see if I was OK, Mum and Dad both left me alone and so I kept up the lie that I simply didn't feel well. However, I knew I'd have to go to school the next day if I wanted to go out with Ashleigh and Charlie afterwards, so I slept through the rest of the night and woke up around 7am to get ready for school.

I truly hated school by this point in my life. Even though I had not yet even made it into secondary school, all the bullying was making me feel so depressed that I had seriously thought about killing myself, and I constantly wondered if it would hurt any less than the pain I was feeling now. I had heard my older sister Callie talk about a suicide which was mentioned on the news one evening, and I had been contemplating the idea ever since the sexual abuse started getting serious. She said she thought it was selfish of someone to do such a thing, because they must not be thinking about the people they are leaving behind and what they are doing to their families. After I heard that, I sometimes wished I had no family just so that I could kill myself and end all the pain without hurting anyone else. All the pain would be gone in an instant, and I'd never have to deal with the school bullies, or Drew and James, or even the self-hatred I constantly felt for being too fat and not good enough... But I did have my family to think about. So I knew I had to put up with the pain for their sake.

Ashleigh and I packed our school bags and left to walk to school together. It was two short roads to the park and then one long road to get to school. Tomlinscote Secondary School was nearby and was a right turn from the park, leaving Ashleigh and I to turn left to go to Ravenscote Junior School with the younger kids. Charlie went to a different junior school and was always driven there by his mum, but Drew and James both went to Tomlinscote, so it was normal for us to cross paths if they were running late. As we walked closer to the park, Drew came out of nowhere and although I could not see James, Drew was still walking with a huge group of boys from his school. They started shouting names at us from the other side of the road, swearing and throwing stones at me and Ashleigh. They must have been in the park before school because there were ripped pieces of tarmac lying around the park that they had thrown after vandalizing it, and I could also see thick smoke in the air from rather large cigarettes they were smoking... But this didn't smell like cigarette smoke. I couldn't quite put it into words, but the smell was like nothing I had ever come into contact with before. I didn't get close enough to see their faces properly but even from the other side of the street, I could see that their eyes were red and glazed and they were all walking really slowly even before they stopped to hurl abuse at us.

Drew shouted, 'Fucking skanks! Look how ugly they are, everyone!'

I had already picked up pace to speed-walking and as they continued to throw tarmac and stones at us, I turned to Ashleigh, who stayed close by my side. 'Come on Ash,' I said quietly so the boys wouldn't hear, 'let's get out of here.'

I tried so hard not to cry, but the sight of Ashleigh upset would always conquer me in the end. When we got to school, Ashleigh and I split up to go to our separate classes. I tried to wipe my tears away in the toilets so as to compose myself before entering the classroom, but a group of girls from the year above followed me in.

'Why are you crying?' one of them asked unsympathetically, whilst staring at my red face. 'Is it because you're so ugly?'

I was so embarrassed and upset that all I wanted to do was to run out of there as fast as I could, but they had surrounded me and were now blocking the door. Through their hysterical fits of laughter, they managed to continue pushing me around whilst calling me every name under the sun until the school bell rang. After what felt like hours, they left to go to their classes and I was left alone in the toilets. There was a large mirror above the sinks and it was at that very moment I gazed upon my reflection, truly absorbing how ugly I was. I stared at every aspect of my face and body, which I despised more with every second that passed and if I hadn't overheard my older sister's opinion on suicide before, I would have quite happily attempted it there and then.

After finally arriving to my lesson, I sat down and got on with my work in silence to try and take my mind off the bullying. No one bothered to talk to me anyway as I was 'that weird kid who no one likes', but that helped me concentrate on my schoolwork, which seemed to be the only thing I was good at besides Judo. I managed to get through the rest of the day without breaking down or crying until I got home, although there were many occasions on which I almost did.

For the rest of that week, I spent most of my spare time crying alone in my bedroom. I didn't ponder too much on the sexual or physical abuse from James and Drew as I could deal with the scars and bruises, but the words and name-calling really got to me. When I closed my eyes and shut myself away from everything else, the words would still be there inside my head and I could never escape. It was like a thousand voices stabbing my ears every time I tried not to listen, and no matter how hard I tried, they would always be there. If I tried to fight or ignore them, they would only get louder inside my head so eventually I began believing that all the awful things people said about me were true.

A few weeks rolled by and I was running out of Ritalin, so I knew I'd have to meet up with Charlie sooner or later to get some more. After school seemed like a good time of day because Drew and James finished school over an hour later than us, so we could go out without running into them, which would mean no trouble. We soon got hold of Charlie, who agreed to meet us at the garages by the park after school. We hadn't built on our base up there for a while, so it seemed like a fun place to hang out when the three of us met up. School had been tough that day because as usual, the other kids had been making fun of me all day. However I stayed in a reasonably good mood because I knew it would only be a few hours until I could pick up my Ritalin from Charlie, so I restrained myself from crying and focused on the positives. Ashleigh and I were both excited to be building our base again, but we were also very cautious of being around Charlie as we knew that Drew and James could show up at any moment.

As soon as we changed out of our school clothes, we walked straight to the garages to wait for Charlie, who had finished school the same time as us. When we arrived I heard Charlie shout to us from the garage roof, 'I've got your pills! You all right?'

I said hello and smiled as I went to give Ashleigh a foot up, but I soon noticed the confused look on her face as she crawled onto the roof and looked around. After pulling me up by my arms, Charlie and Ash walked to the back of the roof where our shelter had previously been. The rope from our swing was nowhere to be seen and the wall we had made out of mud had been kicked to the ground. The mattress wall had been knocked down and the sheet of tarpaulin had been ripped up and thrown all over the roof… Everything we had built had been destroyed, as if someone had walked through it with a sledge hammer, smashing everything to pieces. I started to feel scared as I asked Charlie, 'What happened?'

He didn't answer me. Instead he simply handed me the Ritalin as he walked to the edge of the roof and before any of us had time to view the extent of the damage, we heard someone shouting from the park opposite the flats. I knew that voice; it was Drew who was with James, and they were making their way closer and closer to the garages. I started panicking and shouting at Charlie, 'Why did you stand up? Everyone can see us, Drew can see us!'

He also sounded scared as he answered me, 'I'm sorry, I didn't know they were there.'

Drew and James were right beside us now, standing in the car park below the garage roofs. Drew started smiling at James, who then looked up to face Charlie, who they could still see from the ground.

'We know you're all up there, we found your little base. Do you like what we've done to it?' Drew sniggered as they started to look for a way up. Ashleigh and I stood either side of Charlie, who approached the edge of the roof, shouting, 'Fuck off Drew! You fucking ruined it!'

He then backed away with me and Ashleigh as we tried to get as far away from Drew and James as possible, but they were already climbing up and so we had no option but to stay put. I watched Drew as he jumped from the back of the roof into the garden we had been building in, only to watch helplessly as he destroyed what was left of our base. I felt so hurt and angry because we had worked so hard to build that base and it had previously been a secret place to which I could escape, but now all I could do was hope that nothing worse was going to happen. Ashleigh tried to jump off the roof but Drew stopped her getting down, grabbing her legs if she tried to lower herself and throwing stones at her if she tried to jump. She eventually did jump off the roof but not until Drew had climbed up and pulled her under a sheet of tarpaulin, which he used to cover up what he was doing to her.

Charlie soon jumped off the roof too, and he didn't seem as much of a target for Drew, who let him down without a fight, but James was still down there as he was too big to pull himself up. Drew quickly approached me on the roof, leaving Ashleigh and Charlie in the carpark whilst they waited for me. James was not as psychotic as Drew, which meant Ashleigh and Charlie could leave any time they wanted to, but I was still trapped on the roof and there was no way Ashleigh would leave without me. I was petrified at this point because not only was I being held hostage, but I had also been separated from Ashleigh, whom I could no longer protect from James.

Drew started walking around me in circles whilst looking at the remains of our base, as though he was searching for something. I knew running was no option as he'd either pin me down or push me off the roof, so I sat still in the hope that he would let me go if I was quiet and did what I was told. However I could never agree to do what he asked of me... There was another piece of tarpaulin beside me which Drew picked up and threw over my head like a bed sheet, crawling under it as he wedged his body closer to mine.

'Take your clothes off,' he ordered. I hated him touching me, so I pulled my trousers down myself as he pulled his down and pushed me onto all fours in front of him. He pulled his penis out of his underwear, which he had rolled down, ripping my underwear away from my legs as he forced his penis into me from behind. I don't think he cared which hole it went into, just that it went in, so I felt lucky to have escaped full-on vaginal sex. It still terrified me, however, and I did not stop crying whilst he continued to force it in and out, though I was too scared to try and fight him off. I knew from experience that it would achieve nothing as he was so much bigger and stronger than me, and I was too exhausted to fight anymore. The pain was already agonizing and I didn't want to make it worse by resisting, so I froze and did nothing until he finally stopped after a few minutes and allowed me to leave from under the sheet.

He said I could go, but after what felt like hours of abuse, I was too traumatized to move a muscle without assistance. He grabbed my arm and pulled me up, before dropping me so hard that I hit my head on the roof floor. I suddenly forced myself to regain my normal senses, which had been blocked out in an un-controllable attempt by my body to defend itself. I then stood up and ran to the edge of the roof, where I jumped down to the ground and was reunited with Ashleigh.

She had been crying since Drew made her jump off the roof, but I was so upset myself that I found it hard to comfort her. I felt extremely guilty for not being able to protect her when Drew had forced her to jump, but I was being held hostage myself and thought she would understand. She had stopped crying by this point and we had left the garages to walk home, but she was refusing to talk to me and would just shake her head, giving me a disgusted expression. 'Why did you do that?' she said, more angry than upset. 'I could have broken my ankle jumping off the roof, and all you did was stay up there and have sex with Drew.'

She had never spoken this way about the abuse we were both suffering before, so I was slightly taken back by how mean she was to say those things. It then became clear I had embarrassed her when she added, 'People in the flats saw that sheet moving up and down. Even adults were laughing.'

I started crying and she put her arm around me, but I told her to 'fuck off' because I was so angry at her for telling me it was my fault. Maybe it was my fault;I mean if I wasn't so weak I could have fought him off or protected Ashleigh when she needed me most.

When we got home I ran straight to my bedroom, refusing to speak to Ashleigh as I took five Ritalin pills and lay in bed. I couldn't sleep as I was still upset about what had happened, but I didn't care as long as the Ritalin kicked in soon. Ash left our bedroom to have a shower, so I took another three Ritalin pills before hiding the rest under a loose floorboard whilst she was gone. I didn't want to go downstairs to eat dinner, but knew I'd have to or else Mum would know something was up. Dad shouted to us from the bottom of the stairs when dinner was ready, so I went to the kitchen to take my plate. My brothers and older sister Callie were sitting in the lounge with Mum and Dad and Ashleigh was still in the shower, so I was alone in the kitchen. I saw the food on my plate and thought it was far too much for me to eat if I wanted to continue to lose weight, so I sneakily put half of my dinner onto Ashleigh's plate. I deliberately walked into the lounge with food in my mouth so that if Mum or Dad caught sight of my half-empty plate, they'd assume I'd eaten it. Looking back now I know it would not have been enough to cause any significant weight gain for Ashleigh, but at the time I was still satisfied that it would make me skinnier than her. Even though I knew we both felt equally bad about being fat, I didn't care that she could gain weight from this because as long as I was losing more weight than her, nothing else mattered.

CHAPTER 8

Don't Fall

My behaviour started to get worse after that day because I was gradually falling into a deeper, darker state of depression. As I became more withdrawn and lonely, I started to care less about consequences both in and outside of school. I would regularly meet up with Charlie to throw eggs at houses and we would often go shoplifting, as well as start fires in the woods. I knew we couldn't get in any real trouble for it because I was only ten years old, which meant I was only just old enough to take legal responsibility for my own actions. Since Charlie was not even old enough to be arrested, he would always take the blame if we ever got caught by police. I started slacking in Judo, too, because I would prefer to stay out and cause trouble with Ashleigh and Charlie. When I was causing trouble, I was no longer the victim, which gave me a sense of comfort, because although I knew it was wrong, I felt happier than when I was being bullied or abused, as that made me start questioning my own life.

A few months went by and I was still being bullied at school but apart from name-calling and threats, Drew and James hadn't sexually assaulted me since the garage roof incident. This was because I became increasingly cautious of being near them and therefore avoided them altogether. I would not go to Charlie's house as Drew or James could be there, and I started walking to school twenty minutes early every day to avoid the possibility of running into them on the way. I still went to the park now and then, but only if Beth was there, as her mum would stay with her or watch us from her bedroom window. Ashleigh and I hadn't really seen Beth since before we built the garage base, so it was nice to catch up and play together as we got along so well. We treated her like a younger sister and she looked up to us because we looked out for her.

After Christmas that year it started to get really cold outside until it eventually snowed in late January. Ashleigh and I were still doing Judo, but when we weren't training we would build snowmen with Beth or have snowball fights with Charlie. I enjoyed their friendship because I didn't have any friends at school, so it was nice to feel wanted just like any other child my age. One morning before school, I saw Mum listening to the radio before she told us that school had been cancelled because of the snow. I was so excited to have the day off school because it would mean a day away from the bullying, so Ashleigh and I went to the park to meet Charlie and Beth. On the way there we passed some students from Tomlinscote, who were walking to school because it was only the junior schools which had been closed. This added to my sense of satisfaction, because Drew and James both went to Tomlinscote, which meant they would be nowhere near us all day if we were to stay out and play in the snow. As the path of fresh snow crunched beneath my feet, I watched it glistening in the rising sunlight. It was still partially dark as it was winter but I liked going out at that time of day because I could see so many beautiful colours in the sky, and that was enough to take me away from the world for just a moment.

When Ashleigh and I arrived at the park, we built a five foot wall of snow which we hid behind whilst we threw snowballs at Charlie and Beth. Beth's mum came out to take a photo of the four of us playing together, next to a snowman that Beth had spent all morning building. A group of other kids from our street came to the park to join our snowball fight, so we stayed to play for hours. By this time we were all soaked and Beth wanted to go home and change, so we told her we'd go home, too, and meet her later. Charlie wanted to come home with me and Ashleigh so we walked out of the park together as Beth went home. Ashleigh asked me, 'Do we have to go home? I don't want to go yet.'

I didn't mind staying out but I was a little bored of the park, especially since Drew and James would be finishing school in a couple of hours, so I asked Charlie if there was any other place he knew to play in the snow.

'We could go to the lake?' he suggested, though Ashleigh was convinced it would be boring. 'It'll be all frozen over!' he added excitedly, trying to make Ashleigh feel keener for the idea. I wondered if it would be strong enough to hold the weight of a person, or if anyone had tried to walk across it already. Suddenly Ashleigh said to Charlie, 'I heard someone talk about that lake, actually; they said it was strong enough to skate on… But if it's not, we can go swimming!'

She was laughing as she said the swimming part, but I knew she was only joking as she'd never go swimming in a freezing cold lake. We walked to the lake with Charlie and talked about how cool it was going to be when we got there. I was excited to see the lake as I had never seen it frozen before, but I was also worried that one of us might fall through it. I had seen a movie once where someone fell through ice and drowned, but it didn't scare me too much because I thought I'd be strong enough to break the ice from underwater if I was sucked under. When we arrived at the lake it was completely frozen over just like we'd imagined and we noticed that all of the surrounding snow was untouched, meaning no one else had been here. There was a small island in the middle of the lake where ducks and swans were nesting, and the whole thing was surrounded by bushes and trees, which kept it out of sight. Ashleigh was first to point out a quiet spot we could sit at, although it seemed like we'd be the only ones there all day.

'I dare you to jump on it!' Charlie said, to which I replied, 'Fuck that. It would never take my weight… You're lighter than me.'

Charlie wanted to walk to the island in the middle but he wouldn't go on his own, so Ash suggested we all go. I didn't like this idea, because I might have been naive but I wasn't completely stupid. I knew the ice would not hold all three of us and I didn't want Ash to go, but before I knew it she was walking on the ice with Charlie. She shouted back to me, 'This is so cool, you should try it, Robyn!'

I ignored her as they continued to walk across the ice, but as they made their way closer to the middle of the lake, I found myself panicking. With every step Ashleigh took, I could feel my heart pounding faster and faster. I was still worried about Charlie of course, but Ash was my twin sister and the reality of what could happen at any moment was sinking in. Suddenly I heard a crack. There was no sound except for the trees rustling in the wind so when the ice creaked below their feet, both Ashleigh and Charlie instantly froze and turned to face me. 'Did you hear that?' Ashleigh said quietly, with pure panic in her voice. 'Don't fucking move, Charlie!'

They were holding hands now as they were so scared and there was not much distance left between them and the island, but in Charlie's state of panic and shock, he was about to try and run on the ice.

I shouted to them from the side, 'Wait there! I'll call for help!'

I wanted to go and look for help properly, but I was not prepared to leave Ashleigh and Charlie stranded on the lake out of fear that they'd fall through the ice whilst I was gone. I shouted away from the lake and towards the houses nearby, 'Help! Help! Someone, please help!' … No one answered. Charlie was closer to the island than Ashleigh so he managed to pull himself off the ice using a thin branch that was hanging from a tree on the island. He ripped it off and held the other end out for Ashleigh to hold onto as he pulled her off the ice and onto the island with him. I was temporarily relieved, but I knew this was not over yet as they'd have to cross the ice again to get back. I was so scared I was crying now, but I hid my tears from Charlie and Ashleigh as I didn't want them to panic more just because I was.

After roaming the island in an unsuccessful search for anything that could help get them back, they both stepped onto the ice again, with their arms out for balance. Ashleigh walked first and told Charlie to keep at least a fifteen foot gap between them. This would prevent too much weight causing pressure on the ice, which could cause it to break. I feared for Ashleigh's life as she slowly made her way back out into the lake. Stepping one foot in front of the other, she took a few cautious steps and then stopped to turn and face Charlie, who was close behind her. 'You're too close!' she shouted. 'You need to stay back or we'll both drown.'

I had both my hands together and was quietly praying by this point. I'd never been brought up to be religious, but in my darkest hours I secretly hoped that if I pleaded hard enough with God, he'd send down an angel to protect us. All I remember thinking was, please don't die Ash. Please... I love you. I can't do this on my own.

Charlie backed off from Ashleigh and they slowly made their way towards me. They were still in the middle of the lake when a man came out of nowhere and shouted at us, 'Get off that lake! Don't you know a boy died there last year? Get over here now!'

He was obviously too stupid to realize that Ashleigh and Charlie were trying to get off the lake already, so I told him to fuck off in the hope that he'd leave us alone. I knew he was only worried for our safety, but there was nothing he could do for us to help the situation, which he was only making worse by being there. Seeing that he was not going anywhere, I changed my tone around him and said, 'I'm sorry, I'm just scared. They're getting off the ice now... Please don't call the police.'

He eventually calmed down and told me he wouldn't call the police, but he still refused to leave until Ashleigh and Charlie were safely off the ice. They had both made it half way back by now and I started to feel a false sense of security as though everything would be fine, but any feelings of relief were soon swept away when the ice cracked a second time. It wasn't like the first crack... This was much louder, echoing through the whole lake as it cracked the entire under-layer of the ice. Charlie started to run.

'Stop!' Ashleigh and I shouted together as the cracking continued. Charlie fell through the ice and Ashleigh knew she could not walk slowly any longer. She took ten fast steps towards the bank, where she fell flat on the ground. Charlie was lucky to have been so close to the bank when he fell in as the water was only up to his waist, but it was still so cold it took his breath away. I gave him my coat to wrap around his legs after he took his trousers off, which were soaked, before hugging both him and Ashleigh in relief that they were both alive. 'Fucking hell!' I said to them, 'Don't ever scare me like that again! I thought I was going to lose you.'

After calming ourselves down enough to walk home, we said our goodbyes to Charlie as we split up to call it a day. We still played in the snow after that but we never went back to the lake whilst it was frozen. Ashleigh and I went for a run that evening as we hadn't exercised all day and were still trying to keep our weight down for Judo, but my frequent overdoses on Ritalin made it impossible to ration out daily amounts. This made it harder to stick to the restrictive diets I was constantly creating, but I stuck it out most of the time. When I did occasionally lose control of my eating habits I would only go over by a few hundred calories at most, but would make sure I burnt twice as many calories off through running and other exercises. Judo was still a huge part of my life and although all the abuse from other kids at school didn't seem worth the fight at times, it was all worth it to see my parents' faces every time I won a medal.

A few months went by without too much hassle from James or Drew. They still continued to touch me inappropriately and shout abusive comments every time I bumped into them, but nothing as bad as what Drew had done to me on the garage roof. I was still being bullied at school and the name-calling was getting worse, but I would only cry now and then at school as I was learning to hold it in until I got home. I think the mixture of endorphins and friendly environment made me feel happy and safe at Judo, but I still never fitted in there either. Even at Judo, some kids would bully me. However, the majority of them didn't hassle me at all, so I continued to enjoy the sport when everything else in my life was going so wrong. I still enjoyed causing trouble with

Charlie and getting up to mischief, but if I had Judo training I would always drop Charlie for Judo. I didn't skip training very often to hang out with him instead, but one evening at the beginning of the summer holidays I was due to pick up some Ritalin. I felt guilty for missing Judo as my parents always made me feel like I'd let them down if I said I didn't want to go, but the Ritalin was my only hope at staying under my weight limit and so I had to miss Judo that night to meet Charlie.

It had been a hot, sunny day and although it was cooling down now, it was still warm enough for me to go out wearing just a t-shirt and leggings. Ashleigh chose to go training, which left me to meet Charlie at the park on my own. There were no adults or other kids in the park as it was almost 7pm, so I waited quietly by the swings until Charlie arrived. I heard the gate squeak as he entered the park. 'Hey mate, you alright?' I said to Charlie as he reached into his pocket to hand me the Ritalin. He answered me, 'Yeah, I'm fine, my brother's just got home with James.'

I didn't think much of it because if they had only just arrived at Charlie's they'd probably be there for a while, but the thought of them coming to the park was still bothering me in the back of my mind.

'You don't think they'll come out, do you?' I asked Charlie, as I feared for my safety around them, but he told me they'd have no interest in going out as they had just bought new video games. However, this assumption turned out to be wrong as I would soon realize in the most brutal way possible. They entered the park after spotting us on the swings, before heading straight towards us. I quickly slipped the Ritalin pills into my shoe so that they wouldn't try and take it off me, but that would become the least of my worries when they surrounded us at the back of the park. It was starting to get dark by now and we were the only ones in the park, so I started trying to back off from them as I began to feel further at risk of danger.

James had walked to the bottom of the hill behind the swings that was hidden by a small collection of trees and bushes. I thought he had gone there to urinate on the fence behind it, but he shouted my name and told me to go down there. I didn't want to go, but I felt extremely threatened by Drew, who pressured me into it and insisted the two of them only wanted to talk to me. I don't know why or even if I believed Drew for that moment, but whenever he or James were around I felt so afraid of them that I would do as they said. I thought if I did what they wanted me to do, they would let me go. Drew pushed me down the hill and stayed at the top whilst James put his arm out next to my face and took a light grip of my t-shirt. He continued to move so close to me that I ended up with my back against the fence whilst standing face to face with him. Well, face to chest, since that's how much taller than me he was.

He started to put his hands down my trousers and through my underwear, whilst leaning down to kiss me… All I could hear except for my petrified heart pounding was his warm breath down my neck, sending shivers down my spine. His hands were cold and big, with his dirty nails digging into my vagina. I wasn't crying yet as I was used to it by now, but the pain was becoming unbearable. I tried to pull away for one stupid moment, but he reached out and pushed me to the ground with a single hit. He then lifted me to my knees by my hair and spat the words at me, 'You don't like kissing, do you?'

He then took his penis out of his trousers and ordered me to suck it. I had started to cry by this point as I was so scared, but he continued to pull my hair whilst threatening me through his gritted teeth. I suddenly felt the courage to stand up for myself, and told him "No! I don't want to anymore…" With that, and after giving me one final chance, he raised his arms and pushed me to the cold ground. He pressed his body up against mine whilst keeping me lying on my back, as he pulled both my legs apart with what seemed like almost no struggle for him at all. His penis was still out of his trousers, which he had rolled all the way down and he ripped my leggings away from my skin, which he bruised as he forced his penis into my vagina. I felt so helpless, crying in agonizing pain whilst I struggled to breathe with his hand covering my mouth to stop me screaming. I couldn't have screamed anyway, because I was panicking so much about my breathing that I eventually gave up and stopped moving. I froze and accepted what I could not control as I started to think this was how I would die…

After what felt like hours, he stopped thrusting in and out of me and began to stand up. I stared blankly into space, still trying to catch my breath as I felt everything fading. I watched him pull his trousers up after wiping a disgusting white liquid, which I was all too familiar with, onto the grass beside me. Before turning to walk away, he leant down to my face and whispered, 'If you ever tell anyone about this, I'll kill you and your twin.'

Drew, who had been keeping guard at the top of the hill, suddenly shouted for James and the two of them casually walked off as if nothing had happened. Despite the semi-conscious state I was in, those words stabbed me instantly and I felt like I was bleeding from them. Then I realized I was in fact bleeding… As I rolled over and reached down to pull my leggings up, my hands suddenly became covered in blood. My vagina felt so sore, as if something inside it had ripped, but it was too dark outside to see it properly. I could feel a lot of blood covering my upper thighs and abdomen because I was soaking wet in the area surrounding my vagina, but luckily I was wearing mostly black so it didn't show up through my clothes. I would still have to get rid of them, however. When I finally managed to regain my senses, I knew I had to get out of there, but I was too scared to move in case James and Drew were still there. Realizing that I could not remember hearing the gate open or not, I crawled up to the top of the hill and stuck my head up to look around. James and Drew were nowhere to be seen and neither was Charlie. I didn't even think to worry about where he'd got to, because all I was concentrating on was getting myself home where I would be safe. I also knew I'd have to hide it from everyone at home, and that scared me more than anything.

After finding my feet and wiping the majority of the blood onto my socks, which I threw over a fence, I started to run out of the park and towards home. I was usually scared of the dark but after the ordeal I'd just been through, all my fears seemed too small to bother me. My only worry was getting myself home, bathed and in bed without being seen. I tidied my hair up before reaching for the front door, which was always locked from the inside back then. Luckily Ash had just got home from Judo training so the door was still open and I could walk through without Mum or Dad physically seeing the state of me. I ran up to the bathroom before locking the door and shouting, 'I'm in the bathroom!' so that no one would walk in. I started running the water and lay in the bath from the moment the taps were on, leaving all my clothes scrunched up in a bin bag on the floor. I felt so disgusting and dirty, the same way I always felt after Drew or James had touched me, and I just wanted the water to wash it all away. On that particular night I think I wanted the water to wash me away too, but I knew that wasn't possible. I knew I'd have to ignore it and stay strong for my family's sake, but at that particular moment I couldn't think about anything positive.

The bath water had turned to a muddy red colour and I felt absolutely disgusting. My knees were grazed from being pushed to the floor and my head hurt from when James had pulled my hair, but my private parts were hurting the most. As I looked down at my bruised body, so upset that I didn't even notice all the fat that usually bothered me, all I could think about was how much I wished I wasn't me. I felt so ashamed of my life that I just wanted to be someone else and if I couldn't, then I wanted to be dead.

Whilst I emptied the bath and rinsed myself with fresh water, a terrifying thought suddenly came over me... What if I was pregnant? We hadn't yet been taught about sex education in school but I was old enough to know where babies came from, and so I wondered if what happened tonight could have made me pregnant. In reality there was virtually no chance of that as I had not yet started my periods and when I took a closer look, the bleeding was coming mostly from outside rather that inside my vagina... But with my ten-year-old brain, I was under the assumption that all sex makes a baby and I was strongly convinced I would become pregnant unless I did something about it.

After drying myself with a clean towel, I took my bin bag full of blood-soaked clothes and hid it underneath my bed. Ashleigh and I shared a bunk bed and I had the bottom bunk, so I hurriedly shoved the bag under my bunk before anyone could see it. We had so much junk under our bed that it was easy to hide and the carpet was old and darkly coloured, so it wouldn't matter if the blood leaked through a little and stained it. This was when I remembered I had Ritalin stashed under the mattress. My shoes were still outside the bathroom and I knew my new box of Ritalin pills might still be in them, so I put my pyjamas on and went to look inside my shoes. The Ritalin was a bit crushed up from running home but it was still there so I took it to my bedroom and put it with the rest of my Ritalin stash. After lying in bed for hours unable to sleep, I decided how I would get rid of the baby. I couldn't tell anyone about it, not even Ashleigh, as she would tell Mum and Dad, who would think it was my fault, so I took the Ritalin out from under my bed whilst coming up with the most horrific idea I'd ever had.

After making sure Ashleigh was asleep, I took every single pill out of both packets and filled a bottle up with fresh water from the bathroom. The pills that were crushed from running home were hard to swallow as they tasted so foul, but they numbed my mouth and throat enough so that I couldn't taste anything after the first few. I swallowed around fifteen Ritalin pills before sneaking downstairs to see if Mum had left any paracetamol lying around, but all I found was half a packet of ibuprofen, so I took the rest of them and went back to bed. I didn't think I had any tears left to cry that night, but I broke down silently when I closed my eyes and cried myself to sleep. I don't remember what time of night it was when I woke up, only that all the lights were off and everyone in the house was asleep, but I was woken abruptly by a roaring pain in my stomach and chest, which caused me to cry out in pain.

I leapt up and ran straight for the bathroom but didn't make it to the toilet, so instead ended up vomiting all over the bathroom floor. The noise woke Dad, who rushed straight for the bathroom to see what was wrong. He gagged at the smell but made sure I was OK, before cleaning it up and going back to bed. He hugged me and said I should try to get some sleep, though I didn't feel like sleeping as I felt so dizzy. I couldn't tell him this of course, so I said I felt better after being sick and was going back to bed. I did go back to my bed, but I hardly slept at all until the early hours of the morning when the sun was coming up.

As I lay in bed trying not to wake Ashleigh, I realized my heart was beating abnormally fast. I didn't take too much notice of it because at the age of ten I would not have known about side-effects from drugs and mixing them, but it was causing me to sweat heavily, which became extremely uncomfortable. I hated being unable to sleep too, because whenever I was alone, all I could think about was how lonely I was from all the bullying and abuse, and how awful it made me feel. I didn't understand the meaning of words such as 'worthless' and 'fading' back then, but looking back now I can see that both those words really underestimated how I felt. Worse now, I had a pregnancy to worry about, something I didn't understand at all, but with no adult knowledge of the human body I thought that by overdosing and vomiting I would have got rid of any possible chance of being pregnant.

I cried deep into my pillow once again before finally falling asleep, only to be woken again by nightmares about James and Drew. Then I started wondering, where did Charlie disappear to in all this? How could he just leave me with his brother and James when they were being so cruel to me? I knew I could no longer risk seeing them again, but Charlie was my closest friend besides Ashleigh and I couldn't bear the thought of losing him. I didn't care that he didn't stick up for me because I loved him and he was my friend, but I could no longer take the pain from being abused by James and Drew. I regretted giving up Charlie's friendship and for a very long time I felt guilty about it but in the end, the Ritalin was not worth the pain and so I stopped seeing Charlie, which stopped the sexual abuse.

CHAPTER 9

Trouble

A few weeks went by without seeing Charlie, or anyone really. I stayed in for months after that final incident at the park and didn't bother trying to socialize with anyone outside school, except for when Ashleigh occasionally brought a friend back to the house to play. If I left the house it was only to go to school or Judo training and the more time I spent alone, the more focused I became on losing weight. I knew I'd have to fight so much harder to lose weight now that I no longer had the Ritalin to stop my hunger pains, so I started to become even more obsessed with exercising and counting calories. I was still competing heavily in Judo and would focus as best as I could, but after the rape I was finding it increasingly difficult to deal with my emotions. When the bullying kicked off at school, which it often did, I would find myself feeling alone and unable to talk to anyone. I was still unaware of the fact I had actually been raped as I was too young to understand, but that made me feel even worse, because I could not talk to anyone about what had happened since I didn't know how serious it was. I also thought that no one would be able to do anything about it as nothing had been done in the past, so I tried to forget as best as I could by spending all my time writing songs and exercising.

My bulimic tendencies started here, too. When I was upset I would comfort eat and feel ever so guilty about it afterwards, so I'd end up panicking if I didn't burn off every single calorie. This made me even more frustrated about my weight, because although I still weighed the same as I did when I was eight years old, I wanted to weigh less than I ever had, even though I was almost eleven now. It was also proving much harder to lose weight as I was still growing, but unless I saw that number drop on the scales I would feel disappointed with myself. And that's another thing that really got me upset… My height.

Kids at school would pick on me because of my height and, among the many other names, they would call me Gigantor, as well as exclude me from their games because I was 'too tall'. By the time I turned eleven I had given up on making friends because I had never fitted in anywhere, but a few weeks after my eleventh birthday I received a knock on the door from Beth, who we had previously hung out with at the park. She was standing with a taller girl named Emma who I had not met before and she looked a bit older than us, but she seemed nice and so I invited them in. I always felt slightly awkward around new people my age because I was socially excluded at school as a result of being bullied, which led me to spend a lot of time alone. Because of this I found it hard to interact socially with other kids, especially as I was so depressed due to all the abuse, but I tried my best to fit in around her and we soon became good friends.

I refused to go to the park where all the abuse had happened, but without telling anyone why, I managed to convince both Beth and Emma that we should try hanging out in a different park. Emma suggested we go to 'Marconi's', which was a bit further away from our house but still within walking distance, so I soon got dressed and walked out of the house with Ashleigh, who came along too. Marconi's seemed nicer than the park right by our house. There was a cricket club next to the recreation area, which was situated in front of a large field with bright green, freshly cut grass. There was a tall office building fenced off next to the field, but everything seemed clean and looked brand new. In the actual park there was a sandpit with a slide for the younger kids, with swings and a climbing frame for the older children. We sat on the swings and shared a huge bag of sweets we had bought from the shops on the way there, whilst talking and listening to music on our phones. It wasn't long before we spotted two girls walking towards us from the back of the field, and I realized I recognized one of them.

It was Fiona from Judo training, who we cruelly referred to as 'Fat Fiona' behind her back. She had never been mean or bullied us like some of the kids at Judo, but whenever Mum or Dad had caught us eating sweets they would jokingly make comments, such as 'Don't eat that or you'll end up like Fat Fiona!' We said 'hello' and she introduced us to her friend. She was an extremely tall, thin girl who was at least six feet tall, named Laura. She spoke with a very deep voice, which seemed funny at first, but Ashleigh and I never laughed at her or said anything about it as we knew what it was like to be bullied. Beth had gone home after a few hours but Emma stayed out with us and we spent the rest of that day at Marconi's, before eventually walking home that evening. Emma and Fiona were both older than me and Ashleigh, which meant they were allowed to stay out later than us, resulting in the two of them having a closer friendship as they found they had more things in common with each other than with us.

The two of them would talk about boys and sex, but Ashleigh and I always felt awkward and uncomfortable around those conversations as we had only known abuse. I later found out that Emma was in the same year as Drew at school, which made it harder for me to feel comfortable around her when she talked about sex as she would often talk about having feelings for Drew. Sometimes Charlie would turn up to the park and as Emma knew his brother, she would call him over to us. I didn't want to talk to him as I couldn't go back to the abuse from James and Drew, but after contemplating what was the worst situation that could happen, I decided to be friends with him again because it wasn't him who had hurt me in the first place.

A few weeks went by and Ashleigh and I continued to hang out with Fiona, Laura, Emma and Charlie, but on this particular day we left for Marconi's without Emma as she was hungover from a night out. I noticed that whenever Laura was with Fiona, they always seemed to have huge amounts of sweets and other goodies with them. However, it wasn't until I went to the shops with them that I realized everything they had was from shoplifting. We started to call Laura 'Magnet' as it seemed she could walk into any shop with any amount of security, and still walk out with hundreds of pounds' worth of things we hadn't even see her steal. The five of us would walk into shops and as Ashleigh was always too afraid of being caught to shoplift, she would stand guard or block the camera view whilst Fiona, Charlie and I took whatever we wanted with Laura. We never got caught and the more time we spent doing it, the better we got at it. One afternoon we had been hanging out on Fiona's estate, when we decided to walk to the building warehouse opposite her street. It was a large DIY superstore which sold items from floorboards and roof tiles to scaffolding and paint. I don't know what we were expecting when we walked in, but we were immediately drawn to the brightly coloured paint section at the back of the store.

Charlie picked up a can of spray paint but noticed the barcode was printed on the metal, which meant we couldn't simply rip the tag off, as it would still set off the alarm when we walked out of the shop. Laura took a closer look at it and realized the barcode and tag were only on the lids of the cans, so she took the lid off the can Charlie was holding and shoved it into her bag. All five of us were wearing string sports bags, so we were able to fill the bags up with cans of spray paint. Ashleigh kept watch for any security staff whilst Fiona stood in front of the camera, blocking us from view. I turned around with my back facing Charlie and Laura, who ripped the lids off as many cans as they could before throwing them into my bag. Then Charlie turned around whilst Laura and I filled his bag, before swapping once again to fill Laura's bag to the top. We then kept watch whilst Ashleigh and Fiona stole even more spray paint, before taking some free colour samples and casually leaving the store. We continued to walk until we were at the end of the car park, at which point we ran the rest of the journey back to Fiona's house where we could hide if anyone called the police.

We emptied our bags onto Fiona's bed and as we counted the cans, we started to realize just how much we had stolen. I think all of us felt an incredible sense of satisfaction because we had not been caught, but we were still weary of the fact the police could show up at any moment. We knew we had to either use or hide the cans, so we went with the first option and walked to a fence at the top of a hill that separated the housing estate from the motorway. I was first to paint and as we drew large smiley faces and rude words, Charlie started to write his name.

'Don't write your own name, you'll get us all caught!' Laura shouted, as she covered his name up with a different coloured paint.

'What should I write then?' Charlie said to Laura. 'We need to make up a name for our crew!'

He excitedly made suggestions for the name, as we continued to vandalize the fence. After thinking hard amongst ourselves as to what we should be called, we eventually came up with the name 'FA3S', which stood for 'Frimley Adidas 3 Stripes', since that was the name and design of the tracksuit bottoms we all wore. I was amazed at how cool the name sounded, so I said to everyone, 'That's such a great idea! We should only wear Adidas three-striped tracksuits from now on too, it can be like our little gang uniform!'

This suited me a lot because I had recently decided that I would only wear boy's clothes since I was raped, in the hope that nothing similar would ever happen to me again. This was because I thought if I wore baggy, boy's clothes all the time and looked like a boy, no one would be interested in my body and therefore no one would touch me.

We continued to spray paint until it was time to go home, covering the fence and surrounding areas in drawings and markings which I only saw as art because of all the beautiful different colours. Our tag (crew name) soon covered every wall on the estate, and we hid all but two leftover paint cans in a bush behind Fiona's house before we left to walk home. Charlie was still allowed round our house back then, so he stayed for dinner before making his way home later that night. The following day we went out with Fiona and Laura again, who knocked for us with a child's push chair. The baby was Laura's younger sister, Chelsea, who was only three years old, but Laura, who was thirteen, was babysitting her and so she stayed with us for the day. Fiona and Laura didn't want to walk all the way to Marconi's as they had Chelsea's push chair with them, so they suggested we go to the park by my house, which was where all the abuse had happened. They didn't know this of course, but there was no way I could tell them and so I left the house to walk down the road with them. Ashleigh stayed at home to help Dad, who was working on the garage roof as he was building an extension on the house, but I felt better about going to the park without her as I would only have memories and flashbacks of what happened to me and not what happened to her, which I failed to stop.

Fiona and Laura were first to enter the park and although I felt greatly uneasy and uncomfortable at first, I soon got on with it and started to feel much calmer once we sat down together. There was an Asian man pushing his young daughter on the baby swings in the park and Fiona started being extremely rude towards him, for absolutely no reason other than the colour of his skin. I was shocked to hear the names she called him as I had never been so rude towards anyone because of their race, but Fiona seemed to have no morals or respect whatsoever and she continued to hurl abuse at him until he left the park. He didn't swear or react, which I suppose was what she was hoping for, but instead he simply said to her, 'You must have had something really bad happen to you, to make you treat others this way.'

He was completely correct in my opinion and I felt ever so guilty for not standing up for him, but I was scared to say anything as I thought Fiona might have fallen out with me over it. I took in what he said, however, as I had vowed never to bully anyone, because I knew what it was like to be on the receiving end. I did feel ashamed that I had been in the park with her in the first place, because it would have appeared to the Asian man that I was on Fiona's side and agreed with her racist comments, which was far from true

Laura suddenly took a can of pink spray paint out of Chelsea's push chair and since we were now the only people in the park, it seemed like a great idea to start spray painting again. Laura and Fiona painted long pink lines across the tarmac floor as they chased each other round in circles. I covered up someone else's tag with my own design, which was an abbreviated version of my name. I painted the letter 'R' with a huge swirly circle around it, next to which Laura and Fiona painted our crew name in different colours. After spraying the entire park with different colours until all the cans in Chelsea's push chair were empty, we sat under the climbing frame and fed Chelsea her snacks. She was still only a toddler, which meant she needed feeding every few hours, but it was no problem for us as we liked to pretend we were mothers. I threw the empty cans I'd been using through the fence at the back of the park, which had bushes poking through it from the gardens behind, but Fiona and Laura insisted on keeping their cans hidden in the push chair since they would be covered in finger prints.

We had been sitting under the climbing frame for barely ten minutes when suddenly a police car pulled up outside the park. We didn't notice the two police officers until we looked up after hearing the gate open, but by the time we saw them it was already too late to try to make an escape. Fiona quickly whispered to me and Laura, 'Sit still! Don't move… If we try to run they'll know it was us…' She then turned her head towards them and smiled politely, trying to act innocent as they approached us. 'They can't prove anything, we'll just say it wasn't us and it was there before we got here.'

Both police officers made their way to the climbing frame we were sitting under and politely asked us, 'Hello, girls. Would you mind moving out from under that climbing frame so we can see you all?'

I tried to keep a straight face as Laura and Fiona both looked at each other almost laughing, but I think they were laughing with nerves as we knew we'd been caught red handed. Fiona turned to face the police officer and said calmly, 'What's the matter, piggy? Can't you see us from out there?'

Laura was now laughing and I was trying so hard not to. I was petrified of being taken away in their car as I knew I'd be in so much trouble at home if my parents found out, but the fact that Fiona was being so rude and confident made me feel less scared. Both police officers were male, which meant they couldn't search us, but I was still weary of them taking a closer look around the park. They saw the spray-painted graffiti all over the tarmac floor and asked if we did it, to which we replied 'No'. After taking a closer look, they noticed the letter 'R' was painted in various spots around the park. I had tried giving fake names to the police before, but they were beginning to recognize my face now and because I had started to wear a gold chain with the letter 'R' around my neck, it seemed pointless trying to deny my name was Robyn.

It's OK, I thought to myself, I can just pretend there was someone else in the park whose name also began with the letter 'R'. This didn't work, however, and after they asked me a third time whether or not I had painted the letter 'R' around the park, I confessed to the police officers, who then moved closer towards me. They had found the cans that Fiona and Laura had stashed inside Chelsea's push chair, which they took as evidence in case of any arrest. They told me, however, that I wouldn't get into trouble for all of it because there were so many different colours painted in the park that it couldn't have been only me. One of the police officers stood beside me whilst the other stood in front of me and said, 'We're very glad you admitted to that on the third time, as we'd be arresting you and taking you to court if you hadn't.'

I felt a huge sigh of relief as I found out I was not going to be arrested, but when they tried to take me away in their car I simply refused. One of them grabbed hold of my arm whilst the other tried to twist it behind my back, so I pulled away and shouted, 'You can't touch me… I'm just a kid! Get the fuck off me!'

Suddenly the officer who had hold of my arm put his other arm around my chest from behind, which pinned me to him as he pushed me down to the ground. My hands were too small to put cuffs on properly, but they put them on as tight as they would go behind my back and I was forced to stop struggling when the other officer dug his knee deep into my spine. I was out of breath and panicking by this point, but they still would not let me go. Both officers were still holding me down when one leant right down to my ear and said quietly, 'Are you going to behave yourself now? You'll only be there longer if you don't pack it in.'

I reluctantly complied as they pulled me up to my feet, keeping hold of both my arms from either side as they walked me to the car. I took a seat in the back and Laura and Fiona waved goodbye, proceeding to walk to my house to meet me there. The police drove me home and parked outside my house. As they stepped out of the car, I noticed Ash was on the roof with a man named Richard who worked for my dad at the time, and he looked scared at the sight of a police car but started laughing the second he saw me sitting in the back. They opened the back door, which was locked from the outside, before slowly making their way up the driveway at the front of my house. I pushed past them through the front door, which was unlocked, before shouting, 'Mum? I'm home... The police are here, it's a long story... They want to talk to you.'

She immediately sounded angry with me and replied with, 'What do you mean? What have you done?!'

I started to face the floor as I walked into the front room with the police, who looked straight towards Mum and told her, 'We've had a phone call from a local resident about some youths, vandalizing the park. Your daughter has admitted to spray painting.'

Dad had walked into the room by this point and looked even angrier than Mum as he asked, 'What did she spray paint? Is she going to be arrested?'

The police officers went on to tell my parents that I had painted the first letter of my name in various places and would not be arrested because I had admitted to doing it, but that they would need to arrange a day for me to go to the police station. This was because they wanted to take finger prints, photos and DNA samples to put me on their database, which would officially make me a criminal, as the police would now have my details, which they'd keep permanently. They also said I'd be reprimanded, which meant I was given a formal warning as a juvenile for committing my first offence. Dad asked the police officers if they were allowed to take me to stay in a police cell for a night as he thought that would scare me from breaking the law again, but the police officers said that was out of the question as I had not been arrested. After talking to my parents for almost an hour, the police left my house with a fake apology that I gave to be polite. I was still angry at them for pinning me to the ground in the park and I thought it was stupid, how they had so little to do with their time that they could walk into a park and pick on a few kids for developing their skills in art. Mum and Dad didn't share the same opinion, however, and started shouting at me the moment the police left.

Mum shouted at me, 'What the fuck do you think you're doing Robyn?! You know you won't be able to go abroad with a criminal record don't you? So if you get selected at Judo to fight in the Junior World Championships or Olympics, you won't be able to go because you've done something fucking stupid and got yourself arrested!'

Dad was also fuming. He told me how disappointed he was with me, how I'd let both him and Mum down and that they didn't want to see me for the rest of the night. Dad was always terrifying when he was angry as he would throw things and stomp his feet around the room whilst gritting his teeth, so I ran upstairs as fast as I could to get away from both of them. Dad stormed to the bottom of the stairs and said, 'You're not getting nothing from now on, you got that? No going out with your friends, no going out to the park and you are fucking grounded until further notice!'

I slammed my bedroom door shut and screamed as loud as I could into my pillow. Fiona and Laura had been waiting for me outside but my dad told them to go away as I was not allowed out for at least a week. I was so angry... Not so much at how my parents had reacted, because I suppose I expected that, but some of the things they said had really hurt me; the fact that I wouldn't be able to compete abroad and how it would let them down, especially as I was already thinking about dropping out of Judo because I couldn't take the bullying at school any longer. How I had betrayed them, how I had let them down… I already felt like I wasn't good enough and hearing them say it simply made all those horrible voices inside my head even louder. I couldn't take the pain of letting them down, I just wanted to make them proud... Now I had fucked up my chances and it seemed everything would go wrong from here. I wished and wished I still had my Ritalin so I could at least overdose and forget about the pain for a while, but there was no chance of that now that I'd been raped, which had made me stop taking it from Charlie. He had also been taken off the drug now as his mum had realized it wasn't working on him, although that was only because he wasn't taking it as he would give it all to me, so now even if I wanted to go back to that comfort I couldn't. I had nothing left now except the depression inside my head which was starting to make every waking moment a living hell.

CHAPTER 10

Fight

I kept myself in my room for a few days after that. I would only leave my room to go to Judo and I would refuse to eat until my grounding was lifted. It had only been three days, but being used to going out with my friends, I hated being grounded more than anything. Charlie knocked on the door early afternoon and since my parents told him I wasn't allowed out, he started to walk off. I shouted his name from the window, to which he replied as soon as he saw my face. 'Robyn! You alright? You should come out, we're making smoke bombs. Why don't you sneak out?'

I told him my dad would notice as he was working on the garage roof, which would mean he'd see me straight away, but I decided to go downstairs anyway and make a run for it. I threw on my pink hoodie with my Adidas tracksuit bottoms, before sneaking past my mum and walking out the front door. Dad spotted me immediately and so I legged it, sprinting all the way to the bottom of the road before turning right and running as fast as I could to the back of the local shops, which I hid behind in a ditch.

Dad had sprinted after me but was no match for my legs when

it came to running. He was faster than most people, but I had the adrenaline rush of sneaking out, as well as the top sprinting time out of all the girls and boys at school. There was a car park behind the shops and a flat, muddy plot of land surrounded by overgrown weeds, which had a nice little ditch behind it where I could hide. I lay flat on my back as I tried to keep my breathing as quiet as possible, but this was difficult because I was out of breath from sprinting two roads at full pelt. I kept my composure however and stayed lying flat on my back in that ditch. Dad was out of breath too and I could hear he was nearby. He shouted through the top of his puffed-out lungs, 'Robyn? You're not funny... You can come out now.'

I wasn't moving for shit. Though my heart was pounding from both adrenaline and fear, I stayed lying still in that ditch for over an hour to be completely sure he was gone. As I slowly sat up, listening carefully to my surroundings in case I was spotted, I walked out from behind the shops and made my way to the park to meet Charlie. I felt slightly guilty for disobeying my dad, but he had shouted at me to the point I was scared and I couldn't deal with being isolated in my bedroom any longer. When I was out, I was having fun... And no matter how much trouble I got myself into, it was better than being bullied at school or being alone with my thoughts.

Dad eventually found me after a few hours and I was forced to come home. I wasn't grounded the day after that, but both Mum and Dad tried to talk to me to see what the problem was. They didn't know I'd been sexually abused, of course, and there was no way I could tell them at that age, so I simply apologized and listened to what they had to say. They told me how proud they were of me for all my efforts in Judo and high grades at school but the more they told me how proud they were, the more pressure I felt being put on me to please them. I know now that it was just depression taking over my mind and distorting my thoughts, but at the time I didn't know why I was feeling so upset and any time they told me they were proud, I simply felt guilty because I thought I'd never be able to live up to their expectations. The impossible expectations I put on myself were all my own, however, but when I didn't reach them I always felt like I'd let everyone else down too. I think that's part of having low self-esteem, reinforced by abuse and bullying, but it always made me feel like I wasn't good enough. Mum and Dad would tell me I was perfect in every way, but any time I heard positive words I only felt guilty about not being able to live up to them.

The weeks went by and I started getting into more and more trouble with the police, including being taken home in police cars and vans with Charlie four times in just five days. We had a police helicopter out looking for us on one of those days, which was due to the fact we were all carrying knives, which we were using to carve up the bench in the park. We hadn't brought the knives out with us to hurt anyone and it was simply because we'd been stripping copper wires to cash in at the scrap merchants', but after Ashleigh's flick knife broke she attached the blade to a long gold chain which she wore around her neck. We thought it looked really cool, so we took our knives out to the park and had a play with them to try and make knife chains ourselves. I hadn't hung out with Emma for a while, but I still saw Laura and Fiona until the arguments started with Emma. Drew had seen that she'd become friends with me and I'm assuming he didn't like the fact that he risked her finding out what he had done to me and Ashleigh, so he started spreading false rumours that I was bitching about her behind her back. She confronted me one day and was convinced I had called her a slut, so she threatened to beat me up if I ever tried to talk to her again. I was really hurt at the accusations because I had never said anything bad about her and had only ever been there for her as a friend, but she soon had an entire gang of her and Drew's friends bullying me about it.

They started to shout abuse and throw stones at me whenever they saw me and because she lived so close to me, it was hard to avoid her. I had to walk past her house to go to the local shops and there would always be a gang of at least eight of them, hurling verbal and physical abuse at me. They were all the same age as Drew, which I found very threatening as I was only eleven, over five years younger than most of them. They would spit at me as I walked past, as well as filling cups with boiling water to throw at me if they saw me walking back from the shops.

Fiona took Emma's side as she was closer to her age, and Laura didn't go out much without Fiona, but would walk me past Emma's house if she was around. I hated Fiona for this because we'd been such good friends and she had dropped me like I meant nothing, over a few lies and rumours which weren't even true. I specifically remember one incident when I was walking home from the shops, and one of her friends was riding a moped up and down the street outside her house. The girl on the moped skidded over to my side of the road and pulled a knife out of her jacket, grabbing hold of me by the throat whilst she threatened me on Emma's behalf. I was so scared that all I could do was cry, which made the bullying even worse because now they would call me a cry baby as well as all the other abusive names they would hurl at me almost every day. One afternoon I was walking home from school and as I approached the road before my house, I saw Emma sitting on the side of the street with Fiona. They were both laughing hysterically whilst they started skipping and running behind me, shouting, 'Judo freak! Skanky twin freak!' as I tried to ignore and walk past them. Emma was keeping a slight distance behind me as they followed me but Fiona had run right up close behind me and grabbed hold of my ponytail, which hung right down to my waist.

'Ding dong!' she shouted, whilst pulling on my hair. I turned around with my fist out and punched her straight in the mouth, at which point she started bleeding. I screamed at her, 'Don't fucking touch me!'

I couldn't take it anymore. I was being bullied at school, bullied at Judo, and now this... Before I knew it, the rest of her friends had turned up with Drew and were all shouting abuse at me. I suddenly found some courage to stick up for myself and shouted to Emma at the top of my lungs, 'I'm sick of all your shit, Emma! I've had enough now! Fight me tomorrow after school, at Hawthorn Park.'

That was the park by my house where all the abuse had happened, where all the suffering had started... But I didn't care. All of Emma's friends had heard me call a fight, so I would have to push all the bad memories out the way and show her who she was messing with. I didn't like fighting as I didn't like hurting people, but the pain they had caused me had become too much to take any longer. I had to do this, I had to stop the bullying.

School that day was hard. Alongside all the bullying I had to deal with, I was also worrying constantly about the fight that afternoon and what would happen. I knew if I didn't show up they would bully me even more, but if I did show up I'd get my head kicked in by however many of them decided to join in. I was petrified of both alternatives, but I knew which one I had to take, and give it everything I had, because there was no way I could continue living like this. Among the many things I would cry about, the bullying from Emma was really hard for me to deal with because Drew and James were both there a lot of the time too, which made it impossible for me to stand up for myself. On top of all this it was SATS week at school, so I had to concentrate completely as I was sitting through all the exams that would dictate which sets I was in when I started secondary school. The whole day felt like a ticking time bomb, moving closer to the hour that would either make or break my reputation. I'd never seen Emma fight, or Fiona for that matter, but I had seen her shout and make threats, which made her seem very confident about having a fight. I was quiet and depressed, but I did Judo, which meant that maybe I could win this fight. We'd learnt a few different arm locks and strangles and so I kept trying to picture in my head which one would be most likely to help me during my fight after school. Ashleigh tried building my confidence up by saying I'd smash her and I had my mum and dad's full support too, since I told them the night before that I'd be having a fight to end the bullying. They didn't like me fighting, of course, but they'd always taught me to stand up for myself if someone was ever causing me too much hassle.

The school bell soon rang for the end of the day and it was time to go and fight. I packed away my things, walked to the front gates and waited for Ashleigh. She arrived shortly after I did and as we made our way to the park, I felt my heart beating faster with every step I took. I started having doubts and thought maybe she'd call it off, or maybe no one would show up and there'd be no point in fighting. She was a lot taller and fatter than me and all of her friends were the same height or even bigger, so how could I defend myself if any of them stepped in? Ashleigh tried to reassure me, turning to face me as she said, 'Don't worry, Rob, you'll smash that cunt up. No more bullying, babe, you can do this!'

She also promised she'd step in if it got too rough for me to handle on my own, but she didn't even have to say that. It was like an automatic twin instinct that you will always stick up for the other one no matter what and no matter how big the opposing army is- the two of you together will never be defeated. I felt comforted by this and it helped me a lot to know that Ash would be by my side, but I was still scared, like any eleven-year-old would be about to fight someone who was fifteen.

We arrived at the park and I knew I couldn't turn back. There weren't ten or fifteen people with Emma like I'd expected, instead there were at least fifty students from Tomlinscote with the rest of Emma's friends. The girl who had threatened me with a knife was there, alongside the older teenagers from our estate, who were eighteen to twenty years old. Everyone from her school looked like an army in their black and gold uniform, whilst I was alone with Ashleigh wearing our purple Junior School uniform... They had all turned up to see the fight, and running was no option for either of us. As I walked through the gates, one of the older boys shouted, 'She's here, she's here! Ding! Ding! Ding! Round one, are we ready?!'

He patted me on the shoulder and wished me good luck, which told me that half of the people here were probably not even Emma's friends and were only here to see a fight. That made me feel better about not knowing anyone because Emma couldn't have known many of them either, and the fact that they weren't here to back her up meant I might just stand a chance at winning. I walked over to Emma, who was sitting on the swings with Drew and James, both staring at me as I approached her. Everyone in the park had started to make a circle around us by now and Ashleigh stayed close behind me until I was standing face to face with Emma.

As I got closer to her I could sense her fear, even though she was trying to scare me by acting like she wasn't fazed at all by what was about to happen. She stayed on the swings but looked straight at me and said 'You're pathetic. I'm not throwing the first punch', to which I replied, 'Well, I fuckin will!' And before anyone could speak, I grabbed hold of her neck from behind and gripped her tightly in a head lock, before forward flipping over her as she pulled us both off the swings and onto the ground. She screamed and pushed me off her, letting go of my hair, before punching me in my face and stomach from the floor as I sat on top of her and tried to hold her down with a Judo hold. I punched her repeatedly in the face whilst she pulled my hair and scratched mine, before losing my balance and rolling over to one side. She jumped on top of me and was punching me in all directions, before I screamed, which lead to Ashleigh running in for a full-on kick in the face to get her off me. Ashleigh stepped back after that as the crowd were shouting at me for it, but everyone was shouting and cheering so loudly that I could hardly hear what they were saying anyway.

I kept hold of Emma's neck whilst I threw myself on top of her, keeping her pinned to the ground with my legs either side of her arms as I pushed all my weight onto her chest. I took hold of her hair in one hand to pin her head to the floor, whilst punching her in the face with the other hand. She was crying by this point, and no matter how cruel she had been to me in the past, I still felt bad for her so instead of carrying on with the punches I put my face close to hers and ordered, 'Say you're sorry, in front of all these people! Say you're fucking sorry!'

She screamed and cried as she begged me to let her go, saying, 'I'm sorry, Robyn, I'm so sorry! You win.'

I stopped hitting her and got to my feet, raising a fist in the air in front of all the camera phones that were still filming as I left her lying on the ground. By this point a woman had come out of her house, which backed onto the park, and was telling everybody to leave as she had phoned the police who were on their way. She said we were behaving like animals, and she was right in that respect. All the abuse from Emma, James and Drew- they were the animals. I hated fighting but I now had the confidence and felt a great sense of satisfaction when I got an actual apology out of Emma, and when I was beating her up it felt like I was beating a piece of James and Drew up too. No one could begin to understand the extent of the damage they'd caused by what they put me through for years, and it was at that very moment that I finally learnt I was strong enough to stand up for myself. That park was no longer a place where I was left to cry after my innocence had been brutally stolen from me. It was now a holy ground which I could revisit and where I could remember all the great feelings that swept through my entire body when I finally defeated those who had hurt me so much. I felt guilty for hurting Emma that day, but she had hurt me for months and she deserved every bruise.

Ashleigh and I walked home together and saw police cars rushing to the scene, but I hid my face behind Ashleigh so they would not see that I'd been fighting. There was an ambulance there too, but everyone who had watched the fight had left, leaving the police to chase after a few remaining spectators who ran off before they could try to take statements. I was happy not to have been questioned by the police, as I had already been reprimanded, which meant I'd be in even bigger trouble if they had caught me fighting. When I opened the front door, Dad was sitting in the living room as he had just finished working for the day. He took one look at my scratched face and said, 'Did you win, babe?'

I laughed and answered 'Yes', before walking to the bathroom to tidy my hair and wash my face. My head was pounding on one side where Emma had hit me, but it was mainly just scratches, which gave me two identical lines of vertical cuts to my face. They weren't bleeding heavily and Dad told me they were victory marks, which cheered me up, telling me as well that I shouldn't need to worry about her bullying anymore.

Suddenly there was a knock on the front door, which Mum answered. Emma and her mother stood outside.

'Your daughter's beaten up mine! Did she tell you she'd assaulted my Emma today?!'

Mum looked concerned and I started feeling agitated the moment Emma's mum started talking, but I managed to run to the front door and speak to Emma's mother before my mum could answer. 'She's been bullying me for months and I couldn't take it anymore! She makes me I wish I was dead because of how she makes me feel.'

Her mum looked a bit taken back by this and went on to say that she didn't know we'd been arguing, but had told her daughter the previous day that she would not allow her to fight an eleven-year-old child. Mum stuck up for me and I eventually apologized to Emma who apologized to me in front of both our mums, but I didn't mean it for one single breath as she had hurt me so much inside. After settling our differences she finally left, but Mum was now worried about me because of what I had said. With a concerned look of sympathy, Mum asked me, 'Is this true? Has Emma been bullying you? I wish you'd told me so I could have helped you sort things out before it got to this point.'

She put her hands on my shoulders as she bent down to my eye level before saying, 'You can always come and talk to me and your dad, please don't feel like you're ever alone. We love you and we will always stand by you, no matter what.'

Part of me wishes I'd listened to those words more, as maybe my life wouldn't have gone so horribly wrong in later years. But at the time, although I was comforted by my parents' support, I never wanted to tell them how depressed I truly was as I felt I'd be letting them down. They always told me how proud they were of how strong I was, so I felt I had to keep up that strong image on the outside, as it was all I had.

After showering and sorting myself out, I realized I'd left my school bag at the park so Ashleigh and I walked back to see if it was still there. When we got to the park we saw that my bag itself was still there, but all the contents had been thrown around the park or stolen. Although there had been nothing of any financial value in my bag, all the little things that had been broken or stolen were of sentimental value to me. I loved to draw and Mum had bought me a glittery gel pen set of different colours, which were now scattered across the park in the mud. There was also a brand new maths and writing kit which I'd been given by Mum and Dad, who'd bought them for my exams as it was SATS week at school. I picked up the bag and tried not to cry as I left the park. It sounded silly that I'd cry over something so small after everything I'd been through, but I was still only a child and so I'd still cry sometimes over things any young kid would. However, I think it was more a release of every emotion I'd been feeling that day because throughout the fight and the hours leading up to it, I'd been too wrapped up in everything else to cry.

As we made our way home, there was an older boy walking past us on the opposite side of the street. He looked around seventeen or eighteen years old and I started to feel unsure of him as he crossed the road to walk on our side. Then all of a sudden, he put his hand up to hi-five me as he said, 'You're that girl who beat up Emma earlier… Fucking legend!!'

I hi-fived him back and smiled as he walked past us and carried on walking down the street. Little did I know that I would be receiving a lot more attention after that fight, from many other teenagers who now thought I was cool after my fight with Emma. When we arrived home and told Mum and Dad all my things had been trashed at the park, dad took me out to a stationery shop to replace all the items from my school bag. He bought me the loveliest coloured pen set, a brand new maths set with compasses and protractors, along with everything else I needed for my exams the next day. After searching for a new pencil case that I would like, Dad picked out a black one which said the word 'Tough' on it in silver writing. I laughed as we added it to our basket and I was soon feeling back to normal when we arrived home. After packing my school bag for the next day, I went to bed feeling happier than I had in a very long time. I did one last bit of revision for my exams before thanking Ashleigh for sticking up for me, as we went to bed.

When I woke to get ready for school the following day, I noticed that all except two marks on my face had disappeared. The redness that had previously been there had died down completely and I was left with only a graze on one cheek, and a short scratch on the other. It was still obvious I'd had a fight, but I thought I wouldn't be questioned about it too much at school as I could say I'd simple fallen over or been knocked around at Judo if a teacher asked. I had to go to school and wanted to that day as I was confident I'd pass my exams, but I started to feel as though everyone was staring at me when I walked through the front gates.

There was a group of boys from my year playing football in the playground who usually bullied me when I walked past them, but this time they stopped their game and asked me if I'd had a fight the night before. I suppose I felt proud when I answered 'Yes', but I didn't realize they all had seen video footage of the fight from some of their older brothers and sisters who'd been there watching. They still picked on me after that and would exclude me from their games like everyone else at school, but they didn't pick on me so much from then onwards. When I eventually arrived at my classroom, I was asked by the teacher to report to the headmaster's office immediately. I wasn't scared as I knew I'd done nothing in school to get myself in trouble recently, but I was still nervous as I walked to his office because I knew I'd be in trouble for something.

I knocked on the door and waited outside, before making my way into his office when the deputy head teacher showed up too. He said to me in a calm voice, 'We've had a phone call from Tomlinscote Secondary School. Their head teacher has informed us that one of their pupils has been in a fight with you and is quite badly beaten up.'

He could see I was becoming scared as I thought I would now be in trouble, but he changed his tone to caring when he asked if I was OK. I told him I was fine, but that she had been bullying me for months prior to the event and that I had to fight to try to end it. Although I did not go into much detail about the bullying as I tried to defend my case, he said he was not bothered about the fight and was only concerned for my wellbeing. He told me to go straight to him if anything like that ever happened again, but how could I? I couldn't tell him that almost everyone in school was bullying me and even if I had told him how the other kids made me feel, it wouldn't have made them like me, which was all I wanted really. I didn't need people at school to be my friends, but I wanted more than anything for them not to hate me so much. There must have been a reason no one liked me, and I could never work out what it was. That was harder to deal with than anything because when nobody likes you, it feels like everything you do is wrong.

The head teacher went on to tell me that Emma had come out of the fight with two black eyes, a fractured nose and a split lip. I didn't feel good about hurting her or hearing the extent of the damage, but I felt happy in the sense that she probably wouldn't bother me again. I still had no friends my own age but at least I was respected now by people who were older than me, because they'd seen my fight and seen how I stopped it as soon as Emma apologized and maybe thought I wasn't such a bad person after all. This made me feel slightly better about myself because I was nearing the end of my final year at junior school and it was looking like I wouldn't have to put up with the bullying for much longer.

CHAPTER 11

Alone

A few weeks after my exams at the end of school term, I was sitting on the swings in the park beside Ashleigh when a tall boy appeared from one of the houses that backed onto the park. He asked us if either one of us had a lighter he could borrow. I didn't smoke but would usually carry a lighter as we would sometimes start small fires for fun with Charlie, so I handed it to him and he lit his cigarette. He politely thanked me for the lighter, then sat beside me and Ashleigh on the swings. He was seventeen years old but I didn't feel threatened by him as he appeared to have no sexual interest in me whatsoever, so we started talking.

He looked up at me as he inhaled his cigarette smoke and said, 'I know you... You're that girl who beat up Emma!'

I smiled as he laughed then said, 'Pleased to meet you, my name's Nathan.'

I thought he sounded strangely well-spoken for the way he was dressed, but I admired his sense of style and thought I might start dressing like him. He was wearing baggy tracksuit bottoms with a hoodie which was covered in graffiti writing, with a flat-capped hat and lots of gold jewellery. He had a huge fake diamond earring in one ear and wore rings on almost every finger. I started to realize the cigarette he was smoking wasn't actually a cigarette, as it smelt just like the smoke I had noticed a while back on the way to school one morning. Drew and his friends had been shouting abuse at me and Ash whilst they shared between them a large white cigarette, which was twice the length of a normal cigarette and much wider on the lit end. I remembered the smell instantly and so I innocently asked Nathan, 'What's that you're smoking? It smells funny.'

He laughed and told me it was called 'cannabis' or 'weed' for short and that he was smoking what's called a 'spliff'. His eyes were bloodshot and glazed, which I assumed was from the weed, so when he offered me some I was slightly hesitant to try it. I had only ever tried a puff of a cigarette once as Fiona and Laura had pressured me into it and when I had breathed it in, I had immediately coughed and said I would never try it again. Ashleigh told me not to smoke with Nathan as it would screw up my lungs for Judo, but the sadness I constantly felt caused me to care less about my body and so I put my lips around the spliff as Nathan held it to my mouth.

I wanted to cough at first, but I didn't want Nathan to think I wasn't cool. Fiona and Laura had told me how to smoke before and that you were supposed to breathe only through your mouth and not your nose when inhaling, so I took a few more puffs and then passed it back to Nathan. I started to feel a little sick, but that soon went away and I could only feel positive effects from the weed. I was slightly dizzy but felt like I was floating and suddenly, I started to feel incredibly happy, as though all my worries and problems didn't seem so bad. Nathan continued to smoke the rest of the spliff, which he shared with me as Ash didn't want any. Among the many other positive and calm feelings, I noticed that when he started playing music on his phone it seemed I could not stop listening. The music felt like love to my ears, and it was the only thing I could hear clearly apart from a pounding droning sound in each side of my head. It felt like the weed was quietening all other sounds, relaxing my mind and taking me away from depression to somewhere I could finally breathe. I'd found something that momentarily made me feel happy.

I started to see Nathan a lot more after that day and when school broke up for the summer holidays, I would spend all my money on weed. Dad had started taking me to work with him on a building site in Chessington, as he thought I was getting into trouble with the police because I was bored. He worked for himself and would pay me when I worked hard, so I went to work with him a few days each week and would spend all of my money on cannabis. It was nice to spend time with my dad as I was used to him being at work a lot whilst I was growing up, plus being one of five siblings it was hard to get in any one-to-one time with either parent so I appreciated the time we had together. I stopped seeing Charlie so much and hardly saw Laura at all, but being away from Charlie took me away from the memories of abuse by his older brother and James.

Being around Nathan made me feel safe, because if Drew or James walked past the park whilst we were there, they wouldn't start on me because Nathan was older than them. We would dress like gangsters, walking round in huge baggy tracksuit bottoms covered in gold and black graffiti writing with matching flat-capped hats. I had started to grow boobs at this point too, so I would wear a neon pink bra underneath a white skin tight sports top with even more gold jewellery than Nathan wore. As well as working with Dad for money, I would take home scrap wires from the building sites that I would then strip to cash in at the scrap merchants' for even more drug money. I was still doing Judo at this point but would try to skip training sessions often, as I preferred getting off my face on weed to going training. I had also started drinking now and then, so would have no chance whatsoever of surviving a training session or making a weigh-in.

I'd almost got to the end of the summer holidays when I broke my arm after falling off my bike, but in a way I was slightly happy I'd broken it. This was because the hospital would have to put it in a cast for six weeks, which would mean I'd get a break from Judo. Now I could starve myself and stop eating completely, as I wouldn't need the energy to exercise and I would simply need to restrain myself from eating. This didn't work, however, because no matter how hard I tried to fight the urges, I'd always end up giving in and stuffing my fat face. This made me feel so depressed because I was getting fatter by the day in my eyes, whilst Ash was still training and getting skinnier than me. In reality we still weighed around the same as each other, but I was too depressed from all the sexual abuse and self-hatred I suffered as a result of the bullying to even think about going back to Judo. I started to think that maybe if I stopped Judo, the bullying would stop at school. And so I decided to use my broken arm as an excuse to quit, by telling Mum and Dad that I had lost interest in the sport while I'd been away from it for so long. They were devastated and kept pushing for an explanation or 'real reason' why I'd quit, but I couldn't tell them my pathetic excuse. I couldn't tell them that other kids would like me if I gave up Judo and they wouldn't have known how much that meant to me anyway... I couldn't tell them that I'd rather smoke weed and get drunk than train for the Olympics, but I was so depressed I had absolutely no energy for anything that wasn't self-destructive. No one could begin to understand how much I hated myself and even though it felt wrong to quit Judo, my body and mind were too exhausted now to keep fighting. I let the bullies win.

I never forgave myself for quitting Judo and even to this day, I know it is something I will regret for the rest of my life. I boxed all my medals and trophies away after a while and put all two hundred of them in the attic. I couldn't bear to look at them because it would remind me of what I had thrown away, what I had lost, and I felt so guilty that I couldn't take it. The weeks went by and after the summer holidays I started my first year of secondary school, the same school James and Drew were still attending as sixth-formers. I hated seeing them and would almost cry at the sight of them, but I always hid my tears as I was trying to put on a brave face to build a new reputation. I didn't care about fresh starts regarding grades or exams, as all I was interested in was making friends. There was a boy in my class with severe behavioural problems and he was ever so popular, as the other kids would find him hilarious, so I started copying his behaviour and would act up to try and make people like me. I was in the first year of a school I would be stuck with until I left in five years, and there was no way I could let myself be bullied the way I had been throughout junior school.

On the third day of Tomlinscote, I was suspended for setting fireworks off as bombs on the field at lunch break. There were more than ten other kids suspended over it too, most in the oldest year group, but Ashleigh was one of them, which meant I was with her all day when we were put in the isolation room. One morning I had half a bottle of vodka left over from my twelfth birthday which I had spent in the woods with Ashleigh and Charlie, so I decided to bring it into school mixed with orangeade in a plastic bottle. Some other kids in my year found out I had alcohol and after I refused to share it with them, they told our head of year. I was called into his office where he searched my school bag and clothes, but I had already drunk it and refilled the bottle with water. I had chewing gum which had stopped my breath smelling of alcohol and my tolerance was reasonably high from drinking and smoking weed all summer, so I was able to act sober enough to get off with just my chewing gum confiscated as we were not allowed it in school. I was still annoyed at this because it seemed like everyone was out to get me, but after spending so much time isolating myself I preferred to be alone anyway. I still tried to make friends as I wanted that more than anything but after a few outbursts of crying and kids from my junior school talking to those in my new school, I was soon back to being the 'Judo freak' who no one liked. This made me feel awful and alone inside, because no matter how hard I tried, I never fitted in and everywhere I went, no one liked me.

Ash had started to become quiet in school too and I think that was due to her being depressed after quitting Judo when I did, but suffering the same sexual abuse as me must have been horrific too. It was hard to see her upset and I always felt helpless when I couldn't comfort her, but how could I when I was so depressed myself? I started cutting my wrists when I was upset and would feel comforted by the sight of my own blood. I thought that if I could hurt myself more than anyone else could hurt me, then maybe the pain they caused wouldn't feel so bad. Ash had started to cut her wrists too and so it wasn't long before the school found out, and they immediately told Mum and Dad. They were shocked and concerned at first but they soon turned angry about it and told us to 'stop being so stupid', as we were 'only doing it for attention'. This made me cut myself even more, because I was so upset and angry with the world for how alone I was that it seemed my only friend apart from drugs and alcohol was the blood I drew from my own veins. Each time I ripped my skin with that cold metal blade, I felt a sense of release as the blood flowed out and covered my skin. It felt just like crying, except I could hide my tears as they were not on my face. I started listening to depressing music when I was alone too, and would write songs about loneliness and sadness on my piano, which I still played. It didn't make me feel better and it often made me feel worse because it would make me cry, but it felt calming to write my pain on paper where I could turn it into music. In some ways it was like a beautiful sadness.

Ashleigh had carved the word 'Alone' on her forearm, so I carved the word 'Worthless' into mine. All the other kids at school had started to bully us about this as they thought we were weird because we cut ourselves, but if they'd ever known how we felt inside I think they might have just left us alone. One afternoon I was sitting at the front on my English class as I had been moved to sit closer to the teacher after misbehaving and it was too hot to wear my jumper, so I rolled my sleeves up, which revealed the nasty cuts up both arms. The teacher stopped what he was doing and said to me in front of the whole class, 'Roll your sleeves back down now! I don't want to see that disgusting mess!'

I was so upset and angry that I thought, why should I? I had done nothing wrong, so I took my jumper off completely and threw my arms out to both sides. I shouted to him as I stood up, 'What's your problem? A big, old man like you, scared of a few cuts?!'

I then threw my books onto the floor in a strop and stormed out of the classroom, crying. He called my head of year to come and find me, who then walked me to his office to shout at me and talk. I didn't want to talk, most definitely not to him. I hated my head of year. He was an incompetent pig who had no idea how to deal with teenagers. He had no children of his own, which I suspect was what made him so unsympathetic to any problems I was dealing with, so he simply put me on a report, which was the first step towards being expelled. I'd have to get every teacher from every lesson to sign it throughout each day, marking me down for my behaviour, appearance and amount of work done and if I continued to act up or get crosses rather than ticks on my report, I would move onto the next level report before being expelled. My head of year started to watch my every move and if just one person told him I had been rude or naughty, he would give me an hour detention and make me sit in silence in the exclusion room.

I was stressed out all the time because I was trying so hard not to be expelled, as my parents had moved us out of London to get me a better education, and I felt I was letting them down with every breath I took. My head of year would tell other kids not to talk to me and if he saw me crying, he would tell me to go and sort my 'horrible red face' out before attending my next lesson. I started staying awake at night because I didn't want the next day to come as I was so scared of what might happen, but that only made things worse as I became even more depressed from suffering from insomnia. When I stayed awake all night I would cut my arms all the way from my wrists to my shoulders, before staring blankly into space hoping that I didn't wake anyone up whilst I cried for hours. When I was in school I would keep my head down facing the ground, as I walked through countless groups of other kids hurling abuse at me when I walked past them. On the rare occasion that a teacher did ask what was wrong, I would have nothing to say to them, as I didn't even know myself. I was too young to link my depression to what had happened when I was younger, so all I knew was that I was feeling suicidal for a reason I could not explain.

One teacher who I did trust was Mr French, a science teacher who specialized in physics. He would pull me into his classroom occasionally to ask what was wrong and though I never usually told him much, it still felt reassuring to know that he cared. No other teachers at Tomlinscote thought I was anything more than a waste of space who would be expelled soon, but Mr French stuck up for me and would insist that I was not a bad kid, but that something must have been going on to cause my behavioural problems. Sometimes I'd deliberately get a detention with him, just so that I escaped attending a detention with my head of year or any other teacher that I didn't like who had arranged a detention for the same day. Other teachers would either hand me boring work to do, or make me sit in silence for the entire hour. My French on the other hand gave me words of encouragement, telling me that he knew I was smart and would go far in life. Although I was still depressed, this helped massively and I will forever be grateful for his actions whilst I was at Tomlinscote.

I eventually stopped smoking weed and drinking so much because it was making me gain weight, something I couldn't bear, so I was now feeling a huge cloud of guilt above my head that I could no longer hide with alcohol or drugs. I felt guilty all the time because I was depressed, which made me feel guilty for being alive. I was guilty of not helping Ashleigh when she was now being bullied in school, and I was guilty for not standing up for her every time James and Drew had touched her. I felt guilty I'd let my parents down by quitting Judo and I felt guilty about being fat. I started smoking cigarettes often as they would stop me being hungry, which would help me lose the weight I so desperately needed to, but I was more interested in the fact they would stunt my growth. This was because I hated my height and did not want to grow any taller; I thought maybe if I stopped growing, everyone else my age would catch up to me and I'd no longer be the outcast freak who was too tall.

Nathan had started hanging out with people his own age now so I would only meet up with him to buy weed or cigarettes, and I was unable to find any other friends like me. I still dressed like he did when

I wasn't with him and if he saw me he would always stop to say hello, but I started to become even more of a target for bullies since he was no longer there to protect me. The boys in school would bully me for dressing like a 'chav', and the girls would all call me a 'lesbian' or 'man' since I had no interest in boys after what had happened to me. I was still wearing boy's clothes so that no one would have any sexual attraction towards me, in the hope that nothing bad would happen to me again regarding sexual abuse. This caused me to start questioning my sexuality as after hearing it from so many other people, I started to think maybe I was a lesbian or a boy trapped in a girl's body. I never acted on this of course, but it made me think that there was even more wrong with me. Why couldn't anyone like me? I only wanted to be loved or even treated like a person, but it seemed like that would never happen and so I kept myself away from everyone as often as I could.

My bulimia started getting worse too, because now that I was no longer doing Judo, I had stopped worrying about my weight for a few months even though I secretly knew it still bothered me. When I quit Judo I thought 'fuck it' and ate what I wanted for a bit, but when I saw the fat growing on my body I felt so disgusted and ashamed that I went back to starving until I had lost it all again. When I couldn't exercise I would force myself to vomit after I ate, feeling more disgusted with myself than before. Every time I lost 30lb or so from starving, I would soon put it back on through binging and then would starve again to lose it, and that's how I started yo-yoing. This is something I still suffer with now, but whenever I was feeling fat back then, all I would try to do was starve and exercise in the hope that one day I'd be thin. Thin was such a perfect thing to be in my eyes and I thought it would make me happy, which was the only thing I ever wanted to be in life.

Over a year went by with my depression at its peak and I was starting to feel detached from reality. There were scars from the shadows which crept into my head, and there was nothing I could do to stop it. All I could see was darkness, as if life meant nothing and there was no point in existence. The voices of my bullies and sexual abusers from years ago were still inside my head, causing a pain I could never escape. I felt alone even when I was surrounded by people and it felt like I was drowning, only I could see everyone around me still breathing. Ashleigh had started seeing and hearing things, which I think was due to her depression as she was suffering too, but I found it hard to believe her at first. If we were out drinking or walking outside late at night when it was dark, she would sometimes say whilst we approached a dark alleyway, 'We can't walk that way, there's a man down there.'

She started seeing three people she believed were ghosts, one named Eve. She did a paper trick one night where you draw a circle on a sheet of paper which you then set on fire, whilst calling any spirits who may be watching to state their name. She still has the piece of paper to this day and there is a clear black smoke mark inside the circle which spells 'Eve', as if someone had drawn it with their finger. I was with her when she set the paper on fire so knew she didn't do it herself, but I was still very reluctant to believe in ghosts. She described the little girl named Eve as though she could see her standing next to us when she was there, and she would start shaking and crying as it scared her a lot. The man she could sometimes see had a full body, which she described as a black figure in the dark, but she would go quiet when she came to describing his face. She said it was disfigured and partially distorted, with half of it not there at all.

One night we had been arguing because Dad had shouted at me for cutting myself after he walked in on me, but I took my anger out on Ashleigh by addressing the fact that I didn't believe her about the ghosts. I said without thinking, 'You have imaginary friends when you're five years old, not thirteen! Stop being a fucking baby.' I didn't mean to get angry with her and I wish I hadn't, but we were still just kids and it really scared me. Looking back now I can see just how unhappy Ashleigh was, as psychologists suggest that she had felt so alone that her subconscious mind was forced to make her a friend. I should have been there for her. I should have made her realize I was still her best friend, because maybe if I hadn't been so wrapped up in my own depression

I could have been there more for her as a sister and she wouldn't have had to go through what she did.

I would sometimes see figures of people in the corner of my eye when I was alone too, but I knew I was only hallucinating because I'd been awake for three or four days. Once you hit that three-day mark of not sleeping, your mind starts playing tricks on you as your body starts to shut down and you begin to lose touch with reality. It was like a drug in some ways, which I suspect was why I chose to stay awake so often, but one night I remember trying to fall asleep and couldn't because of an agonizing pain in my abdomen. It felt like a stabbing pain which was tearing through my internal organs, but I didn't think much of it because I had a high pain tolerance and thought maybe it was just something I had eaten.

After taking some pain-killers and going back to bed, I saw that Ashleigh's light was still on in her bedroom. We now had our own bedrooms in the attic as Dad had finished building the extension on the house, but it felt strange not sleeping in the same room together so we would often sleep in each other's rooms at night. I took my blankets and pillows into Ashleigh's room, before adding them to her bed and lying next to her. She had been crying and was unable to tell me what was wrong, but I hugged her tight and held her until she fell asleep. I apologized just in case she was upset because I'd done or said something, but she had already fallen into deep sleep.

I was still awake when the pain I had felt in my abdomen came back, and I started to worry now as it was getting worse. I still hadn't started my periods so it couldn't have been that, but I started thinking about the night I was raped and if it could be something to do with that. I knew it had been years since that happened, but what if I had been pregnant after all? I knew my overdose would have killed any chance of carrying a baby, but what if it hadn't died instantly and had been living inside me for a month or even longer?

That was when I remembered the second time I overdosed after the rape and I remembered feeling a pain in my stomach although I did not vomit, so what if that pain in my stomach had been a dead baby which had been sitting inside my womb since then? I know now that this would never have been possible, but at thirteen I was unsure and started panicking at the thought that I might have to go to hospital about it. If there was a dead baby inside me, the hospital would know I'd had sex and my parents would be so ashamed of me. I thought they'd think it was my fault, so I decided not to tell anyone about the pain I was feeling. As well as being petrified of Mum or Dad finding out I'd been raped, I was also beginning to grieve for the dead baby I thought I was carrying. I had grown up a bit now and was starting to think about motherhood in later life, which made me realize there was a good chance I'd already murdered my first unborn child.

CHAPTER 12

Septicaemia

I noticed the same pain over the next few weeks whenever I sat down on a bike seat or swing, and it hurt when I used my stomach muscles for anything. The pain was getting worse by the day, until it suddenly stopped for just under a month. It soon reappeared, however, and I had no option but to call for help this time. Ashleigh had gone to school that morning but had woken to find me in the bathroom before she left, crying in agony as I pulled my top up to show her how swollen my lower abdomen was. The swelling stretched from my right to my left hip, spreading up to my stomach and down to my private parts. Mum rushed me to the doctor, who was surprised I could still walk, as my stomach muscles hurt so much I could not lift my own legs up onto the bed when he took a look at me. He raised his eyebrows in concern and told my mum, 'She needs to go to hospital right away! Would you like me to call an ambulance?'

I wasn't sure about calling for an ambulance as I thought they were only for emergencies, so I told the doctor I'd go to hospital with my mum. He helped me off the bed and I walked slowly to the car as every step was agonizing. When we were in the car it hurt to drive fast or go over any bumps, so Mum did the best she could whilst she tried to comfort me and tell me everything was going to be alright… 'I'm sorry Rob', she said as she could see how much pain I was in. 'We'll be at the hospital soon and they will make you all better.'

She looked like she was going to cry because she could see I was so upset, but she held it together, unlike me, as I cried until we were at the hospital. A nurse saw how much pain I was in as I walked from the car park to the hospital entrance, so she quickly grabbed a wheelchair for Mum to push me in. We sat and waited in A&E to be seen and she rocked me like I was a little baby again. I was seen surprisingly fast, but the doctors were taking forever to find out what was wrong with me. They kept asking if the pain was only on one side, as they thought it could be appendicitis. When I told them the pain was all over, they asked Mum to leave the room for a second whilst they asked me some private questions. I was offended and embarrassed when the doctor asked me if I was sexually active, to which I replied 'No,' but he reassured me it was only standard procedure that they had to ask me.

Mum asked what they had said when she was out of the room and I had no problem telling her I was not sexually active. This ruled out being pregnant or having a miscarriage but I did not tell them I had been raped or sexually abused in the past. They then weighed me to calculate how much pain medicine they could give me and when I stepped on the scales, Mum made a harmless joke about my weight. It was something like 'You'd be fighting the fatties now in the under-63kg category if you were still at Judo!' I laughed as she had meant nothing by it other than to cheer me up with a joke, but felt upset inside because I hated how much that number read on the scale. That made me not want to eat for the rest of the day, but I was in so much pain that I didn't feel hungry anyway.

After asking me a ridiculous amount of blatantly obvious questions about the pain I was feeling, they wheeled me in the wheelchair to a room where I was told to lie down on the bed and take my trousers and underwear off. There was a seat next to the pillow end where Mum sat and held my hand, but I was in so much pain I was scared I would break her fingers by squeezing too hard. I didn't want to take any more clothes off as the other doctors had already seen my naked breasts whilst checking my pulse, but I had no choice if I wanted to find out what was wrong with me. No one had seen my naked lower body except for Drew and James, so I was constantly reminded of what they had done to me.

A male doctor came in and told me his name, saying he was a gynaecologist who had to take a swab. He took out a six-inch needle which he stuck up my vagina after telling me to spread my legs open, whilst another doctor stood next to me and tried to take my mind off what was going on. The doctor was asking stupid questions like 'What's your favourite lesson in school?' to which I could not reply as I screamed in agony whilst this needle was being shoved into my private parts. I was crying partially because of the pain, but more because of the flashbacks I was getting after being reminded of what it felt like back in the park when James had taken advantage of me. After what felt like hours, the gynaecologist pulled the enormous needle out and told me the ordeal was over. There had been around five or six other doctors and nurses standing around my bedside and I felt embarrassed that all of them had seen my private parts. I was eventually allowed to put my clothes back on, but this was short-lived as I was told to go and sit in yet another waiting room.

After they had taken one last look at my swollen, rock-hard belly, I was told I needed an ultrasound scan. With the curtains closed for a little privacy, the doctors took blood samples from the veins in my arm and noticed my scars, but I told them they were all old and that I didn't cut anymore. This was not only because I didn't want their help, as I didn't think I needed it, but also due to the fact that I was scared of professional people finding out, as Dad had threatened to throw me into a mental institution if I carried on cutting. I know now that he did not have the power to do that, but I was still a child and believed him, which was why I never sought help.

When I was called into the screening room, I was told to lie down on the bed and roll my top up from the bottom. I felt extremely self-conscious doing this as I hated anyone seeing my body, which I was so ashamed of, but what the nurse did next would upset me even more. Because the swelling stretched down past my bikini line, she had to reveal half of my private parts as she needed to apply gel over it to scan everything. She tugged my trousers and underwear down without warning and said in a sarcastically high-pitched voice, 'Woo!'

I was so uncomfortable and angry that I wanted to scream at her to 'fuck off!', because the last person who had done that was James when he raped me. It brought back memories of all the sexual abuse and I suddenly started crying. Mum asked what was wrong, but I lied and told her it was only because of the pain. I hated that particular nurse touching me after that and refused to look at her whilst she scanned my body, but I was able to watch the video footage on a screen whilst she was scanning. I was having one of those scans women get when they're pregnant, and I started wondering if they'd find out I had killed my possible unborn child back at that awful time.

It had been hours now since we'd first arrived at the hospital and I had not eaten or drunk anything all day, so was starting to become dehydrated. Mum asked if they could give me any water, but the nurse spoke with the doctor who then said I could only have sips as they might need to operate on me. Mum sounded worried when she asked them, 'What do you mean, operate? You haven't found out what's wrong with her yet.'

The doctors told her that from the results of the scan, it appeared I had what was called an 'Imperforate Hymen'. This happens sometimes when girls start their period as there is a thin line of body tissue which is supposed to break for the blood to come through, but mine hadn't as there was scar tissue on it for some reason. I knew this was because I had been raped before my body was ready for that line to break, but they simply said that because I was not sexually active it must have been a rare mistake on their machine or a harmless body defect I had… Though they did say that left untreated it could kill me.

They booked me in for an overnight stay where I was placed in the teen ward, situated next to all the screaming babies in the children's ward next door. A nurse put yet another needle in my arm to attach a drip, which pumped vital medication I needed before my opp. They said the operation was a standard procedure but I was still scared as I had never been sedated under general anaesthetic before in my life, so I begged Mum to stay with me for as long as she could. I would need to take off my underwear before my operation as they were going to cut open the line that was supposed to break, allowing all the trapped blood to flow out through the hole. I took my clothes off and put on the gown they'd provided, whilst they attached patient name bands to my ankle and wrist. Mum held my hand as they wheeled me off into theatre, staying with me until I was asleep. They injected my arm with local anaesthetic whilst other doctors stood around me with breathing tubes ready to be pushed down my oesophagus, as they told me to count down from ten. I barely made it to seven before I became unconscious. I don't remember anything after that until I woke up in the recovery unit, feeling extremely dizzy and high as I was still heavily sedated. I was waking up when they pulled my breathing tube out and I felt a gagging sensation when it came up through my throat, but I was still too sedated to move or gag though I felt like I was going to be sick.

One of the nurses was walking around at this point and saw me opening my eyes, so she came over to my bedside to see if I was OK. I was feeling anxious and confused as I had forgotten where I was and why I couldn't move, but I soon came round fully and remembered what was going on. I was panicky at first because Mum was no longer there, but I calmed myself down before I could cry as I knew she would only be in another room and if she had left the hospital it would have been because she had all my other siblings to think about too. I knew she'd have to go home sooner or later to care for everyone else and run the household as normal, but a huge part of me still wished she could stay until I left the hospital.

After assuring me that the anaesthetic would completely wear of within the next few hours, the nurses wheeled me back to the teen ward where I was reunited with Mum. She looked relieved to see me and she hugged me tight when I was back in the ward. It was now dark outside so I started to wonder how long I'd been unconscious for, and if I'd be allowed home now that the operation was over. Mum leant over to me looking tired from worrying as she said, 'You took so long to wake up, Rob, we weren't sure if you would. My poor baby.'

She cried a little but only because she had been scared of losing me, and I thought it must have been hard for her to see me like that. The doctors came back to take some more blood samples for testing, using three different needles in the same place in my arm. It hurt a little but I was on such strong pain medication that I hardly noticed it. Another doctor came back with a drip which he attached to my arm, before taking Mum off round the corner to talk to her. When she came back with the doctor they told me I'd need to stay for a few days so they could monitor my progress, but that everything so far had gone to plan apart from me taking longer than usual to wake up.

I tried to stand up as I wanted to go to the toilet, but there was so much blood where I was laying that I found it hard to move as I was still bleeding heavily. Furthermore I was still feeling dizzy and sick from the anaesthetic and I was so light-headed that when I tried to stand up, I barely made it to my feet before collapsing back onto the bed. A nurse wheeled over a toilet chair to my bedside and helped me stand so I could go to the toilet, but it was hard to go whilst everyone was still there. I noticed that my urine was red as I was still losing blood, but the doctors told me it was expected as I'd had so much blood trapped inside me and that it was only infected blood I was losing.

I was still in a lot of pain and extremely sore when Mum passed me her phone so I could speak to everyone at home. Dad spoke to me first and said that he loved me, followed by my brothers who were also home and wanted to say goodnight. Callie was out with a friend but Ashleigh soon had the phone and told me that everything was going to be OK. I told her I loved her and would be home soon, then we said goodnight to each other and I passed the phone back to mum. I was putting on a brave face but really I was scared. I knew Mum would have to leave soon and I didn't want to be left alone in the hospital overnight. This was a strange place to me, filled with lots of sick people with too many white gowns and doctors wearing face masks and gloves. Mum kissed me goodnight and closed the curtain, promising me she'd be there the next morning as soon as Ashleigh and the boys had gone to school at around 9am. I thought it couldn't be that long to wait as I could sleep through most of it, but I was proved wrong throughout the evening and wished Mum or Dad could just come and take me home.

I managed to sleep until the anaesthetic had completely worn off, but after that I found it hard to sleep through all the noise and lights on in the ward. There was no one in the bed beside me but there was a girl who kept crying on the next bed, and I was sweating as I had a fever but was too physically ill to leave my bed and stand by the window. If I had made it to the window it would have made no difference, however, because although my bed was right next to it, there were bars keeping it from opening more than a few inches. I guessed this was to stop people falling out of them or jumping, as there were a few mentally sick patients in the ward, but I was so frustrated because I was so hot.

There were babies screaming in the corridors and wards either side of my ward, but any time they stopped crying another one would start. At 2am I was greeted by a nurse who had come to check my blood pressure and temperature, but I was still awake from all the noise so it didn't bother me too much. However when I eventually did fall asleep around 4am, I was irritable when I was woken at 5am by another nurse who had come to do the same checks. She asked me how I was feeling as she told me they would be putting another drip in my arm for more medication, which they said would take two hours to pump into my bloodstream. When they started the drip I felt sick and then vomited, so the nurse cleaned me up before leaving the drip attached to my arm. I tried to sleep so that I wouldn't feel so ill, but the sun was coming up now and I found it hard to sleep propped up in my bed so I gave up and waited another three hours for Mum to come back.

At around 9am I was surprised to see Ashleigh without Mum, but was relieved to see a familiar face and happy that it was her out of all of my siblings. She hugged me and gave me some sweets she'd bought on the way to the hospital, but I was too ill to eat them so I said she could have them. We talked until Mum came but as I didn't know much about what was wrong with me, I let Mum explain to her later. Mum had been running errands with shopping and housework, but was still there by my bedside as soon as she could get there. The doctors came over to me to check my symptoms and were a little worried that my tummy was still so swollen, but they said it should go down within the next few days. I told them it was still hurting a lot, so they upped my medication and gave me stronger doses of pain relief.

The rest of that week was spent lying in bed with doctors and nurses taking more blood samples and tests throughout the day, before saying they wanted to scan me again as they were worried the swelling was getting worse and not better. I had stopped bleeding the night after the operation but the pain I'd originally felt kept coming back, and my abdomen was hurting more than ever. As the nurse lifted me into my wheelchair with the help of my sister and Mum, I was wheeled down to the ultrasound room for another scan. They wouldn't tell me the results straight away but I knew it couldn't have been good because of the way they were looking at one another. The same nurse who had annoyed me the day before was there, the one who made a stupid noise whilst pulling my underwear down. She saw I looked seriously unwell so didn't make the same stupid joke on the second scan, but I still hated her and didn't want her to touch me.

After wheeling me back to the ward, the doctors approached Mum with some papers as they gathered round my bed. They said they'd need Mum's permission to sedate me under general anaesthetic again as I would need another operation. The doctor looked at Mum and said, 'Now I don't want to alarm you, but it appears the hole we cut when we operated on Robyn has closed up. We will need to operate again and this time cut both ways so that it stays open, as the blood has become trapped again and is filling up her womb.'

They went on to give Mum more details of the surgery they would be re-performing, but I was under such heavy medication that I found it hard to listen. Because the hole they'd cut had closed up, the blood had filled my uterus, which was now the size of a birthday balloon. It had become extremely infected and I needed treatment immediately. This explained all the swelling and pain I was in, but they didn't tell me what else they'd told Mum. I suppose they thought I was too young or ill to be allowed the information, but Mum told me afterwards as she thought I had a right to know. The doctors explained that my womb was now a circle shape instead of a triangle because it was filled with so much blood and left untreated it would burst, releasing all the infection into my main bloodstream as well as making me infertile.

I now had septicaemia because of how rapidly the infection was spreading, and I was immediately wheeled into theatre where they would attempt to drain my womb. Ashleigh said her goodbyes with Mum, who didn't stay with me this time as I'd already done it once before, so she thought I wouldn't be too scared. They injected the anaesthetic whilst inserting a breathing tube as I fell unconscious, and I took even longer to wake up than the first time round. As with the first operation, I didn't remember anything except waking up feeling dizzy and nauseated. I struggled to see clearly for a few minutes, before a nurse checked to see if I was fit enough to be placed back in my ward. I closed my eyes again as they wheeled my bed back to the teen ward, where Ashleigh was waiting with Mum. Dad had shown up with Jake and Jed who had made me 'Get well soon' cards in school. I was too tired to speak to them properly but was grateful for the cards and glad to see them. Callie soon arrived and it seemed like we were taking up the entire ward, but I felt lucky to have such a caring family by my side. Mum and Dad were worried because I looked so pale but the doctors said it was because I'd lost so much blood in the operation. They had drained more than two litres of blood from my womb and had made the cut double in size to make sure it wouldn't close up again.

After everyone had left, I fell straight asleep and only woke when the nurses came to check my blood pressure and temperature throughout the night, whilst monitoring my pulse on a heart rate machine. I spent the next two weeks in hospital under constant supervision, sleeping through most of the day and night unless I was being checked on by nurses or receiving medication; I was on two different drips every day, which both took two hours to complete. I received numerous cards and phone calls from relatives who sent their love. It felt strange lying in bed for so long as I was used to exercising all the time, but I knew I wouldn't put on any weight as I had barely eaten since before I'd been admitted. I felt good about this but was also unsure it had made a difference, as I had not seen my body in a mirror since before going to hospital. This was because I had been bed-washed the entire time I was there, as I had been too ill to leave my bed to even go to the toilet by myself. I remember one evening when Ashleigh came to visit me with Charlie. He had made me a 'Get well soon' card and Ash had bought me some sweets, but like before in the hospital I was too ill to eat and so I let her share them with Charlie. When the nurses came to my bedside to serve dinner, it was chicken nuggets and chips, which I also gave to Ashleigh and Charlie. They asked for some more chicken nuggets and the nurse kindly gave them some, but I still couldn't eat although they smelt good. Charlie picked up my bedside remote and asked, 'What does this do?'

It was a remote control for my bed, which could move up and down at both ends as well as moving the side bars up or down. Charlie thought it was hilarious and since I was making a recovery now, I was well enough to find it fun. Ashleigh had been eating crisps and suddenly started spitting them everywhere with Charlie who joined in, which I didn't find funny at all. They were starting to really annoy me as they were so hyper and acting like idiots, but I was still too weak to move or shout and so I simply started crying. One of the nurses came to my bed and noticed they were upsetting me, so she asked them to leave and that was the last bit of company I had that night.

A few more days went by and Mum or Dad would be there in the morning with Ash, who was the only one allowed off school to visit me. I was feeling better and knew Mum couldn't be with me the whole time, as she had things to do at home, so I told her I didn't mind her only visiting me in the evening with everyone else. I wanted her there all the time of course, but I was mature in the sense that I knew it would be selfish to think badly of her for caring about my other siblings as well as me. I was getting better in the hospital now but Mum would still visit me every day until I was discharged. The day I could go home finally arrived and after some final checks from the doctors and nurses, I was taken downstairs in a wheelchair. It felt good to leave the hospital and although I was still ill, it was nice to be going home. I picked at a couple of sweets for breakfast as the nurses wanted to make sure I was going back to normal with food, so although I didn't feel like eating, it meant I was allowed to go home.

CHAPTER 13

She's Innocent

When I arrived home from hospital, Ashleigh and the boys were all at school. I had asked Ashleigh if she would tidy my bedroom whilst I was gone so that I wouldn't have to struggle myself when I was home, but she didn't. There was no insulation in my side of the loft and there were two large cupboard doors which lead out to the eaves around the edge of the roof. The doors were broken in my room and had come off their hinges; one of them had completely fallen through, which meant my room was freezing cold as well as smelling like a squatters' house. My bed linen was damp because it had been exposed to the outside cold for over a week, and my wooden floor was too cold to walk on in bare feet. I was still too ill to walk properly as my stomach muscles were still sore from the operation, which I had not fully recovered from, so I needed assistance walking around the house.

Ashleigh eventually helped me tidy my room and put the cupboard doors back in place, which helped heat up my room, but it was still cold. I lay down in my cold bed and slept for a few hours before Mum brought me the antibiotics I had to take for the next couple of weeks. I had to take five different pills, four times a day, as I was still receiving outpatient treatment from the hospital. Mum would leave a phone beside my bed so that I could call her if I wanted to get up, but if I dropped it I was totally screwed. I still struggled moving around by myself, but I was slowly getting better. I managed to weigh myself after being home for a bit, too, and I was ecstatic at the results. The scale read 58kg (127lb), which meant I'd lost over 5kg (11lb) since I'd been admitted to hospital.

I was still too ill to attend school but I didn't mind that so much because I hated school. Ashleigh would tell me lots of teachers and pupils were asking about me and being really nice, which was strange as no one had cared much before. I was recovering fine until one morning when I was abruptly woken by a pain in my chest, which was stopping me from breathing. I was petrified because I couldn't breathe, but I was in so much pain I couldn't call for help. I had left the phone mum gave me in the bathroom the night before, which was only ten feet away from my bed but it still seemed impossible to get to. Too weak to stand, I crawled off my bed and tried to pull myself along the floor to the bathroom. It hurt too much to move but I kept trying as hard as I could, and eventually made it to the bathroom after two very long hours. I called Mum, who helped me back to my bedroom, where I stayed for the rest of the day. My chest had calmed down and didn't hurt again until later that night, but this time I was sitting downstairs with Mum and Dad. I remember feeling an intense burning pain inside my chest which was stopping me from breathing and felt as though my rib cage would break any minute. I whispered to Mum in a weak and petrified voice, 'Mum, I can't breathe… I can't breathe…'

She immediately phoned an ambulance and I was rushed to hospital, where they put me on an oxygen machine to help me breathe until they found out what was wrong with me. I sat on the bed whilst they took my pulse and tapped at my chest, asking me if I felt any pain. After another doctor had given his opinion, I was sent for an x-ray and it was back to being in a wheelchair for me. Mum rocked me whilst we waited for the results and I cried because it felt as though I would never get any better.

After a few more blood tests, the doctors came back with my results from the x-ray and told mum I had costochondritis. Mum asked what that was, as she had never heard of it before. The doctor explained that it was an inflammation of the breast bone, causing swelling underneath the ribs between my lungs, which was causing enormous pressure on both lungs as well as my rib cage any time I tried to breathe. They sent me home with some antibiotics and said that if it got any worse I had to go straight back to hospital. The antibiotics helped a lot and I was soon well enough to go back to school, but I was still continuing to eat as little as possible. I was motivated by how much weight I'd lost through being ill and didn't want to regain it, but I soon went back to binge/purge habits I'd developed through bulimia.

Throwing up my food became a kind of stress relief as I felt the same sense of release as when I cut myself, but I was trying desperately hard to fight my way out of depression. I didn't like being depressed and it seemed as though I would never get my head around it, but I helped myself as much as I could and started exercising more instead of cutting. I would write songs and sing them when I was alone, which temporarily took me to a happier place. Ashleigh had also started trying to fight her depression, and over the next few weeks we started to spend less time in our bedrooms and more time outside with other kids our age. Ashleigh had made a friend at school named Jade, who lived on an estate nearby. She was quiet and shy when I first met her, but she seemed nice and soon welcomed both me and Ashleigh into her friendship group. We met other kids on her estate and would hang out with them, getting up to the same sort of mischief we had with Charlie, who also started hanging out on Jade's estate with us.

There would always be loads of us and we'd steal sweets from the shop on the estate, which we'd then share between us as we sat outside in the street or down alleyways. It helped my depression a lot because although I was frequently getting into trouble with the police, I now had friends, which was just enough to stop me feeling so alone. As well as Jade, I had also become close friends with a girl named Lauren who hung out on the estate. We had met whilst bunking off school one morning and because she liked drinking too, we would always get drunk together and smoke weed on the estate where Jade lived. Charlie would usually hang out with a boy named Shane from the same estate, but they would always end up hanging out with me and Lauren if we were out. Shane was a trouble-maker like me who loved getting drunk and fighting the police, so we immediately became close. By this point I'd completely stopped seeing Emma, Laura and Fiona, so it was easy to spend time with my new friends.

There was a girl named Amy who I had also met on the Ansel Estate, but she didn't like getting into as much trouble as us so would usually stay home. One Saturday I'd been drinking on the Ansel Estate with Lauren and Charlie, when suddenly Shane joined us and told me he'd seen my mum looking for me. Someone had told her I was drinking and so I immediately asked him who it was. He wouldn't tell me so I thought it was his mum at first, as she had seen us through her window, so I started to take my anger out on him. We argued and were in the middle of a drunken fight when Amy came out of nowhere and shouted, 'I did it! I called your mum. You're too young to drink, it's illegal!'

I apologized to Shane and quickly turned my attention to her. I was so angry at Amy for grassing me up, but the alcohol was making my judgement even worse. We were now standing in the middle of the road whilst we shouted at each other, with Lauren sticking up for me as Shane and Charlie watched. Amy backed onto the pavement as she shouted, 'You're a stupid fat cunt!', at which point I lost my temper. I had refrained from hitting her as she was younger than me and was very immature for her age, but when she called me fat I simply lost it. I'm sure I had called her even worse names in the argument, but it didn't stop me from pushing her off the side of the road. She dramatically stepped back and threw herself onto the ground, making it look as though I'd pushed her really hard when I'd barely tapped her. I could see she was helpless to defend herself by this point and I didn't want to be a bully, so I ended the fight before it began and walked back towards Lauren. We ran off with Shane and Charlie as we saw Amy's mum come out, at which point we'd already taken all our alcohol and were legging it to a woodland area at the back of the estate. We found a more secluded place to drink and so we carried on drinking, whilst keeping a lookout for any police that might have been called.

When I arrived home later that night I found the police had been called by Amy, but because there was no clear evidence I'd touched her they had little power to arrest me. The police wanted to take me to the station to give a statement, but I refused to go. As I was under no legal obligation to attend the police station, I told them I would not be complying and they might as well just go away. However, that quickly changed when they threatened to arrest me for assault. Because Amy had made an allegation that I'd assaulted her, I was taken to the station under caution to be interviewed. After questioning me about the incident, they told me I was free to go but would need to stay away from Amy whilst the investigation was taking place over the next few weeks. It didn't stop me hanging round Ansel, however, because all my friends were there and there was no way I was going to stop hanging out with them, even if I did risk being arrested for it.

A few days later I was walking to Marconi's Park with Ashleigh, Charlie and Lauren, when we noticed Amy sitting on the swings with Jade. We walked over to them as I was still friends with Jade and although Amy seemed intimidated by my presence, I told her I was not there to fight. I wasn't stupid and knew I'd be getting in trouble soon for our argument, so I decided to pretend to be her friend so that she'd withdraw her statement. I sat on the swings next to her and apologized for pushing her when we argued, whilst convincing her I still wanted to be her friend. She said to me, 'I just want all of this to be over. I don't want to argue anymore either.'

I then took my lying to the next level when I said to her, 'Withdraw your statement then. Here, you can use my phone.'

Ashleigh had left her phone with me whilst she went to the shop with Charlie and as I knew Amy did not have a phone, I insisted she borrowed Ashleigh's. She didn't know what to say, so I told her what she had to tell the police, that she wanted to withdraw her statement because we had made up. She soon called the police from Ashleigh's phone. I thanked her and continued to be civil with her whilst we hung out in the park, before leaving to walk home later than evening. I thought this would all be over now as I would no longer be under investigation by the police, but I was soon proved horribly wrong when they showed up at school the next morning. I had arrived on time to my form class but had barely had a chance to sit down when the teacher told me I was to report to the vice principal's office immediately. Lauren was sitting outside another teacher's office when I knocked on the vice principal's door, before walking inside where I was told to sit down in silence. A tall man wearing a black suit followed me in and stood by the door, which I thought was extremely odd.

I was scared by this point as I didn't know what I had done wrong, nor did I recognize this man, who then told the vice principal to leave. I felt uncomfortable and knew something was up, so I said I needed the toilet desperately, in an attempt to make a run for it. I didn't care about leaving my school bag as I could come back for that later, but when he refused to let me go I started to realize he was not a teacher. As I stood up to push past him, he twisted my arm behind my back and pushed me against the teacher's desk whilst he pulled out a set of handcuffs. I was still resisting when he said, 'Robyn Hennessy, I am arresting you on suspicion of witness intimidation under section fifty-one of the criminal justice act, 1994. You do not have to say anything but it may harm your defence, if you do not mention when questioned, something you later rely on in court. Anything you do say may be given in evidence.'

I started screaming, 'But I haven't done anything! There must be a mistake!'

I continued to plead my innocence whilst he dragged me by the scruff of my neck, keeping hold of my hands, which were in cuffs behind my back. Lauren looked shocked as I was walked past her, which was when I also noticed Ashleigh being walked to another police car. She was walking with an officer who we knew from being stop-searched in the past, but this was the first time we had ever actually been arrested and it was quite frightening. I was panicking inside but did not let out a single tear, as I refused to show my fear to the police. More importantly I had to stay strong for Ashleigh, as I was sure she was even more scared than I was.

When we arrived at the station they took me to the front desk where I was searched and booked into custody by the custody sergeant. I was forced to hand over any jewellery, electrical items, and any items they thought I could entertain or harm myself with. Ashleigh was being booked into custody too and although the officers had told me not to speak to her, I managed to hug her and tell her everything would be OK, before they pulled me away from her and threatened to further arrest me. She was crying and I comforted her as a sister, telling her in front of all the police officers that they couldn't do anything to her and she would be out soon. She seemed comforted by me being there and had stopped crying by the time the police took us in opposite directions, but I still continued to shout to her until she was too far away to hear me.

I didn't care about being further arrested as nothing mattered to me other than making sure Ash was OK, so it didn't bother me too much when they started being rougher with me, so long as I comforted my sister. I was told to take my shoes off before being thrown into a white cell with no doors or windows, except for one thick steel door which they locked behind me from the outside. As I sat on the bed, which was merely a concrete slab built into the wall with a foam mattress on top of it, I looked up at the camera before closing my eyes and trying not to cry. I remember thinking that whatever I had done to get myself in here, Ash was innocent and it was my fault she'd been arrested. She didn't belong here and nor did I, but I couldn't help wondering if Amy withdrawing her statement through Ashleigh's phone had something to do with it. Ashleigh hadn't even been there and had just left her phone with me for a few minutes, but I knew the police had her number stored on their database. It all started to make sense.

When I was eventually taken out of my cell to be interviewed, it all became clear that it was indeed my fault that Ashleigh and I had been arrested. The police questioned me about the incident regarding Amy using Ashleigh's phone to withdraw her statement, and they accused me of forcing her to do so. They kept trying to provoke a reaction from me by talking at me rather than to me, stating things such as, 'I think you're a bully, which is why you threatened Amy and made her withdraw her statement.'

Amy hadn't even reported this to the police; this was all done on their part, after noticing Amy was using the defendant's sister's phone to withdraw her statement. I stayed calm throughout the interview and answered all their questions, being sure to make note of as many as I could remember when I left the station. When I was eventually allowed to go, I was bailed to reappear at the police station on a later date, by which time they would have decided whether or not the case would go to court.

Mum picked us up and drove us home, but we were not in trouble as she knew our arrests had been a mistake. The case was eventually dropped because Ashleigh and Amy both told the exact same story I had told when interviewed, and I continued to hang out on the Ansel Estate with Lauren, Jade, Shane and Charlie and would not make a fuss if Amy came out. Lauren was dating Amy's older brother at the time and so we had to be civil with her, but she would rarely come out as she didn't drink or get into trouble like us.

Most thirteen-year-olds would have been scared into behaving after being arrested and thrown into a police cell, but all it taught me was that nothing actually happened and there were no consequences to my actions. Drinking and causing trouble seemed to be helping my depression at the time, as I would always have fun, and now that I wasn't scared of being arrested, I was no longer afraid of being caught by the police. I knew that nothing would come out of it as they would never follow through with their threats, so after that day I became fearless of the law itself.

A few weeks went by and I was still getting into trouble at school, but I'd behave myself just enough so that they didn't throw me out. I would still cut myself and purge but only when I was stressed, and I continued to get drunk and smoke cannabis every weekend. My grades were still pretty good at school as I didn't have many friends there so would focus on my work, but my depression caused me to have frequent outbursts during lessons, where I would end up being kicked out of the classroom or sent to the exclusion room. I hated that room because there was boards between every desk so that you couldn't talk to anyone and there was a rule of complete silence all round. Seven hours in that room would be enough to drive anyone insane, but I ended up spending most of my school hours in there as I was deemed incapable of sitting through mainstream lessons.

One morning in school I received a letter from the head teacher, who had teamed up with the local police and surrounding schools to nominate all the badly behaved thirteen to fourteen-year-olds to attend a three-day army-styled boot camp. I was excited to go as the few people I got on with at school would be there, and I thought it would be fun to dress up in camouflage and run around the woods like idiots for a few days. The school and police thought it would 'kick us into behaving' but it seemed that along with all the kids attending, I had other ideas. A girl from my year named Toni was asked to go; she had already been expelled from Tomlinscote in the first year. I had stayed in touch with her through Facebook and as soon as I found out she was going, we started planning how to smuggle alcohol and drugs in for the boot camp weekend. I was excited when the weekend finally arrived and after meeting everyone at the police station, two men in army uniform drove us in a minibus to the army barracks where we were shown what we'd be doing over the next few days. There were a few more people there than I'd originally expected, but we soon started talking and immediately became friends.

They showed us the assault course we'd be racing on in teams later that day, as well as handing out army trousers for us all to wear.

The instructors took us into the woods and painted our faces with camouflage to play some team- building games, whilst I stood close to Toni as she was a familiar face. Two boys approached us and asked if we wanted to go with them to find somewhere to smoke, so we ran off from the rest of the group and tried to hide behind some bushes. The army instructors were shouting at us to come back as they chased us, but we were laughing too hard to hear them as we lit our cigarettes and carried on running. We eventually found a nice little ditch where we could hide and so the four of us lay down, whilst opening up cans of beer the boys had snuck in. They passed a can each to me and Toni and we stayed there until we'd finished drinking all the boys' beer, as well as smoking more cigarettes.

When we eventually joined the rest of the group, we were asked to hand over any cigarettes we had to the instructors. I knew we'd probably be asked, so I'd already hidden my weekend supply in my bra. Toni and the boys had their cigarettes hidden on them too, so we lied and said we had smoked our last ones. They told us to get on the floor and do fifty push-ups each for running off, but I found it no struggle because I had always kept myself fit. We were then shown to the dorms we'd be sleeping in, where we were told to pick a bed and leave all our belongings beside it. Girls were in one room and boys were in the other, but everyone ended up sneaking into each other's rooms anyway. Everyone was warned that if they misbehaved past a third warning they would have to sleep outside in a tent which they'd put up themselves, but those who had followed rules could also choose to camp outside.

Toni and I hid all our alcohol and weed in our suitcases, which we locked in lockers beside our beds, before barricading the door shut so that we could smoke out of the window. The army instructors eventually kicked the door down and we were given a second warning, but I didn't care because I could easily do the push-ups and sit-ups they used as punishment. Once everyone had settled in, they told us to put our hiking shoes on as we'd be going for a ten-mile trek. I couldn't be bothered to go for a walk and neither could anyone else, but they said we'd be playing games along the way.

After a full day of assault courses, muddy walks and marching, we sat outside where we were given our meal for the evening. It was a dehydrated, packaged meal which we would cook in a pan over a fire, but it looked revolting so I refused to eat it. I didn't want to eat much anyway, as Toni and I would be drinking later that evening and we'd get drunk faster on empty stomachs. At around 11pm, we were told to take whatever we needed for the night from our suitcases in our dorms. I was given a tent to put up with Toni, who was also sleeping outside as a punishment for acting up all day, but we didn't really mind because most of the boys ended up sleeping outside too. In the end, all but three out of the twenty kids at boot camp decided to sleep outside. My tent was nothing more than a wooden pole, holding up a green sheet of tarpaulin. All of the tents were two-man and exactly the same, except for the instructor's tent, which was much like a large canopy with all the walls rolled down except for the one they were watching us from. Theirs was an eight-man tent with six of them sleeping in it, but we were still sneaky enough to get all our alcohol past them and into our tent.

Toni and I had been lying inside our sleeping bags for around ten minutes, when she pulled a mirror out of her bag. I told her we should place it on the inside of the tent, facing out of the tent door, and leave the door slightly unzipped so that we could see if anyone was coming. We could just about see outside using the mirror, which meant we could hide our alcohol and pretend to be asleep before they unzipped our door. We started drinking and soon enough, the two boys who we'd been running off with all day showed up. They had even more alcohol that they'd snuck to their tent, so after finishing off a bottle of vodka between us we crept back to their tent for more booze. It was almost 1am now and we hadn't smoked since before dinner, so we started talking about how we could smoke without being caught. One of the boys took out some papers and a grinder from his pocket, then we added our weed together to roll a gigantic spliff which we would take to the woods along with cigarettes. We crawled out of their tent, keeping our bodies close to the floor until we had made it to the woods, at which point we started running away from camp. Toni whispered, 'Quick! I think someone heard us,'

No one had noticed however, so we walked further out into the woods before sitting around some logs and putting our alcohol into a pile. We lit our cigarettes and passed round the spliff we'd rolled in the tent, still drinking beers as we laughed and talked about why each one of us was there. I didn't feel proud about saying I'd been arrested in the past, but the boys seemed to think it was cool and I was trying to fit in so I felt glad I'd told them. After almost two hours, we were still in the woods when I received a phone call from Ashleigh.

She had been out all night with another girl and they'd been to a party which had been raided by the police, so they were now on the run. I felt jealous when she'd told me Mum had believed her that she was staying at a friend's house without checking with their parents, as Mum and Dad would know straight away if I was trying to pull an 'all-nighter'. I was glad she was having fun, however, so I said goodnight to her before she hung up as she was still running from the police. We eventually headed back to our tent but still had no intention of sleeping, so we collapsed everyone else's tent including ours before running back to the boys' tent. We had finished all our alcohol by now so we were extremely drunk and hungry as we hadn't eaten for most of the day, so we decided to sneak off to the instructors' tent, where they had sugary snacks in a crate.

The crate of food was easy to access and so we stole what we could, before one of the army instructors started to wake up. We legged it back to the boys' tent, which was the only one still standing, but that was soon collapsed by the main man in charge of the boot camp. He stormed over to our tent, shouting for anyone who was still awake to go to sleep, before smashing our tent down with a sledge hammer from the outside. He commanded us to step outside immediately and either go to sleep now, or we'd be forced to go for a run. It was 4am by this point and although I was still drunk, the alcohol was starting to wear off so I said to Toni, 'Fuck it. Let's go for a run!'

They told us that unless one of us finished the run we would all be sent home, so we started running with one of the instructors who was the youngest and fittest. I was also still fit from all the years of Judo and having an eating disorder, however, so once the others dropped out after a few miles I continued running with the instructor. He gave up after eight miles and said he did not know how I could run so fast after drinking as he could smell the alcohol on me, but there were no drinks left to confiscate as we'd finished them. He reluctantly walked me back to base camp and told me they'd be waking everyone up in less than thirty minutes, so I decided to try and get some sleep. I met Toni and the boys, who were still awake, and they thanked me for finishing the run so that they didn't have to. Sure enough, we were told to wake up and pack away our tents for the next day's training.

I had vomited on the run, which stopped me feeling too sick for the rest of the day, but I still refused to eat anything as I had a phobia of eating in front of people. When Mum came to collect me at the end of the day, the instructors told her I hadn't eaten much but they didn't say a lot about my behaviour, as I hadn't been caught for much other than running off. Ashleigh was in the car and told me all about her night when we arrived home, telling me that she was eventually taken home by police who found her asleep on the street at 4am. She had tried lying about her age but one of the officers recognized her as he knew my face, so there was no denying she was only thirteen when they realized she was my twin sister. She was grounded after that, but had started going to army cadets, so I went along with her when she was allowed out to go training. Some of the army instructors had been on the boot camp but were very welcoming towards me, despite the fact I'd acted up throughout. I enjoyed army cadets for a little while, but as it was winter, it seemed all we did was history lessons and marching so I soon stopped going along with Ashleigh who also quit because she got bored. I still worked out but only to lose weight and that was becoming hard because I was drinking so much, but it was temporarily helping me escape my depression.

CHAPTER 14

Catch Me If You Can

Over the next few months I continued to drink all the time and would often bunk off school to do so. I hated school because it would constantly remind me that I was never good enough, and no matter how hard I tried to be good, I was still kept on student reports throughout my entire second and third year. I was fourteen years old now and would get myself arrested frequently, usually when I was hanging out on the Ansel Estate, and I started to hate the police so much that I would shout abuse any time I saw them. One evening I'd had a huge argument with Mum and Dad about my behaviour at school, and my frequent drinking outside of school. It seemed like everyone at home had started hating me, including Ashleigh. She would tell me to stop cutting myself, saying I was only doing it for attention, whilst Mum and Dad would say things such as, 'Why do you have to get in trouble all the time? Why can't you just be normal?'

I had stormed out on this particular afternoon and was drinking as usual, when I met up with Shane and Charlie on the Ansel Estate. Shane let me stay at his that night and after I refused to come home, Mum and Dad called the police to come and look for me. We met up with Jade and Lauren, who hung out with us for the rest of the night, before Shane and I went back to his house at around 1am. His mum was deaf which meant we could play music as long as it wasn't loud enough for her to feel the vibrations in the floor, but we could still talk loudly as it wouldn't wake her up. We drew tattoos on each other with marker pens as well as smoking weed once we'd finished all our alcohol, but sure enough the police soon turned up. I had run from them on two occasions that night and got away, but it seemed as though I had no way out this time because they had the entire block of flats surrounded. They pressed the buzzer for us to unlock the outside door from upstairs but Shane's mum was asleep, so we decided to shout at them from the window instead. With a balaclava on Shane's face and a bandana covering mine, I leant out of the window and shouted, 'Fuck off! She's not here!'

They knew it was me and told me I needed to give myself up right away or I'd be arrested, but I didn't care and was prepared to put up a fight. They continued to bang on the door for almost thirty minutes before a neighbour let them in, at which point I had already made an escape plan. I waited until all of them were upstairs and kicking down Shane's front door, before leaping out of the window and running for my life. Shane held the police off for as long as he could but when they saw the lounge window was wide open, they knew I was no longer inside the flat. With the sirens blaring from the police van, two of them drove after me whilst the others chased me on foot. It was pitch black outside as it was 3am by this point, but that made it easier for me to hide once I could no longer run. There was a fence behind some houses with a communal garden split into sections, so I hid behind one of the fences and kept myself out of the light whilst I tried to catch my breath.

One of the police officers who had chased me on foot climbed over the fence and entered the garden, but he was also out of breath from running. As he slowly made his way around the garden to see if I was there, he shone a bright white torch around, which passed me without spotting me at first. He shone it right past my body, which was hunched over as I was still hiding behind the fence, but he quickly shone the light back on me and shouted for me to put my hands up. I hopped the fence and carried on running, out through an alleyway and back onto the road. Suddenly the police van came out of nowhere with another car and the officers stopped in the middle of the road, then ran towards me. I sprinted as fast as I could but the officer who had shone the torch on me was now behind me by inches, so he threw both arms around me and forced me onto the floor. The other officers came to help him restrain me, whilst I continued struggling until they had strapped my legs together as well as cuffed my hands behind my back. I reluctantly complied as they pulled me back up to my feet and threw me into the back of the police van, before a female officer came over to search me.

They took me home without arresting me as I had not caused any real damage, but they told me if they were called out for the same situation again I would be taken to the station to spend the night in a police cell. Dad came to the door to let me in when I arrived home and some of the neighbours were staring out of their windows as the lights from the police van had woken them up, but I ignored them and walked inside. Dad barely said a word to me as he walked up the stairs to go back to bed, but I could feel the atmosphere turning cold as I made my way up to my bedroom. I felt guilty for keeping him and Mum awake all night, but I was angry at the same time. I hated the way my parents seemed to hate me for being depressed, but I knew I was not helping by constantly getting into trouble with the police.

I hated the police too, but whenever they'd lay a finger on me, it felt comforting in a messed-up way because it provided someone to fight and someone to take all my anger out on. They would always overpower me in the end as there were usually lots of them against just me, but when I felt the strength of five or six police officers holding me down I felt happy to know that there was someone stronger than me. When there was someone stronger than me, I felt less pressure to be strong myself, which was slowly killing me inside. It made me feel safe to know that they had complete power and would make decisions for me, so that I no longer had to myself... Even if some decisions would have been better off left unmade.

Mum and Dad didn't ground me after that as I would walk out of the house anyway, which would always cause more arguments than what it was worth. I was still hanging out on the Ansel Estate and would stay out as much as I could because I hated being home. When I was home I would stay sober, which made it hard to deal with the guilt I felt for my actions. I hated myself and felt utterly ashamed of my life, but I continued to drink as I preferred to block out my thoughts with alcohol rather than deal with them head on. Mum and Dad would hardly speak to me since when we did we'd just argue, and if we weren't arguing we'd just get upset, as they'd ask me, 'What happened to you, Robyn? What happened to our little girl?' I sometimes wished that I'd chosen a different path, but I was still in denial of there even being a problem. All I saw was me trying to have fun, whilst everyone else was causing problems over nothing.

One evening I had been arrested over a drunken fight on the Ansel, when two female police officers tried to walk me to their car to take me home. I saw that they were both half my size and I fancied my chances, so I made a break for it and ran. I was so drunk I'd barely made it to the bottom of the road when a male police officer, who'd also chased after me, swung for my legs with a baton. The pain hit me instantly and I fell straight to the ground, my drunken body passed out as he pushed his body weight on top of me to hold me down. He cuffed my hands behind my back as he arrested me, before calling for a larger police van to take me to the station. I knew the drill by now; photos and finger prints, custody search and check-in then a cold night in a cell followed by an interview in the morning. Once I'd sobered up in a police cell I became a lot calmer, but I would often find myself crying once I was alone. It felt like I'd been left to rot any time I was in a police cell for more than a few hours, but I was used to spending six to twelve hours in police cells by now. Every time I got arrested I would fall into the same routine, fighting with the custody staff until they threw me into a locked cell where I would cry myself to sleep, before waking up and repeating the same process over and over again until I was released.

After being bailed the next morning, I was given a fourty-eight-hour ban from the Ansel Estate. Though I knew the police would be out looking for me, I ignored my bail conditions and decided to drink with my friends on the Ansel the next night anyway. I don't remember who I was with, just that we spent most of the night running from police, and the fact that they kept chasing us made me even more determined to run. At around 8pm I'd already been drinking for three hours when a police car drove past me before turning the sirens on and stopping. They immediately got out of the car and chased after me, but I legged it down an alleyway which led back to Shane's house. After hiding in his flat for a few hours whilst smoking weed in his bedroom, we left the flat to continue drinking outside. We kept a constant look-out for the police and if we saw them we would wind them up by running out into the road where they could see us before running off when they chased us. We would run using all sorts of escape routes, climbing over fences and garage roofs as well as sprinting through people's back gardens and into woods. They'd been chasing me for over six hours now and since I was trying to make amends with Mum and Dad, I ran once more from the police before making my way home. I'd only just left the Ansel Estate when a police car drove up behind me and stopped, but since I was no longer on banned turf I thought I'd stop running and try to act innocent. The police officer approached me with his colleague and immediately said, 'I am arresting you on suspicion of breaking your bail conditions…'

He had already grabbed hold of my arm before saying a word, but when the handcuffs came out I desperately tried to pull away. Using all my strength, I pulled my arm away from his grip and close to my chest whilst he dragged me to the floor. By this point he had his legs either side of me as I continued to resist my arms being pulled away from my body, whilst pushing up with my legs as hard as I could to get this idiot off me. I felt his body weight practically leaving mine as my legs were almost strong enough to lift him completely off me, but four other police vehicles had arrived at the scene and were all stepping in. They pinned me to the floor whilst holding down my head, as I kept banging it on the concrete floor, but I continued to struggle until I was completely exhausted. My brother Jake had walked past and seen that I was being arrested, but was told to leave by the police, who threatened to spray him if he took one step closer to me. I didn't realize this until I spoke to him later, which was probably a good thing as I would have gone ballistic, but he stayed calm and walked past me to go home. I shouted to him, asking him to tell Mum and Dad I'd been arrested and that I was sorry so that they wouldn't be surprised when they received a phone call, but he didn't seem too impressed by what I'd meant as caring. He told me I was selfish and stupid for getting arrested and that Mum and Dad shouldn't have to deal with me, but I was surrounded by so many police officers that I couldn't even try to defend myself against his accusations.

I cried in the back of the van and continued to bang my head forcefully against the metal cage which surrounded me, whilst threatening to commit suicide that night. I told the police officers exactly what I thought of them and how I thought they were pathetic for starting on my little brother, but they simply told me to 'shut up' as they drove me to the station in Woking. I didn't like staying at Woking Police Station because the cells were a lot smaller than Guildford, which was where I'd usually be taken for overnight stays, but I had no choice over this and was forced to sit in the back of the van until we arrived. I had been shouting and banging on the metal cage for the entire journey and as it was a Saturday night, there was a queue forming at the custody suite, which meant they refused to let me out straight away. I was beginning to feel claustrophobic by now as I'd been locked in a box-like cage for over an hour, and I started having a panic attack in the back of the van. They eventually opened the doors and let me out, on the condition that I would stop acting up. I behaved myself for a little while and sat quietly against a wall until my breathing had calmed down, complying with the police by no longer resisting my handcuffs.

Worthless

My head was bruised and bleeding from banging it continuously in the back of the van, so they wiped the blood away with a bandage before holding an ice pack against it. My wrists were swollen from the handcuffs as well as my hands and knees being bruised from resisting arrest, so as soon as the swelling on my head went down I pressed the ice pack against all the other bruised parts of my body. I was ready to be booked into custody now which meant being searched, but the second I took my hoodie off, the custody sergeant started questioning me about my mental state. After noticing the numerous scars and fresh cuts up both my arms, he asked if I was self-harming. I told him my injuries were not self-inflicted, but he was not as stupid as the people who had questioned me before, so he put me under twenty-four-hour supervision, which meant being constantly monitored so that I didn't try to kill myself. It didn't help that I had threatened to commit suicide upon my arrest, as the officers used that against me, making my stay in custody even harder than it already was.

I was told to hand over my hoodie, shoes and tracksuit bottoms as they had strings in them which they said I could harm myself with, as well as being ordered to remove my bra from under my shirt as it was wired with metal. I felt extremely self-conscious after this as I could no longer hide my face by keeping my hood up, which was the only thing making me feel remotely safe, as I'd sometimes pretend that my hood made me invisible. When they took my bra away I was extremely worried about how I looked, as without it my large breasts made me look even fatter than I already was. As for the tracksuit bottoms, they were keeping me warm and now all I had was one blanket, which was not enough to get through the night. Police cells were made of concrete, which felt cold on my skin and was far too cold to sleep on without shivering. I eventually fell asleep after a few hours and although I was cold, I was still slightly drunk, which helped me to stop thinking about where I was. Once I was locked in a cell, the game was up. No one to fight, no one to talk to… Just me alone with my thoughts and so it was best just to try and sleep.

The night was eventually over and after being woken by new custody staff who were working the morning shift, I was interviewed before being bailed to appear in court. I didn't like going to court as it was intimidating to stand in front of a judge and court marshals, because they would always look down on me as if I was worth nothing more than the crimes written on the piece of paper they were holding. I hated dragging Mum and Dad to court too, as I felt ashamed because they had not brought me up to be like that, and I knew I'd failed them just by the look on their faces. Part of this guilt-ridden mind-set was due to my depression, but the choices I'd made in life had always left me to blame because of all my flaws. I couldn't help getting into trouble as I couldn't seem to help drinking, but the outcome was always the same. I drank because I was depressed and I was depressed because I drank, so it became a viscous cycle I could not get out of.

School was becoming increasingly difficult too. I was trying ever so hard not to be expelled, but the pressure of pleasing certain teachers who I despised was proving more challenging than coping with the bullying. The bullying itself wasn't bothering me so much now as I was growing older and less bothered by it, but I still felt lonely in school as I didn't fit in with anyone. I wasn't accepted with any academic friendship groups as they knew I misbehaved a lot, but I never fitted in with the badly behaved kids either because I was so much smarter than them academically. I didn't fit in with the boys because I was a girl, but the girls thought I was weird because I was not interested in boys. Everyone seemed immature to me as I had been through and seen so much in my short life, so I found it hard to relate to anyone my age.

I was eventually put on a final warning at school, the white report. It was a twelve-week probation plan which would monitor my every move, and though I came close on several occasions throughout the rest of year nine I was not expelled. When school broke up for the summer holidays in July, I was required to attend a meeting with my parents about my place at Tomlinscote. There were still six weeks left of my report, so I was told I would need to think carefully over the summer holidays about what I really wanted. Mum and Dad had talked about moving me to a different school as it would give me a fresh start, but as much as I hated Tomlinscote I knew it would provide me with a good education. I needed to stay at Tomlinscote if I wanted to make Mum and Dad proud, so I told them my behaviour would be immaculate after the summer holidays, which would allow me a six-week break to clear my head… Clearing my head seemed to be the last of my priorities, however, as I spent the entire six-week holiday getting drunk and arrested. I'd stand outside the shops for hours waiting for anyone to go in to buy alcohol for me, but if the shop staff found out I'd simply move on to a different shop. One of the shops on the high street had started serving me alcohol but soon stopped once they realized I was underage, however, I continued to walk into that same shop to try and buy alcohol. If they refused to serve me I'd simply pick up the alcohol I wanted, whilst saying to the shop owner as I approached the counter, 'Do you want the money or not, mate? Because I'm going now.'

With that they'd usually shout at me to stop what I was doing, but as I always left the money on the counter they never phoned the police. I got away with this frequently and would do it in front of other customers, until one of them turned out to be an off-duty police officer who tried to arrest me. I still managed to run out of the shop holding enough alcohol to get drunk, but I knew I had to be more careful after that. My friends would drink with me some nights but when I continued to drink in the daytime, they could not keep up with me and so I often ended up drinking alone on the streets all day. One afternoon I'd been drinking on the Ansel and was making my way home to pass out and sleep, when I heard someone shout at me 'Pisshead!'

I knew I had an alcohol problem by this point but was still in denial and it upset me, as I was still trying to accept the fact that I even had a problem. When I turned around to see who it was, I noticed Drew and James standing with a crowd of their friends. The friend of theirs who had shouted at me was riding a moped and I tried to ignore them and carry on walking, but he sped up to follow me as I made my way up the hill. Drew and James followed with all their friends, mostly boys, who continued to shout abuse at me until I stopped walking. I turned around to face them as I knew they were going to start a fight, so I threw my arms up in the air and shouted, 'Come on then!'

The boy on the moped stayed put, but Drew and James followed behind another one of their friends, who was older and taller than me, which felt threatening. I knew he was going to hit me, so I poured bottle of wine over him before dropping it as he took a swing with his fist. After missing my face, he picked up my wine bottle and I was scared he was going to smash it over me. I couldn't fight when I was drunk, I had no chance of protecting myself, but I was also too drunk to run. He dropped it beside me and grabbed my hoodie with his hands, before letting go and backing away from me as he saw some of my friends arrive. It was only Shane with his mum but his mum was known to police and so if she was around, there would usually be police arriving any minute. Maybe he had a little dignity left in his body, which was why he didn't beat up a girl, but I felt relieved when he stepped back as I could walk away. Once I was out of sight from James and Drew's friends, I ran to Shane's mum, who gave me hug and told me she would get them back.

I went back to their flat and drank more with Shane, before heading home, where I passed out and fell asleep. The police came round that evening as they had been called to the scene shortly after I left, but I told them what had happened and how I had been assaulted but did not wish to press charges. Whenever I had occasionally gone to the police for help, they'd end up arresting me whilst I was in the station and so I thought it was best to stay away from them as much as I could. This was also part of the reason I never told the police about what Drew and James had done to me and Ashleigh, but I was also still too young to think that the sexual abuse had anything to do with how I felt now. I tried never to think about the sexual abuse as it would only get me upset and as drinking temporarily took the pain away, I couldn't see any reason to seek help.

Worthless

The summer holidays soon passed and I was back at school starting the beginning of year ten, which meant being on my best behaviour as I was on my final warning. The school had never followed through with their threats to kick me out, so I never felt much more pressure to behave than before. However, I knew they were being serious this time as they were constantly calling my parents in for meetings with my head of year. I had made it through almost two weeks with no trouble, but as I was still smoking weed I would often be questioned by teachers who could smell the smoke. One lunch break I had been searching for a place to smoke, but unlike most days there were teachers patrolling the field, so I felt I had no option but to smoke in the toilets. There were many toilet blocks around the building, but one of them was quiet and hardly used as it was practically outside.

There were no classrooms around it and it was on the ground floor, so I walked in alone and lit up my spliff. I had smoked around half of it when two girls from my year walked in, lecturing me about how I shouldn't be smoking. They said I'd get caught by a teacher and that they were worried about me anyway as they'd heard rumours about my drinking problem, so I eventually stubbed it out to avoid the hassle they were giving me. I hung out with them for the rest of lunch break but had barely made it to my next lesson when my head of year came into my classroom with the vice principal. They ordered me to go with them to the principal's office, where they stood either side of me and told me to empty my bag out on the desk. I reluctantly complied and started to take out my books and pens, before admitting to them that I was carrying some cigarettes. They saw my smoked spliff, which I told them was nothing more than a roll-up, and they seemed oblivious to the fact that it was in-fact weed. When they ripped open the spliff they still thought it was a roll-up, even with all the green bits lying around with the tobacco. I was glad to have got away with smoking cannabis in school, but I knew I'd be in trouble for smoking in the toilets. They told me exactly how they'd found out and as they gave the names of the two girls who'd told them, I felt devastated and betrayed. It was

Shannon and Hannah who I'd spent lunch break with had found me in the toilets, then pretended to be my friends before grassing me up to the teachers. I was incredibly angry with them as they had gone behind my back and completely lied to me, but I was even angrier at the fact that confronting them about it would jeopardize my final chance at Tomlinscote. Despite the threat of being expelled, I went looking for them as soon as I was sent back to my lesson. I knew which class they were both in and so I walked straight into their lesson and said to the teacher, 'Our head of year wants to speak with Shannon and Hannah. He told me to come and get them.'

She stupidly believed me and sent both girls out of their classroom; they then followed me as I led them into the toilets. I stood in front of the door so they couldn't walk off as I shouted, 'What the fuck's your problem? I know it was you two who went and told on me. Don't you know you've probably got me expelled?'

They both told me it was my own fault and that they only did it because they were my friends and were worried about me, but how on earth was snitching going to help me? If anything it only stressed me out, which made me smoke even more, so I told them to 'fuck off' back to their classroom and not to tell anyone I'd pulled them into the toilets. They didn't tell any teachers on me as I assume they were scared, but I didn't care as long as I didn't get in any more trouble. I eventually did end up fighting over the situation, but not with Shannon or Hannah. One of their friends, who was also supposed to be my friend, stuck up for them and after calling me a 'Fat cunt' I simply lost it. I grabbed hold of her hair and threw her head against the table, knocking her almost unconscious on the floor. I stormed off and told everyone they were next, before walking out of school to speak to Mum and Dad before the school did.

I was so angry that I said I wouldn't care if I was thrown out, but deep down it was all I wanted to avoid. Mum and Dad were angry at me but could see I was upset, so they agreed to take me into school to try and talk it through with my head of year. He told them there was no option but to get rid of me, which was exactly what he wanted. He had hated me from the moment I arrived because I was classed as a 'problem child', which would potentially bring down the reputation of their school, which was all they cared about. I knew I'd misbehaved a lot but not once had they tried to help me, or ever cared to ask me what was wrong. The only teacher who had ever been there for me, Mr French, did not have the power to change my head of year's decision and I felt incredibly guilty, because he had helped me so many times yet I still ended up where I was. He had even turned up at court to support me in the past, as well as giving me a piano CD because he knew how much I loved to play.

I was eventually given the choice of being thrown out with expulsion on my permanent record, or choosing to leave and apply for another school with a fresh start. I hated Tomlinscote so much, but I didn't want to leave because it would have meant I'd failed Mum and Dad, by not getting the best qualifications I could, which was all they wanted for me. However, Mum talked me into the second option and signed the papers to say I'd chosen to leave. I felt betrayed that I'd had no say in it, but leaving Tomlinscote came with a huge sense of relief. I felt like a huge weight had been lifted off my shoulders and although it upset me deeply for a very long time, I started to think more positively as Mum and Dad began the process of finding me a new school.

CHAPTER 15

Fernhill

I continued to drink as I was still depressed and leaving school seemed to have made it worse, but it was almost the end of autumn term, which meant everyone else was soon off school for two weeks. I was reunited with all my friends as they would also be out during the day-time, meaning I was no longer drinking alone, which seemed to be all I had done since being expelled. I still got myself arrested on a number of occasions, but things seemed to be looking brighter. I was excited to attend a new school with a fresh start, and until then I could drink without worrying about its effects on my school work. Mum had started up an animal care business and so I helped her with dog walking on some days, which helped my depression as it got me out of the house. She had lost a lot of weight by now too, so it was nice to go for walks with her as it was having a positive effect on both our diets. I never told her how thin I really wanted to be, only that I wanted to lose a few pounds and 'get healthy', but it was still nice to be able to do it together.

A few months went by and although it seemed to be taking forever for me to be placed in a new school, I was soon asked to attend an interview meeting at Fernhill Secondary School. Fernhill didn't live up to the same grade results as Tomlinscote, but I knew I would gain more qualifications than I would have if I'd stayed at Tomlinscote. The uniform looked easier to comply with than Tomlinscote too, as there were no 'shirts and ties' or stupid rules about asking permission to remove your school jumper. I dressed smartly for the interview and was happy to start shortly after Christmas. I cut down on the drinking as I wanted to lose a little weight before starting my new school, but I continued to smoke weed as I still needed something to take my mind away from reality. I stopped hanging out on the Ansel Estate so much because I had cut down on drinking, and when I wasn't drinking, I seemed to have no interest in going out. I was also focusing on cleaning myself up before starting school so apart from going out to buy and smoke weed, I would spend most of my time writing music and fighting my depression. When the start date finally arrived for my new school, I felt nervous but also excited. I was starting a school where no one knew my past and I was determined to make some friends, as well as get a good education.

I woke up early that morning to do my hair and make-up. First impressions were always important and I knew I'd be labelled as 'the new kid' as soon as I arrived, so I wanted to make a good impression on my first day. I was fifteen years old now and at halfway though year ten, I was joining a year group where most kids would have known each other since year seven or even before. I didn't want to be the outcast; too quiet, ugly or just different, and after all the years of bullying throughout Ravenscote and Tomlinscote, I knew I had to do everything I could to make sure this school was different. I had to look perfect for my first day at Fernhill, which, at the time, was my fresh start and chance to meet new friends. More importantly it was my last chance to gain some qualifications in my final attempt at education.

I felt like a small child on my first day at school as I wandered up through the front gates, leaving Mum behind as I walked to reception alone. Tomlinscote School was a lot bigger than Fernhill, which appeared slightly run down and rough on the edges, but the untidiness of its appearance gave it a warmer, more welcoming feel than Tomlinscote. It was as though by stepping through those gates, you would not be judged by anyone based on how much money you had or what equipment you could afford. Everyone was valued as a person and I greatly respected that because it was a treatment I was not used to. After leaving Mum behind, I was greeted with a firm handshake at reception by the head teacher, Mr Daniels. He was a tall man, smartly dressed and well spoken. He was very professionally strict but also seemed down to earth and showed a continuous level of mutual respect, something I had never felt back at Tomlinscote. Students there were constantly made to feel inferior to members of staff, like they simply felt the need to remind you that you were less of a person than they were because of your age or lack of life experience.

I was given a timetable to show what lessons I had and what rooms they were in, before being escorted to my classroom, where I was introduced to my form tutor. I smiled politely as he introduced me to my new classmates, before pointing me towards a small desk by the window. I sat down and felt my heart pounding as I tried my best not to look nervous. This was it! My chance to clean myself up and make a fresh start.

After what felt like seconds after sitting down, the bell rang and it was time to change classes for my first lesson. I don't remember what subject it was, but I do remember feeling out of place as I was paired up with a girl named Alice who would 'look after me' that first day and make sure I didn't get lost. She was a short girl, petite build with dyed bright red hair and green eyes. She seemed nice, which was a relief, since we'd be spending most of the day together. We didn't talk much as we walked to lesson one but she smiled and told me a bit about the school day ahead and that I had nothing to worry about, as I would only be 'the new girl' for a few days and would eventually find my feet. From what I could see, Alice enjoyed going to school and worked hard in class as well as staying out of trouble, which was something I desperately wanted for myself.

Worthless

We stood outside the classroom and waited in the hallway. There were so many people we could barely move through the corridors, which were overflowing with crowds of students, shouting and screaming. This typical school environment was one I was no longer familiar with after being away for so long. It brought back memories of Tomlinscote, which my mind only associated with fights, stress and depression. This terrified me, but by this point in my life I'd learnt to distance myself from any feelings I was uncomfortable with. It felt as though by flicking a switch in the back of my brain to shut off all feelings, good or bad, I could withstand feeling absolutely nothing as an alternative to feeling hurt.

Alice walked into the classroom with me where I met yet another teacher, who introduced himself before introducing me to the whole class. This continued in every new lesson I had for the first week. Alice made sure I was settled before leaving the room as she was in a different class. I thanked her for showing me around but told her not to worry about 'babysitting' me all day as I assumed she would not want me tagging alongside her, and I didn't want her to get in trouble for being late to all her lessons after walking me to mine. I figured I'd be alright on my own anyway. As a last resort, I could always ask a staff member or student where my next class was if I was unsure where to go. The teacher pointed to a spare seat next to a blonde girl with glasses and told me to sit there. The girl was very friendly and immediately introduced herself, seeming overwhelmingly struck on becoming my friend. 'My name's Dina…' she said politely, 'I love your hair! Did you dye it yourself?'

My hair was jet black with a blue tint and I had spent hours straightening it before school, so it was nice to have someone notice. I thanked her for the compliment and we continued to talk throughout the lesson. The teacher didn't mind because it was my first day and he could see I was simply trying to make friends, so he left us to it and also didn't seem to mind that we only did half the work we were supposed to do. At the end of the lesson, Dina asked me what my next lesson was. It was in the same room as hers so we walked together, carrying on our conversation as she introduced me to friends of hers who we passed on the way.

Dina was smart and had a small but very close group of friends, who seemed to be more popular with the teachers than with other students. It occurred to me that Dina was a far cry from the types of friends I had chosen in the past, but this was good because it meant I'd have to be more like her if I wanted to fit in. This would up my chances of succeeding in school and completing my exams because if I was friends with her, I would have no reason to be in trouble or in bad situations where I'd make stupid decisions. After lesson two finished it was break time, so I stayed with Dina and she introduced me to her other friends who I had not met yet. There were six or seven of them and I don't recall all their names, but one girl who stood out was called Roxy. She was almost six feet tall, had black curly hair and was fat, in my opinion. I don't know why, maybe it was because of how immature she acted for her age, but I didn't like her one bit and I'm certain she felt the same about me.

I liked Dina. She made me feel welcome and always included me to make sure I wasn't left out. Whether it be a group task in class or just a conversation between friends, she'd always go out of her way to include me. A few days went by and I hung out with Dina's group of friends, trying my hardest to fit in. I struggled with this as I was so used to being in trouble all the time, and Dina's friends were almost geeks. However, I found it easier than most 'naughty' kids to fit in with geeks because I was academically smart and in higher-level classes. I was capable of achieving A* grades whether I acted up or not, and that left me with a strong sense of security because I knew I could skip twenty lessons for almost any subject and still score top marks on the test paper when it came to exams. But this was all about to change, as I found out when I fell out with Roxy. She had started giving me dirty looks and making sly comments when no one was around, which confirmed my assumption that she had taken a dislike to me for no good reason.

I was standing with Roxy, Dina and a few of their friends waiting to be let into a lesson and Roxy was deliberately trying to make me feel as though I didn't belong with them. I think she was the leader in their group of friends and felt threatened by me being there because of how well I got on with everyone. She had been ignoring me all day, trying to push me away by deliberately excluding me from any conversation and belittling every word that came out of my mouth. She was wearing a silver charm bracelet and I wanted to break it off her stupid wrist, but I had a better idea. I wanted to show everyone that I was still going to be friends with them, whether she liked it or not, so I complimented her on how pretty the bracelet was. No sooner had I said it, than she slipped the bracelet off her wrist and into her bag, then said, in front of everyone, 'I'm not wearing a bracelet. Err... Fucking weirdo!'

She'd succeeded in what she was trying to do. I felt completely embarrassed and stupid. Dina had seen the whole thing and told me not to worry about it. She told me she had seen the bracelet too and didn't know why Roxy had it in for me. I felt so frustrated because it was so hard to make friends, especially for me as I was clinically depressed. My depression caused me to hate being around people anyway, but I knew I needed to make friends at school and I was so frustrated that this stupid cow was making it even harder for me. I said to Roxy, 'What's your problem?'

She laughed, turning around pulling faces to her friends and shrugging her shoulders. 'I don't know what you mean. You're the one who's starting on me.'

I was so angry but I ignored her. The rest of that day I only spoke to Dina when she was alone and I smoked behind cars, outside the front school gates when I was on my own. I met a few more people from different classes, mainly boys. Some asked what music I was into and were surprised when I told them I like dubstep and rap, but it was something I had in common with them and I knew their friends would ask them 'Have you met the new girl yet?' So this played in my favour as more and more people were beginning to like me. At 3pm, Mum picked me up from school like she would do every day that first week. I won't deny that I was relieved to be going home and getting away from school, which hadn't been so enjoyable that day.

My depression was pretty bad at the time as I was having an insomniac episode anyway, but the stress with arguments at school had made it worse. That evening I logged onto Facebook and saw that Roxy had posted abuse on my profile wall so without thinking of the consequences or rather caring about them, I argued back until the argument reached a point where words could no longer suffice. I felt a rage I hadn't felt since my fight with Emma. I was so angry that for a moment, I didn't even feel depressed... All I felt was the anger dominating me as I sent one final message to Roxy. I'd had it. There was only one thing left to resolve this for me, and that was a fight.

We arranged to meet outside McDonald's the following night, which was a Saturday. There was a huge field behind McDonald's and it was halfway between my house and hers, so neither of us had any excuse not to be there. I gathered my troops in the evening, as many people as I could get from Frimley, and we set of in the rain to walk to McDonald's at 10pm. I counted twenty-seven people walking with me before we decided to split up, so that we would not look suspicious if any police drove past. We were all wearing darkly coloured tracksuits with our hoods up, bandanas and scarves over our faces to protect us from CCTV. It might have seemed threatening to most people, but that was just how we dressed. I didn't care how masculine anyone thought I looked as I was still deliberately dressing like a boy so that no one would have any sexual attraction to me. We had made it to McDonald's just before 11pm, when we headed straight to the field behind it. The streets were empty by this time and all the people following behind me were growing increasingly violent awaiting the fight. I hadn't felt nervous up until now but as the fight grew closer, I became increasingly anxious. I never showed this to anyone, however. To them I only seemed quiet, as though I was mentally preparing myself for beating Roxy half to death.

We looked up and down the field and sent around ten people out to search the car park, but still no sign of Roxy. Where the hell was she? I tried to call her several times but she didn't answer her phone. I never left a voice message as it would be used as evidence against me if the police got involved, but right now all I wanted was to show her up in front of all her friends. With all mine cheering me on, I didn't care that she'd probably take a beating that would land her in hospital. Right then I just wanted to reclaim my reputation after she had made me look so stupid, in front of what seemed like everyone at Fernhill.

Almost an hour passed and she never showed up. My friends were starting to leave, disappointed that I couldn't deliver the fight I'd promised them. At almost midnight I left with the remaining five or six people who had stayed to back me up. I made my way back home in the rain, cold and tired. I felt extremely disappointed. Not only about being unable to let my anger out on Roxy, but also by making all those people walk all the way to Farnborough for nothing. However, I still felt this was not over and a physical fight would have released all the anger which had built up inside me. Not only about the situation with Roxy, but all the pain I was feeling from everything that was eating me up inside. Despite this, looking back now I suppose it was for the best we didn't end up fighting. It was such a pitiful argument in the first place and I don't think it would have done either of us any good to fight and probably get arrested, which would have been way more trouble than it was worth.

The following Monday I returned to school, with a few of Dina's friends telling me to 'just leave it' and that Roxy acts up because her parents died in a tsunami so I shouldn't be mean to her. This pissed me off because it's as if the world believes that if you have one bad thing happen to you in your life, you have an excuse to act like a total ass because no one will ever touch you. I was raped when I was ten years old and no one had ever treated me with that attitude, probably because it was still a secret. Anyhow, I saw I was outnumbered by these kids who were by no means threatening but I decided it was not worth carrying on, so I left it and didn't bother trying to be friends with them anymore. It bothered me that I had once again screwed up my chances of having friends like a normal person, but I tried to remind myself of the real reason I was at Fernhill, which was to gain qualifications. I was not here to make friends, so it didn't matter that I had failed in that respect.

I spent all of that break time alone outside the front gates of the school, chain smoking until my lungs were so dry I could barely breathe. I sat upright against a spray-painted wall of a derelict house, reminiscing on my life and how I got it so wrong. I thought about my twin sister and how much I missed her. Simple things such as not being at the same school as her was hard and upsetting, because I was so used to having that one person I could turn to if I was having a bad day. Now she was miles away in a separate school hanging out with her own friends, far away from me. I thought about my parents and how I'd let them down by being kicked out of Tomlinscote, which was one of the reasons we moved out of London in the first place. They wanted my siblings and me to have a better education than what could ever be offered by the rough estate where we lived in South London, and I had fucked all that up too.

Someone must have seen me leave school because when I went back I noticed one of the deputy head teachers standing by the gate, with another teacher who I had not met yet. He was six-foot-ten, stocky, and had a strong but safe presence about him. I decided not to walk back into school and that was because I would have been sanctioned for truanting, so I found a hole in the fence leading onto the field where I could cut through. He saw what I was doing as he noticed me walk back between the parked cars beside the fence, but to my surprise, he didn't tell the other teacher he had seen me. Instead he winked at me, so I smiled back and went unnoticed as I crawled through the hole in the fence. I was never questioned about my whereabouts that break time, so I stuck out the rest of the day as if nothing had happened. When I went to my next lesson I felt a huge sigh of relief as I had not been caught leaving school premises, but I knew I'd have to be more careful from now on.

My next lesson was French. I had always hated French lessons even back in Tomlinscote, and the only times I had ever enjoyed them were when we were winding up our teacher, who could not control us. We'd spend hours chanting and swearing, refusing to do any work and throwing sweets at each other around the classroom. On the rare occasion I actually tried to learn French, I struggled because I had trouble concentrating on a subject I had such little experience in. This made it even harder for me to focus, as my mind could no longer associate French lessons with anything other than testing teachers and deliberately behaving like a complete idiot. I sat down in my usual seat at the front of the classroom but was asked by the teacher to swap with a boy named Marco, who was sitting at the back by the window. He had been acting up all lesson and the teacher wanted to be able to keep a close eye on him, so I picked up my things and went to sit at the back. I liked this because it reminded me that teachers here knew nothing of my past, and would not treat me any differently to a student who had always been well behaved and played by the rules.

I was now sitting in between a girl and a boy named Ellie and Bradley. Ellie was tiny, less than five feet tall, with the most beautiful long brown hair. Bradley had black spikey hair and they both had the brightest blue eyes I'd ever seen; the moment they both smiled at me, I felt a warm friendship brewing. They had been passing notes to each other and it was obvious that they were best friends at the least, and I was quickly consumed by conversation with them. We got along so well that the three of us ended up spending lunch break together and I was introduced to all their friends, who seemed so much more lively and outgoing than Dina's friends. There was a girl named Kat with gothic-style hair and make-up, then there was Lewis who was tall and chubby with bright pink hair, Rick who wore a hat wherever he went, which I later found out was because he had alopecia, and finally Becky who would dance and sing up and down the corridors until the teachers kicked her out. They were such a nice bunch of kids and I felt I could relate to them, particularly when talking to Lewis, who I found I had a lot in common with. He was gay so had been bullied and struggled to fit in, and at times was depressed and lonely. It was sad to know someone else could feel the pain I felt, but reassuring at the same time to know that I wasn't the only one and there was someone to talk to who had been through similar situations.

One method of coping with my depression was to casually smoke weed as I had done since I was eleven years old, but it was becoming more and more of a habit as I became increasingly addicted to the disconnection from reality. Being high gave me a false sense of wellbeing. It gave me confidence I did not have and needed in social situations, so the day after meeting Bradley and Ellie I brought some weed with me into school without a second thought as to how they might perceive me. Although this new friendship group I'd attached myself to made me feel welcome, I still never felt a complete sense of fitting in, as they didn't smoke weed or drink. They were smart and worked hard in most of their lessons but would still mess around and joke with each other at any opportunity; laughing, flirting, making lots of noise and just generally acting how kids their age should. However, I found this behaviour difficult as I was still unable to completely relate to anyone my own age, so I joined in with their jokes as best I could whilst trying to act like them.

Despite how welcoming they all were, none of them smoked, which meant I had to go out alone on breaks as I had not yet met any other smokers. I walked out into the field past the children and teachers into a secluded area behind a thorn bush. It was not huge in height, but was long enough that I could crouch down behind it and smoke without being seen. Shortly after lighting up a spliff from my bag, I heard footsteps coming my way, so I quickly stubbed it out and ran back into the field where the other children were so I would blend in. Behind the classroom where Ellie and Bradley's group of friends were hanging out stood two huge blue containers, like the ones you see on building sites. I hid behind one when nobody was looking and began smoking my spliff, then stayed there for a few minutes with my music on quietly, simply enjoying the buzz. As I crept out from behind the containers I was greeted by a tough-looking girl with her friend following men as they approached me. She had long blonde hair and piercing blue eyes which shone abnormally brightly, reflecting the sunlight and revealing her tiny pupils, which gave her a mysterious look as though she could see right through me and into my soul. Her friend was a stocky, shorter girl with blonde spikey hair, wearing boy's school uniform and shoes.

I felt threatened but knew I couldn't run away. I was still building a reputation for myself and did not want to be known as a coward, so I turned to face them as they walked closer towards me. The girl with long hair asked bluntly in a threatening but soft voice, 'So what's going on with you and Roxy then? I heard you were having a fight.'

As words began to form in my mouth I took a step back towards the containers, trying to keep it unnoticed that I was ready to run at the first sign of the situation escalating. I stubbed out my spliff as I replied, 'We arranged to fight but she didn't turn up.'

I then explained why we were having a fight to begin with, going on to say, 'When I asked her why she didn't turn up, she said she was waiting round the corner with forty or fifty people, ready to fight me.'

The girl answered, 'What a fucking liar! She hasn't even got ten friends, let alone fifty to back her up! Fuck her. I'm Danielle by the way, this is Sam', turning to her friend with the shorter hair who nodded at me as she caught my eye. 'What's your name?' they asked.

'Robyn,' I replied. Danielle and Sam both put one hand in front of them to form a fist pointing towards me, so I did the same and we touched knuckles. Then Danielle spotted I had a lighter in my hand.

'You don't want to be smoking round there, it's well obvious. Come with us, we'll show you a good place.' And with that, Danielle and the ever-increasing crowd that followed behind her began to introduce themselves to me one by one as we talked and laughed on our way to the field to smoke.

'Do you smoke weed, then?' Sam asked, the girl who had originally followed Danielle when they approached me back at the containers. I casually told them, 'Yeah, now and then… I have a spliff on me now actually, do you want to share it?'

They all started smiling and I noticed a few shocked faces as a few of them began to stare, but only in amazement as though they thought I was really cool and wanted to know more about me. This also broke the ice dramatically and by now, Danielle had her arm around my shoulders whilst the rest of the group were fighting for my attention. I knew from that very moment I would fit in, so it didn't bother me that this was obviously the wrong crowd and these were the 'bad' kids. All I cared was that I had just made friends with kids with common interests and so no matter what they got up to, I wanted to be a part of it!

CHAPTER 16

Totland

Over the next few weeks I grew extremely close to both Danielle and Sam, who I would drink and smoke weed with almost every single day. I started to go to Danielle's house after school and would stay there at weekends, which we'd spend getting out of our minds on booze and weed. Her dad smoked cannabis which was great for us because we would never have to pay for it, as she could simply do a few jobs around the house and he would buy it for us. Their next-door neighbour also smoked weed, so he would go to their house to get high with Danielle's dad whilst we smoked with them before going out. I loved drinking on the streets with them because I met new friends every time we were out, and it seemed that everyone on the estate would fight for our attention any time they saw us. We were the 'cool kids' and no one could bring us down.

The first night I stayed at Danielle's was a lot of fun as we had over five litres of cider each, as well as free weed from her dad. Her parents both complimented me on my looks and took a liking to me from the moment Danielle introduced me, so I enjoyed going to her house as I always felt welcomed. She had two brothers who were eight and twelve years old, both of whom would hang out on the streets like us. We had met up with one of Danielle's friends named Lisa, who had joined us outside to get drunk. We were sitting on a field when she noticed the scars up my arms and asked me, 'What happened to you?'

I told her I'd fallen off my bike, to which she replied whilst pulling up her sleeves, 'We've all fallen off our bikes!'

She had the same amount of scars up both arms, so I immediately felt I had something in common with her as I knew she was or had been depressed too. The four of us had drunk around two litres of cider each, when we spotted a police officer walking towards us. We immediately picked up our alcohol and ran, heading for an alleyway at the back of the field. It took us out to a building site with an overgrown garden behind it, so we jumped the fence and made our way to the back of the garden where we hid behind a shed. The shed had been burnt down but still had four walls and a roof, so we sat inside it and stayed quiet until we were sure the police had gone. We carried on drinking until we had all puked up, at which point we simply rinsed our mouths out with more alcohol before finishing the rest of our cider. We had hot-boxed the shed by covering any air gaps with our hoodies, which we then used to cover our faces when we left the building site as we noticed a camera.

Some different police officers chased us later that night and though we were extremely intoxicated and stumbling all over the place, we managed to get away a second time. It was gone 2am when we eventually made it back to Danielle's house, at which point I passed out on her kitchen floor. She was also too drunk to walk upstairs to her bedroom, so she took some blankets from a cupboard and threw them over me and Sam lying on the floor. Danielle's dad had passed out on one of the sofas and was woken by us stumbling in, but he simply smoked another spliff and went back to sleep. We slept until 8am the next morning, when Danielle's mum walked through the kitchen to sit in the living room. She laughed at the sight of us and said, 'So you had a good night then, girls?'

Sam was still drunk when she nodded at Danielle's mum and

laughed, before standing up to get a drink of water. I apologized to Danielle's mum for the state I was in, but she didn't seem too bothered and simply offered us a cigarette each as she was rolling herself one. I smoked weed often but would usually only smoke cigarettes if I was stressed or drinking, so I shared one with Sam instead of smoking a whole one myself. This was how I became addicted to smoking because I would smoke socially when I was drinking with my new friends, but we were drinking all the time, which meant I would smoke more days than not. We were allowed to smoke inside the house at Danielle's too, so I soon became addicted, since when I wasn't smoking I would still be breathing in second-hand smoke throughout the day.

After spending the rest of the day smoking weed with Danielle and her dad, I slowly made my way back home, which was a four-mile walk. They had offered me a lift but as I was hungover I thought the walk would do me some good, so I smoked my last cigarette and left to walk home. It took me almost two hours but I felt I needed to burn some off some of the calories from all the alcohol, as I knew I had not vomited enough to purge a significant amount that night.

When I walked through the front door, Mum and Dad were sitting downstairs with Ash eating dinner. There was dinner for me on the kitchen side but I felt sick from all the weed I'd smoked, so I headed straight to bed after taking a long, relaxing shower. Ash came into my room to say 'goodnight' when she went to bed a few hours later, but I was already asleep so didn't speak to her until the morning. When morning came she asked me how my night out with Danielle was and I told her I'd bring her out next time, as I was excited to introduce her to my friends from Fernhill. Ash was used to hanging out with younger kids on the Ansel Estate who would never drink as much as we did, so I thought it would be nice for her to hang out with me on the Totland Estate where Danielle lived. Totland seemed like a party all the time, as everyone our age and older would be out drinking and smoking weed almost every day and night.

The next few weeks flew by as I would smoke weed with Danielle and

Sam before and during school, then go to the Totland Estate afterwards with them. Every night was a party and though I'd never remember much of it the next day, I'd always remember that I had fun. This was greatly helping my depression at the time because although I would usually feel worse than ever when I was hungover, it would only last a few hours as I'd soon be drinking or smoking weed again. Mum and Dad started to notice I was getting high more often, as they'd realize I was trying to avoid them when I was home, so we started arguing about the amount I was drinking and smoking. I never told them I was smoking cannabis but they weren't stupid and all they had to do was take one look at my eyes, which were glazed and bloodshot with tiny pupils. We started to argue more often as I continued to smoke and drink more, but I'd avoid arguments by staying out as often as I could. I felt guilty for lying to them whenever I told them I was only drinking and not smoking weed, but at the time it was my only escape and so I couldn't help but continue doing it.

One afternoon I had met up with Danielle and a few other kids from the Totland Estate and as we had been unsuccessful in finding someone to buy us alcohol, one of the boys suggested we did a 'crate-run'. I asked him what he meant as I had never heard the expression, so he told me it meant one of us would walk into a shop and run out with a crate of alcohol. I laughed at the idea at first as I pictured it inside my mind, before volunteering to do it myself. I knew it was risky as the shop owner would almost certainly chase after me, but I was still trying to build a reputation for myself and I knew this would set a high bar for anyone else to compete with. As we walked to a small corner shop at the top of a hill, Danielle looked at me and asked, 'Are you sure you want to do this?'

She then laughed in disbelief, telling me she could not believe I had the guts to do a crate run as she had only ever heard of one other person doing it in the five years she'd been drinking. Sam was with us by this point and as I walked into the shop, she waited outside with Danielle and the boys, who kept a close watch for any police cars. I walked around the shop once to appear innocent, then casually picked up a crate of Super Tennents. They were almost 9% alcohol, a lot higher than the lager we'd usually drink, but I thought my friends would think even more of me for providing beers with such a high alcohol content. The crate I picked up had twenty-four cans and felt a lot heavier than I'd originally thought it would be, so I stood in the line by the counter whilst I mentally prepared myself for what I was about to do. I was feet away from the door when I suddenly legged it, running as fast as I could with Danielle and Sam as we laughed until we were at the end of the road. We sprinted to the opposite side of the street as we ran down a steep hill, whilst realizing we were being chased by three of the shop owners.

One of them was running close behind us on foot whilst the other two were driving in a transit van, waving a baseball bat at us, which was for anything but playing baseball. I was running so fast I lost my footing and accidently dropped the crate of beers, forward-flipping over them as I landed on the ground. I quickly stood up and picked up as many cans as I could, before sprinting again to the bottom of the hill with Danielle and Sam, who had also picked up as many cans as they could carry. The cans we had left were spraying all over the road as they had effectively been shaken up and dropped, but luckily it stopped two of the shop owners, who gave up chasing us to pick up the remaining cans. We carried on running until we could run no further, at which point we jumped a fence and hid behind a car in someone's back garden. We could still hear the shop owner who had chased us on foot as he was just the other side of the fence, but we stayed silent, keeping our breathing as quiet as possible, and he soon left.

A man came out of the house we were hiding in as we were in his back garden, but he saw that we were not trying to damage his car and so he asked us if we wanted to come inside. He knew we were hiding as the police had now been called, but I didn't feel safe about going inside with a complete stranger. Danielle and Sam felt the same but we soon spotted a police helicopter circling us, so we knew we had to hide somewhere better than where we were. The man was alone and much older than us but I felt safe, because there were three of us against only him if he tried to do anything. He offered us some weed as we opened our beers, so we shared our alcohol with him and ended up drinking and smoking with him for a few hours. We thanked him for letting us stay and though we would never meet up with him again, he said the three of us were welcome in his home anytime from then onwards.

The police eventually caught up with us later that evening at Danielle's house but since they had no physical evidence of our involvement, we walked away free. I went home that night and told Ashleigh about what had happened, but she didn't find it as amusing as I thought it was. She was annoyed that I kept getting into trouble and said if anything had happened she would never have forgiven me, but I didn't care because I was having fun. She was depressed too and hated how I got more attention than her because I always acted up, but I couldn't see what she was getting so angry about. We were both depressed about the same thing and dealt with it in different ways, but it just so happened that my methods of coping led to more serious actions. The police had put me on a referral order for some other offenses I had been prosecuted for and because I kept getting arrested, they had started to offer me help from counselling services. I never accepted the help and fought it with every bone in my body, but it meant I was diagnosed with depression on paper, which caused Mum and Dad to be more lenient with my behaviour. They would still get angry with me whenever I got arrested, but I think Ashleigh thought that I was simply seeking attention and it annoyed her that I was getting more than her. She had recently announced that she was gay and in doing so, had cut off all her hair and dyed what was left jet black. She turned up to school on the first day of year ten wearing a full boy's uniform along with the drastic changes to her hair, which appeared to have brought out her anger for the depression she was feeling.

I dealt with my depression by taking drugs and drinking, and it seemed she had chosen this method of coping with hers. We were both bulimic and self-harmed on top of everything else, which made it impossible to interact socially with anyone positive. I think our depression was made worse by each other, as when one of us was feeling low the other one would be too, and we were constantly reminded of the mess we both were anytime we caught sight of each other. Mum and Dad were struggling to cope with this as they thought it was all their fault, since they did not know about the sexual abuse we had suffered as children, but that made our depression even worse because we felt guilty for how Mum and Dad felt, on top of our own heavy guilt. I couldn't stand being sober anymore as I hated to witness the effect my depression was having on my family, so I continued to drink and smoke weed as often as I could just to escape.

School was becoming difficult as I would walk into lessons high on cannabis and would sometimes 'whitey' in the middle of the lesson. It's called a 'whitey' when you've smoked a little too much weed too quickly, because your face turns ghostly pale as you start to vomit and feel as though you're going to die. I had whiteyed on a few occasions in the past so knew I would be OK, but I still thought I would vomit when I sat down in my English class. Break time had just finished and I had been smoking weed with Danielle, but I must have smoked too much as I started to feel sick whilst suffering cold sweats. The teachers at Fernhill were smarter than the teachers at Tomlinscote who had seemed completely oblivious to drugs, and knew exactly what to do as I started to gag at my desk. The teacher ran straight towards me and held a small bin under my face, telling me to puke up into it. She asked if I'd smoked anything 'funny' but as she didn't search my bag, I was not accused of smoking drugs. I made my way to the medical room where I lay down on the bed and slept it off, before being woken by Danielle, who asked me if anyone had found out we'd been smoking weed in school. I told her no one knew and that school only thought I was ill, so she kept me company until I went back to sleep. She said she'd wait for me at the end of the day and I could go to her house so my mum wouldn't find out, so I sobered myself up before attending my final lesson of the day.

When school finished at 3pm, Danielle was waiting for me with Sam at the front gates. I had completely sobered up by now so we walked straight back to Danielle's house, whilst discussing whether we should get drunk or high that night. We shared spliffs and beers provided by her dad, who was high like always, and I was in the mood to get fucked yet again. It was a cold but sunny day so we sat round a glass table in her back garden, enjoying the sun as we drowned our stomachs in alcohol. I never smoked quite as much weed as Danielle did but I'd drink like there was no tomorrow and in the mind-set I was in, that could have easily been possible. Back then I had always felt this invisible feeling, like it didn't matter how much I drank to escape because I'd never become dependent on the substance. I could give it up any time I wanted to and not feel the need to be intoxicated every single day, unlike the people around me who clearly relied on the drugs just to get through the day. I always kidded myself that I was only doing it because I was depressed and that one day, I'd be strong enough to deal with my depression properly, so it didn't matter how much I drank because I'd never become addicted.

I regularly witnessed both Danielle's and Sam's parents living a lifestyle I had previously been alien to, which revolved around heavy doses of drugs and alcohol on a daily basis, with the constant worry of where their next fix was coming from. Since hanging out with Danielle I had started to learn the impact drugs could have on someone, and the full extent to which they could control that person's life was upsetting. Being around Danielle's and Sam's parents brought to light the addictions associated with 'that first hit' and brought me to the awful realization that this could happen to anyone. However, it still did not stop me from being openly willing to try out drugs other than weed. I know this was due to my depression and self-loathing mentality at the time, but I had also learnt that I could temporarily block out my emotions with drugs, and amphetamines were top of my wish list.

We had always joked about trying speed as all three of us had heard stories from people who claimed to have done it. From what I understood, its main and most enjoyable effect was the surreal energy rush on which the person could race around through their daily activities without eating or sleeping for days. This appealed to me because I was still very conscious of my weight and although I was great at starving myself, it would be nice to have a break from the hunger. Obviously that was not the sole reason to try 'upper' drugs, as I was chancing any alternative to feeling suicidal, but it added to the absurd list of reasons inside my head as to why this was a good idea.

Sam had to go home to check on her mum, who had overdosed twice that week and it was only Wednesday, so I stayed with Danielle getting drunk and high in her back garden whilst we discussed where we would buy speed. Danielle phoned her cousin who I had not yet met, but could get hold of speed, which we were ever so curious about trying. Her cousin had just bought a new car so she picked us up and we went for a ride round the estate. Her name was Shanice and she seemed to have an attitude almost as big as her hooped earrings. She had bleached blonde hair and looked orange because she had so much make-up on, but it went well with her fake tan and I could tell immediately what sort of people she hung out with... chavs. This didn't surprise me. After all, we were going to pick up a bag of speed, so what did I honestly expect when I got into that car?

She drove us for miles whilst we drank and smoked weed with the windows wide open, listening to rave music on full blast through her newly fitted speakers. Neither Danielle nor I were wearing seatbelts, but I quickly put mine on when we reached over 120mph on the motorway. Shanice had sped up so fast and without warning that we were all screaming and laughing at the fact we could have died, but it was then that I suddenly realized what she was doing.

'You feel that rush?' she said. 'That's what it's going to feel like the first time you take speed. You sure you only want one gram?'

I had twenty pounds on me which I had originally thought would only buy us one gram, but she said it only cost ten pounds per gram from the person we were buying from. I trusted Shanice because

Danielle trusted her, and it seemed like I could never get ripped off if she was there. I felt safe taking drugs with Danielle because although she had only previously tried the same drugs as me, she had grown up around all kinds of drugs and would know what to look out for. She'd know how much to take and what to do if someone overdosed, and how to calm someone down who was out of their depth on a new substance. We drove a little more, into the car park of a caravan site and picked up a boy named Billy. Quite ironic really, since that was the code name on the street for speed. We drove through a narrow back road which took us to a dead end where Billy handed a small bag of white paste to Shanice. She dipped her finger in it then put her finger in her mouth and jerked back in her seat as she spat and suddenly said, 'What the fuck is that?' with a shocked look on her face.

Billy answered in a strong Irish accent, 'Ay so I see you've not tried the new stuff that's going round? It's "base"- pure speed- it's not even powdered yet... Have fun, ladies, and give me a call later, you'll be wanting more when you run out!'

He smiled and nodded at us as Shanice handed him the twenty pounud note, then he disappeared into a dark alley behind a block of flats where I'm assuming he spent the rest of that night selling more little bags of drugs. Shanice passed me the bag of speed then drove off with me and Danielle still sat in the back. We lit up cigarettes and danced with the music blaring through the speakers, as we laughed and smoked for the entire ride back to Totland.

It was almost 8pm when Shanice eventually dropped us back outside Danielle's and although it was cold there was no way we could do this in sight of her mum and dad, so we put our hoods up and walked to an empty children's park five minutes away from her house. It was dark by this time and completely deserted, so we used our phone lights to observe the white substance we had just bought. We smelt it and dabbed our fingers in it. It didn't smell like much other than chemicals, but it tasted so bitter it made us both gag. Danielle pulled a paper out from her tobacco pouch and ripped a small piece off to wrap the speed in. She used around one fifth of a gram to create the first 'bomb' and then did the same with one for me. It was funny to think that less than a few hours ago we had been fantasising about what it would be like to try speed, and here we were with two grams about to get fucked on the stuff. Danielle swallowed hers first. We didn't have any water to take it with so I stuck my tongue out and placed the little wrap as far back in my mouth as I could, then swallowed twice to get it down. It was the size of a one pence coin and I could feel this hard lump making its way down my oesophagus and into my stomach. The paper must have split because I could taste the bitterness in the back of my throat which tasted so awful I thought I would vomit.

We sat on the swings in the park then left to go for a walk because we were cold. It was almost 9pm now and had been forty minutes or so since we took the speed, and it was starting to kick in. As I walked along the footpath beside Danielle, I suddenly felt an intense flutter in my chest that made me stand up straight, leaving my back almost arched as I took the longest deep breath in as though it would be my last. I looked upwards but straight ahead of me and could feel every drop of blood being pumped through the veins in my body at one hundred miles per hour. I stood onto my tiptoes and felt like I was being lifted off the ground by an angel, with my eyes and mouth so far wide open that I could feel the cold air rinse through my teeth, which were chattering so fast I could not talk. I lifted my arms up beside me, leapt up off my feet and started running, turning to face Danielle as we both laughed in amazement and sprinted to the end of the road. We screamed as we jumped up in the air and spun round in circles holding hands, gazing up at the stars as we tried to take in the adrenaline rush we were both feeling. We tried to leap into a wooded area when we saw a police car drive past but the red and blue flashing lights stunned us, so we simply collapsed on the ground and lay staring up at the sky as we felt the full impact of this euphoric buzz. It was out of this world and completely surreal and for that moment in time, I did not feel depressed. All I could feel was happiness taking over my body, like I had forgotten who I was... and it felt great.

CHAPTER 17

Flying

After finally finding our feet and standing back up, I found I could not stop moving. My arms and legs felt really bizarre if I tried to keep still, as though the blood was rushing through them so fast that it was moving me too. My face was twitching on both sides and my teeth were vibrating uncontrollably, in time with my entire body, which appeared to be shivering… Except this couldn't have been from the cold because by now our hearts were beating so fast we were sweating. I was so hot I had to take off all of my school uniform as well as my hoodie, leaving me wearing only my underwear and strap top as we walked and walked until it was time to go home.

After racing round for just over an hour, we walked back to Danielle's to pick up my school bag, before saying goodbye to each other as I left to go home. It was a four-mile walk back to my house, which usually took over an hour and I was supposed to be home by 11pm, so I sprinted home as fast as I could, trying to sober myself up by running all my energy out on the way. It didn't work, however. No matter how fast I ran, it didn't even touch the sides of the adrenaline rush that was still pumping through my veins. With every minute that passed I was growing less and less aware of what was going on around me, more and more disconnected from reality, as though I had become detached from my body and was now a spirit watching over it. No words can describe how this felt.

After running for almost the entire four-mile journey home, I quickly put my layered clothing back on in an attempt to appear as normal as possible when I went in. If I had been sober I would have been freezing by now as it was so cold outside, so I dried as much sweat off my face onto my hoodie as I could before I walked through the front door, locking it behind me.

'Goodnight, Mum and Dad,' I said quietly up the stairs, to announce that I was home but without waking anyone up. One of my brothers was still awake and was sitting downstairs watching TV so I said to myself out loud so he would hear me, 'I'm off to bed... I'm shattered.'

He said 'goodnight' and so I walked up the stairs, heading straight towards my bedroom, where I sat down on my bed and opened the window that was directly above it. There was a large bottle of water on the floor which I picked up and downed in one go, leaving me out of breath from drinking so much so fast. There were some sweets on top of my chest of drawers at the end of my bed and I had not eaten since lunchtime at school, but just the sight of them made me gag. I remembered what I'd been told about how drug users never eat when taking amphetamines and it was here I learnt that you don't choose not to, you just simply can't.

I broke one sweet and put a tiny piece into my mouth. It tasted like cardboard, so foul I spat it straight out, which left me thirsty for even more water. My water bottle was completely empty by this point so I walked to the bathroom to fill it up and this was the first time I had caught a glimpse of myself in a mirror... I was so mortified that I gasped in shock as I dropped my bottle of water, which spilt all over the floor, thinking this could not possibly be me. My face was such a pale white that I looked as though I'd been poisoned. My lips were almost purple and I noticed the same blueish tint on my fingernails as I took my hand up to touch my face, staring at my reflection in disbelief. My hair was such a mess it drew me away from the fact that my make-up had almost completely sweated off, but the very first thing I noticed were my eyes… My pupils were so dilated that I could barely see the green colour of my eyes, which looked more like black contact lenses with a tiny green ring around each of them. The white part of my eyes appeared enormous too, as it seemed my eyelids were stretched so far open I could not close them. Visually I looked as though I was daydreaming, because I was unable to focus my sight on anything directly in front of me.

I was still breathing fast because the adrenaline rush was still pumping through my body, but I felt even more of a rush when I tried to stay still, so I soon left the bathroom to lie down in my bed. I was so hot that I decided to lie on top of my blankets, wearing only my underwear, and I opened my window as far as I could. I had a fan beside my bed which I switched on below the window, filling my bedroom with freezing cold air from outside. My head was spinning but my body felt like it was floating. My mind felt so at ease that all I could do was smile and as I gazed up at the stars, I started to dream with my eyes wide open. I let my teeth chatter as my head bobbed up and down, whilst my arms and legs shook uncontrollably in time with my racing heartbeat. I felt as though all my worries had been washed away, leaving my mind at peace as I let this euphoric rush consume my mind and soul.

After almost three hours of lying on my bed, I decided to try and get some sleep as I had school the next day. This proved impossible, however, because no matter how hard I tried to shut my eyes, they'd simply ping straight back open and I was unable to keep them closed. I decided to use this to my advantage, by racing through my homework due for the next day. I was supposed to learn two A4 pages of drama lines from the four-page script I had been given and although I did not have to recite the entire script, I managed to learn every single word on all four pages. When I'd finished that I went on to complete a two-thousand-word English Assignment, before spending the remainder of the night lying down listening to music on my bed. My window was still open and the sun was starting to rise, so I phoned Danielle from my mobile to see if she was still up. To no surprise of mine she had been awake all night too, and had been listening to music and smoking since I'd left over eight hours ago. It was 6am by this point and as it was still too early to get up, I stayed on the phone and talked to Danielle until I heard Mum waking up. At around that time I decided to have a shower, before getting ready to walk to school. The speed had started to wear off by now but I still had over one and a half grams left, so I wrapped half a gram in a small piece of paper and swallowed it. Mum asked why I was walking to school so early but I told her I simply wanted to lose some weight by taking the longer route, at which point she started asking questions… I'd never usually choose to walk to school as it was over four miles away and the long route was even further, so she started to realize something was up.

She had caught a glimpse of my eyes and made a comment about my pupils, asking if I'd taken anything, to which I replied 'No'.… I was trying my hardest to bring my eyes back to a normal range so that I appeared sober, but since the second bomb was starting to kick in now, this was simply not happening. Luckily Dad didn't see me before I left the house as he would have known straight away, but Mum was less aware of the visible effects of drugs. Although I had a feeling she knew I'd taken something, I slipped past her as quickly as I could and left to walk to school before she could ask me any more questions. It was cold outside but I was still hot as my heart was still beating fast from the speed, so I took my school jumper off as soon as I made it round the corner from home. I felt energetic and happy as I walked to school, excited to see Danielle who was in the same physical state as me. When I arrived outside school I saw Danielle sitting down an alleyway with Sam and a few others, so I walked towards them as I lit up a cigarette. Danielle was shouting and dancing to some music on her phone, so I joined her as we laughed and told each other all about the night before. We'd both been up all night and felt the same euphoric adrenaline rush, but at the time we could barely put it into words. As Sam passed round a spliff, I split half a gram of speed with Danielle and we both swallowed it in one go. I only had half a gram left now, which I was saving for later that day, but I wasn't too fussed about rationing it as we'd decided we would try to get some more that evening anyway.

After smoking more weed and cigarettes, we sprinted in circles as we laughed and talked on the way into school before splitting up to attend our separate classes. When I made it into my lesson I was immediately asked if I was feeling OK, as the teacher had noticed how pale I was. He had also noticed the size of my pupils and my inability to stop moving, but he let me off as I lied and told him I was simply overtired from a late night. As I left my form class and walked to my next lesson, I found I could not stop talking. Throughout my entire next lesson I talked continuously to the boy sitting next to me, who I'd never spoken to before, as well as shouting out the answers to every single question the teacher asked. I swung back and forth on my chair and sang loudly, whilst fidgeting and tapping my legs uncontrollably. My head was bobbing up and down and side to side, whilst my heartbeat continued to race for the entire school day. In my next lessons I offered to hand out books for the teachers as I could not stop moving, and I deliberately ran from one end of the room to the other with every single book. My third teacher of the day was starting to show suspicion of my drug use as I would normally sit in her lesson quietly without interacting with anyone, but I passed her off like everyone else that day, as no one could force a drug test. At morning and lunch breaks I still had no intention or desire to eat as the drugs were enough for my stomach, so I smoked more cannabis and cigarettes with Danielle until it was time to go back to our lessons.

I raced through all my schoolwork that day and only consumed cold water, which I would down in one go so that I could leave my lessons to run laps around the building as I filled up my bottle again. I stayed in school doing coursework until 6pm that evening, whilst arranging to meet up with Danielle afterwards. I walked home which was an extra four miles on top of the four I'd already walked that morning, whilst listening to music from my phone. I called Danielle and told her I would be out as soon as I'd showered and changed clothes, so she waited for me at her house until I came out. It was a struggle to sneak past Mum and Dad without being noticed, as my eyes were a complete give-away, but I managed to slip past everyone at home by telling them I was in a rush because Danielle was waiting for me. I soon swallowed my final bomb, which was half a gram of speed, saving a tiny bit to give to Danielle when we met up. As with every walk that day, I sped to Danielle's house with a smile on my face, wearing next to nothing.

When I arrived at Danielle's house she had phoned her cousin Shanice, who was going to meet up with us later that night. We decided to walk to Aldershot which was a further three miles from Danielle's house on Totland, but we were still buzzing so much we didn't care about how far it was. As we drank and smoked weed with Sam and a few others, we started to walk to Aldershot where we spent the rest of that night smoking and drinking. I was unable to drink much as the speed made everything taste foul, but I still smoked weed and sipped at a can of beer. Shanice had refused to buy us any more speed as she didn't want us becoming addicts, but she stayed with us for an hour or so and said she'd buy us some more another time.

When she caught a glimpse of our eyes in the light, she asked us how much we'd taken in single bombs. When we told her we'd been swallowing half-gram bombs, she was completely shocked and told us we were only supposed to dip our finger in it and swallow less than half the amount we had been taking... But how were we to know? No one had taught us how to take the drug, we'd been figuring everything out on our own. We assumed we'd snort it if it was powdered and swallow or smoke it if it was anything else, so without realizing we had taken over double the amount of what was safe... Though no amount of illegal drug is significantly safer than another, so what did it matter how much we'd taken?

After roaming the streets of Aldershot for the rest of that night, drinking and smoking, I left Danielle and my other friends to walk home. I was feeling strange as I had been awake for almost forty hours now, but I was still heavily under the influence of speed so I didn't feel tired. My legs ached a little as I'd walked so much, but the speed was telling me to keep moving as my heart was still beating ridiculously fast. As I made my way home, I continued to shake and jitter like I had all day, because the speed was still forcing me to keep moving. When I made it to my front door I felt extremely nervous about bumping into any one of my parents or brothers and sisters, as they would know straight away that I had taken something. I sped up the stairs past Mum and Dad, who were still awake, trying hard not to let anyone see me.

By the time I made it to my room, my heart was beating even faster than it had been all day, as I was now scared of anyone seeing the state I was in. This made it even harder for me to relax as I was in constant worry of my family finding out, but I managed to distance myself from everyone at home by staying in my room and keeping my bedroom light off. This was so that if anyone did walk in, I could simply pretend to be asleep to avoid confrontation. Ashleigh walked in to my room to ask if I was OK as she had barely seen me in the past two days, but I told her to go away and that I was trying to sleep. This was untrue, as there was no way on earth I'd be sleeping that night, but I still had to keep myself away from her as she would definitely tell Mum or Dad. I know she was upset about the way I spoke to her as I seemed almost angry, which was completely uncalled for, but although I felt guilty about it, I had no choice if I was to remain unseen.

As I opened my window and switched on my fan just like the previous night, I lay on top of my blankets and plugged my headphones into music which I listened to for the next few hours. The drug was starting to wear off by 3am but I was still unable to sleep as my heart was still beating fast, among the many other side effects, and it seemed the only thing wearing off was the euphoria. By 5am I was feeling completely drained as the positive side effects of the drug had completely worn off, but I was still unable to relax or feel normal as I was beginning to experience my first come-down. A come-down from a drug is similar to a hangover after alcohol, except different drugs give different levels of come-downs... No one had told me before but a come-down from speed is worse than any other drug because not only does it cause depression and suicidal thoughts, but the feelings stay with that person for weeks and can last for many months.

As I sat in my bed, I felt increasingly anxious and worried for what seemed like no reason. I was paranoid of Mum and Dad finding out I'd taken speed, but also scared of what I was feeling physically and mentally, as I was experiencing something I'd never felt before. I felt like I was being watched by every shadow in the corner of my eye. I felt an increasingly strong urge to cut myself and although I had recently thrown away my blade in an attempt to stop self-harming, I found myself raiding my cupboards in search of anything that I could harm myself with. I eventually found an old razor blade and by this point I was feeling so agitated I could barely think, but before I knew it I had ripped open more than ten cuts on my left arm. When the blood started to drip down my skin I felt a sense of release, but I was still shaking and panicking because the adrenaline rush I could feel was no longer positive. As the night went on I gradually felt worse, becoming more detached from reality than ever. I cried until the sun came up and my eyes became so dry I just wanted to sleep, but it was time to get ready for school now.

After showering and getting dressed, I waited for Mum, who drove me to school. I felt distant and empty, as though my body was there but I wasn't. It felt like a giant black cloud was hovering above my head, making it impossible to see anything but darkness. Mum asked again if I'd taken anything and although I denied it, she continued to ask questions for the entire journey to school. She seemed angry that I was lying to her and I felt extremely guilty about what I had done, but at that moment I felt too depressed to provide answers. I knew I couldn't openly admit I'd taken harder drugs as it would jeopardize my friendship with Danielle, who I needed more than anyone as she provided an escape from my loneliness. She provided drugs which temporarily masked my depression and although it was digging me into a deeper darker hole, I felt I could not let it go.

When I arrived outside school I waited until Mum had driven off before lighting up a cigarette beside Danielle, who asked if I was feeling OK as I looked like I was about to cry. She put her arm around me and told me I would be OK, before wiping my tears away with her hand as I started crying. She was also coming down from speed but because she wasn't already suffering depression as seriously as I was, she found it easier to cope with the after-effects. I eventually stopped crying and felt ever so grateful that I had such a great friend beside me, but I knew it was not enough to stop me feeling suicidal.

Throughout the rest of that day in school and after, I started to feel worse as my depression took over. Everywhere I went I stared straight at the ground because anytime I looked up, I couldn't see anything except ways to commit suicide. My mind became consumed by thoughts such as 'That looks like a nice roof to jump off,' or 'That would be a great place to hang myself.' I was petrified of my own mind and being on a come-down from speed seemed to make everything worse. I knew I had to get more drugs somehow as I couldn't bear feeling the way I did, so as soon as school finished I headed straight to Danielle's in search of more speed.

Her dad was sitting inside smoking weed when I walked in and although Danielle was happy to see me, she asked me to wait outside. She was also trying to hide the visual effects of the speed she'd taken and although it was easier to hide from her parents as they openly let her smoke cannabis, she knew they'd realize we'd taken something stronger if they caught sight of both of us together. Danielle had been keeping a distance from her family in the same way I had because we could no longer hide the state of our faces, which were ghostly pale with huge black circles around our eyes, so the second she saw me she grabbed the nearest hoodie and made her way out the back door. She appeared panicky and paranoid just as I was feeling, then said to me as soon as we were out of sight from her parents, 'Sorry about that, Robyn, you know we can't let anyone see us like this.'

I was fine with this as I understood completely because it was how I'd been hiding from my parents, so I handed her the twenty-pound note I'd brought with me and told her, 'Don't worry about it. Let's just focus on getting more speed.'

I knew this was how people became addicted and I didn't want to follow that path, but I remembered how amazing it was when I felt the rush of that speed for the first time, so I wanted to take it once more to feel happy like I did after that first hit. We lied to ourselves by insisting to each other that we weren't addicts, we were simply out having fun, so that took away the guilt for feeling the need to buy more speed. I knew in my heart that I had a problem arising but I'd already worn out my excitement with cannabis and alcohol over the years, so I felt OK about moving on to harder drugs in search of a different kind of happiness. When I was drunk or high on cannabis I could choose to ignore my emotions, but deep down they'd always be there. However, when I was high from speed, all negative emotions were completely washed away and I became physically incapable of feeling anything but happiness. This was why I preferred 'upper' drugs to 'downers' such as weed or alcohol, because no matter how low I was feeling before I'd taken it, the drug would always take the pain away almost instantly.

After searching the estate for hours for anyone who could get hold of speed, it seemed we were out of luck. Danielle couldn't ask her cousin as she refused to buy us more, and Sam's parents would only deal speed to people aged seventeen or older. As we were only fifteen, most drug dealers would either try to rip us off or refuse to sell altogether. It seemed we had no option but to buy cannabis instead, when suddenly Danielle received a phone call from an old friend who lived nearby. Danielle had tried to call him earlier that evening but his phone had been switched off, so he called her back to ask what she wanted. I listened as Danielle spoke on the phone, 'Hey, it's Dani. I'm with a friend who wants to buy some speed, do you have any?'

She looked disappointed as he started talking and presumably said no, but her face suddenly lit up as he went on to tell her he had something even better... What could possibly be better than speed? I wondered as Danielle continued to talk on the phone, before saying, 'Thanks, mate, see you in a minute,' and hanging up. She smiled excitedly as she told me he had something called 'MDMA', which was pure Ecstasy that had been cut with cocaine. This meant that when the dealer originally bought the substance he had mixed it with cocaine, but it was still mostly MDMA, which he only described by saying 'It will mess you up!'

I was excited to try out this drug as I had not heard of it before and had never tried cocaine or Ecstasy, so although I knew it was wrong I still couldn't wait to get my hands on it. Danielle explained to me that we'd have to snort it rather than swallow it in wraps like speed and although the thought of snorting cocaine scared me, I felt safe with Danielle because I knew she'd know what to do if anything went wrong. After walking a mile to a dark alleyway behind a school where we had arranged to meet the dealer, we waited quietly whilst sharing our excitement to try out this new drug.

CHAPTER 18

Crossing Lines

As we waited in the dark so that no one could see us, a tall, stocky man soon appeared from the shadows at the other end of the alleyway. He was wearing a black tracksuit with his hoodie pulled up and over his face, with dark eyes staring down at us as he told us to follow him. I felt uncomfortable at this point as I rarely met anyone taller than me so was easily intimidated by those who were. However, I knew this was my only chance of escaping my depression with a buzz that matched or even proved better than speed, so I followed him alongside Danielle as he led us into a tunnel-like woodland area. He then pulled out a small bag of white powder, opening it as he dabbed his finger in it and told us to open our mouths.

One by one he placed the tiniest bit of white powder inside our mouth, which almost instantly numbed our gums and gave a rush that felt like the initial effect of speed. As Danielle and I smiled, he told us it usually cost twenty pounds for half a gram but he was willing to sell us our first gram for the same price. This was a typical tactic that most drug dealers used to gain clients, as the person taking the drug would usually come running straight back to them to buy more as soon as they ran out of drugs. The dealer would then continue to sell the drugs cheap until that person became addicted, at which point they would raise the price to ensure they took every penny that person had. At fifteen years old we were both too naive to understand the reality of these tactics, as we were simply searching for a better high, so we willingly opened ourselves to the dangers associated with harder drugs. Inside I knew that I was crossing a fine line between safe drug use and addiction, but I was prepared to try anything to get away from the vicious come-down from speed.

The dealer smiled as Danielle and I both agreed that the drugs he gave us were very good, so we handed him our money before touching knuckles with him and saying goodbye. As we walked back towards the alleyway where we had initially waited for the dealer, Danielle pointed to a metal handrail that stood between a muddy river and some trees. She pulled out the bag of cocaine and tipped some of the powder out onto the handrail before scraping it into two neat lines, using her bank card. We hadn't been shown how to snort before so instead of crushing it down to a finer powder to avoid nose bleeds, we simply racked up the uncrushed powder before attempting to snort it. As I used my phone to shine a light so that we could see what we were doing, Danielle took a five-pound note out of her pocket and rolled it up to use as a snort. She took the first line, shoving the snort as far up her nose as she could before holding it in place using her hand, with her fingers holding down her other nostril as she placed the snort over the powder and began to sniff. I could tell by her facial expressions that it wasn't very nice and must have hurt, as her entire face twitched, but she simply carried on sniffing to make sure all the cocaine had gone. She then passed the snort to me and it was now my turn, so without giving myself time to become nervous I pushed the snort up my nose and copied how Danielle had snorted her line.

After breathing out slowly and facing away from the cocaine so as not to blow it away whilst making sure I'd be able to finish it in one go, I lowered my face and the snort down to the handrail. It was hard to keep my eyes open as the coke hurt my nose, but I needed to keep my eyes on it so that I could sniff in a straight line. After I'd snorted it and raised my head back up, I felt an extremely uncomfortable sensation as the powder ran from the back of my nose down to the back of my throat, where I could taste it. I thought I was going to throw up but before I could gag, Danielle placed one of her hands on the back of my head, with the other hand holding my mouth shut as she told me to swallow. If I had coughed or gagged I would have wasted the cocaine by coughing up powder from my mouth, so I was thankful to Danielle for helping me keep it all down. After only minutes, the rush suddenly hit me and I collapsed to the floor in amazement as Danielle laughed and tried to pull me back up to my feet. She was feeling the rush by now too, so we stood up and started running around in circles as we gazed up at the stars in amazement, just like we had done when we took the speed. The rush came much faster than it had done when we tried speed, which took almost an hour to kick in, so we were soon racking up and snorting more lines before moving to a different part of the estate to avoid being caught by the police.

With every line I snorted, I found it easier to sniff as the coke had numbed my entire mouth, nose and throat, taking away the initial pain I felt when I snorted my first line. The rush felt similar to the effects of speed, except everything seemed more intense and I felt so euphorically happy that I could not stop shaking in shock. The adrenaline was pumping through my veins at one hundred miles per hour and it felt like every dark shadow and memory was now being replaced with feelings of pure joy. I felt like I was back at Judo, except I didn't quit this time and I had gone on to win the Olympics... I felt like I was back at Tomlinscote and had passed every one of my exams with flying colours, forgetting what actually happened there... I felt myself back at home as a child again, before the sexual abuse or bullying... It felt like it had never happened and I was finally free. I wanted to feel like this forever. I was in a parallel universe where all my demons never happened and I was actually worthy of love, wrapped inside a warm blanket with which the drugs surrounded me. I decided at that moment, I didn't want to go back to reality again... I had a much better life here, on drugs, so I pledged to do everything in my power to stay that way.

As we roamed the estate feeling higher than ever, I started to realize there was no way I could go home in the state I was in. Mum and Dad would surely realize I was taking drugs, as I could not avoid them a second time, so I decided to stay at Danielle's that night. Because her parents were more lenient with discipline than mine, we were able to stay out until the early hours of the morning, which seemed to come round sooner than expected. One side effect of being intoxicated with harder drugs is the loss of short-term memory, which leads to a diminished sense of time, meaning that we had been out all night before we knew it and we were soon getting ready for school. Since neither of us wanted to go to school in the state we were in, we decided to bunk off and find somewhere to carry on our night by snorting cocaine and smoking weed all day... And that was when we found the abandoned warehouse.

We had been walking through back roads of the estate by Fernhill, in an attempt to avoid being caught out of school. We were making our way towards the motorway bridge as it seemed a good place to hide under, when we noticed a gigantic warehouse, which had been fenced off from public view. There were bramble bushes surrounding the fence, which was over fifteen feet high, but had cracks along the bottom which eventually led to a hole. Danielle and I were both small enough to crawl through it, so we cautiously made our way through the fence and stepped closer to the warehouse. It was even bigger than it had first seemed, over one hundred feet tall and much longer than it was wide. There were two storeys of office blocks attached to the side of the building, as well as evidence of an underground basement. As we stood side by side right up close, we examined it as closely as we could to try to find a way in.

There were steel bolted doors which ran across the back wall of the warehouse, one door every twenty feet or so. There was a rusty, metal ladder attached to the same wall, which started ten feet off the ground and led all the way up to the roof. Surrounded by a metal cage, the ladder also had a sign beneath it which read 'No Unauthorized Access'. As we checked each door to see if any were open, I soon heard a scream from Danielle, who had been kicking at one of the doors. The metal from the door had caught her hand as she had pushed it open, leaving blood on the floor as the hinges creaked like old floorboards. She started shouting from the floor she was lying on, 'Robyn! You have to come and see this!'

It was pitch black inside the room she had broken into, which we could only assume was gigantic because of how much our voices echoed. I was scared but excited, curious of what we might find, when suddenly it dawned on me… What if we found a dead body, or someone dangerous was hiding in there? Part of me would have listened to the voice telling me to keep out, but since we were still heavily intoxicated with cocaine, it seemed our state of delusion had taken over and stopped us caring.

As I crept inside with my eyes open wide to let them adjust to the dark, I noticed a huge mess all over the floor. The entire warehouse floor was made of concrete and seemed to be covered in rubble, dirt and a general mess. There were sharp pieces of glass scattered across the floor with plenty of other things to cause injury, so Danielle and I kept close together as we cautiously made our way inside. After walking through over fifty feet of rubble, we shone our phone lights far into the distance and could now see the back wall of the warehouse, which led to a new room. There was a small staircase with light coming from the top, beneath which was a doorway to a staircase that led downstairs to a basement of some sort. When we shone our phone lights down the basement stairs we couldn't see much except for metal boilers and pipes, but the sound of the door creaking open freaked us out and so we headed straight upstairs. Danielle insisted, 'Let's go upstairs first, we can look down there later.'

I agreed with her and we began to walk slowly up the stairs. Since there were no signs of any previous fire, our footsteps gradually became less cautious. The stairs led up to the office blocks we had initially seen from outside the building, which now seemed bright and energetic as light from the office windows filled each room. Every room was locked and as we walked through the long corridor which ran down the middle of all twelve rooms, we decided we would come back later with Sam and some other friends. We could have more fun with more people there that night, as I was sure we'd trash the place after calling it ours, but for now we were quite happy sitting quietly by ourselves in one of the rooms which we had broken into. Danielle passed me a CD case she had brought out with her to snort lines off, so I started racking up and snorting cocaine whilst she rolled a spliff with some cannabis which she had stolen from her dad that morning.

As we sat snorting lines and smoking weed, I began to think more deeply about how the drugs had affected me since I'd been taking harder ones. Aside from the fact we were in a secret place that no one else knew about, the rush we shared from the harder drugs made me feel as though I'd entered a special part of me which was only visible to those who knew me when I was high. The warmth I experienced when taking drugs felt like all the pain that had built up inside me from years of abuse was finally fading and my soul was temporarily released, to a place where I felt happy. If I felt alone or scared I knew I could take myself away in a split second by simply taking harder drugs, so I started to think about ways to make money for feeding my ever-increasing addiction.

Although the warehouse had been stripped down to the bare minimum on the inside, there were still copper wires and pipes left behind, which ran through the walls and ceilings of each room. I knew scrap metal was worth a good amount of money as we could exchange it for cash at the scrap merchants', so I decided with Danielle that when we returned later that day with our other friends we would bring the tools we needed to take as much scrap metal as we could find. Since we were too high on drugs to even move at the time, we closed our eyes and enjoyed the buzz until we were out of drugs and sober enough to walk back to Danielle's house.

It was dark when we returned that evening. Danielle had picked some tools out of her dad's shed with Sam, leaving me to carry the bags we were going to fill up with scrap metal. As we approached the warehouse we noticed another group of kids standing outside it, before realizing it was Danielle's younger brother with his friends. Some of them were old enough for me to recognize from school, so we talked to each other and it soon became clear that everyone was there for the same reason. I wasn't too bothered about finding huge amounts of scrap metal as I had already seen how much there was inside, but Danielle's brother wasn't interested at all which meant more for me. Danielle's brother and his friends only wanted to have fun, smashing the place to pieces, so we made a good team as they decided to give me any copper they found once we were inside.

Entering the warehouse proved difficult as the downstairs door which Danielle had previously kicked open was now locked along with the others, so I stared at the roof as I tried to think of a way up. I remembered the second floor from when Danielle and I had been in the office blocks earlier that day. I remembered the glass windows on the ceiling of the second floor, which was only a four-foot jump from the caged ladder attached to the warehouse wall. The warehouse was around twice the height of the office blocks, which were only two storeys high, so I knew if I jumped from the third floor of the warehouse I had a good chance of landing on the roof of one of the office blocks. Now all I needed was a foot up onto the ladder as it only started a few feet off the ground. As I was strong enough to pull my own body weight up, I let the others lift me just high enough to hang from the ladder. After pulling myself up and beginning to climb, I looked up and to the left of me where the office blocks were. Now that I was up on the ladder, the smaller roof seemed much higher and the gap between the office blocks and the ladder seemed even wider. However, I knew I had to do this to retrieve the scrap metal as that was my only hope of paying for my next dose of cocaine or speed, so I continued climbing until I was high enough to jump from the ladder.

As I looked down from the third floor, all I could see were Danielle and Sam reassuring me that I could do this. I knew if I missed and didn't jump far enough I would fall three storeys, but I was fearless from the depression and over-confident from the drugs. As I climbed out of the cage which surrounded the ladder, I used the rusty metal as a platform to jump from. Although I felt uneasy, I soon took a leap through the sky and jumped twelve feet down from the ladder and onto the roof… I made it! Danielle and the others cheered me on before asking what I could see, if I could get in that way after all. As I walked closer to the window on the roof, I stamped on it repeatedly with one foot to smash the glass. I wanted to smash all the glass through as I would be jumping through sooner or later, so I tried to reduce the chance of cutting myself as much as possible. After kicking the remaining glass away, I jumped through the window in the roof with my arms by my side to avoid hitting anything on the way down.

'It's clear!' I shouted, before making my way downstairs to let the others in. I used my phone light to guide me downstairs as the entire building was a complete blackout in the dark. This left me cautious of cutting myself on broken glass or tripping on rubble, as no one would be able to help me if I had any kind of accident. I eventually made it to the inside of the warehouse where I kicked open the door from inside, letting Danielle in along with everyone else who had waited outside. There were at least twenty of us by now and we were all trespassing, but the chances of being caught by the police were slim as there were so many of us. With our hoods up and tools out, we began trashing the place whilst bagging up scrap copper. The younger kids smashed every window, door and wall, whilst the older ones helped me bag up all the scrap metal we could find. We set off fire extinguishers and drew markings on the walls with spray paint which Danielle's brother had brought out, whilst hiding round corners and jumping out on each other throughout the warehouse. It was the most sober fun I'd had in months.

After almost three hours, too many cuts from broken glass and one close call with the gas pipes, I had bagged up all the copper I could carry and was now ready to leave. Danielle and Sam had also bagged up lots of copper wires and we would struggle to carry the amount we had, so we decided to call it a day and headed back to Danielle's house. Leaving the warehouse proved harder than entering it as there were more police patrolling the estate at night, but we took the back roads as much as we could and avoided being spotted for the entire walk back to Totland. When we arrived I decided to take one bag home and leave the rest at Danielle's to come back to the following day. We decided we would strip the wires together and split the money from all three bags, but I could take one bag home to start stripping myself. I didn't realize at this point that Danielle was trying to cheat me out of my money for the copper, but it didn't bother me as long as I was getting at least some drugs out of it.

Over the next few days I spent less time at home and even more time with Danielle. We spent hours stripping copper in her back garden with the help of her parents and younger siblings, who all seemed to want to join in. I felt accepted in their family because I got on with her parents better than my own and her brothers looked up to me like a big sister. I'd had so many drunken heart-to-hearts with Danielle and her parents on different occasions, telling them things that I felt I could not tell my own family. Mum and Dad always seemed angry with me for taking drugs and getting arrested, so it was nice to be around people who didn't know that side of me.

After spending three days stripping copper, my hands were covered in blisters and I was physically drained from the hard work. I managed to talk Dad into taking my bag of copper to the scrap merchants, whilst Danielle's dad took her with the copper left at her house. The total for all the scrap combined came to £400, paid in cash, which was split between me and Danielle. We didn't intend on spending much of it until the weekend as we were both at school until then, but I couldn't hold back my physical need for drugs so I brought half of my money into school just in case. Danielle had also brought £100 with her and we soon decided that we would buy a few grams of coke later on, but not until after school as I was trying hard to keep my place at Fernhill. By now I'd argued with almost every teacher, had fights with most of my peers, and had been in school whilst obviously intoxicated with drugs. Because of this I was on my final warning and would probably be expelled if I bunked off again, so I told Danielle that I didn't want to leave school until it finished at 3pm.

When break time arrived, Danielle and I were searching for a place to smoke as the field was out of bounds because it was raining. When we couldn't smoke on the field we'd usually light up behind the containers where we first met, but there were teachers standing in front of them, which left us no option but to sneak out. I didn't jump to the idea of sneaking out as it was only a cigarette and although I desperately needed one, it wasn't worth getting expelled over if I was caught. Sure enough a teacher spotted us from the front gates in the distance, so Danielle and I ran off into a housing estate that surrounded the school.

'Do you think he'll be around now?' Danielle asked, referring to the drug dealer who we had initially met the first time we bought cocaine. I told her I wasn't sure, but it was worth a try as we had been seen now, so would be in trouble whether we went back to school or not. As she began phoning the dealer who I later found out was named 'Kennedy', I listened as she asked him how much we could buy with the £200 we had. He told us he did not have much coke but that he had enough speed for us to spend the rest of our money on, so we started walking to his house to meet him. Danielle led the way and just as usual, I was totally reliant on her to find the way back. I didn't like not knowing where I was or relying on someone else for anything, but I knew Danielle would never leave me anywhere on my own unless I knew my way home. She went on to tell me that Kennedy was selling us two grams of cocaine and six grams of speed for just £200... I was over the moon with excitement because it had been so long since I'd taken speed, which I could now mix with the euphoric rush of coke and this time, we would have enough to stay high for an entire week!

CHAPTER 19

Release

As we made our way along a curved road up a slight hill, Danielle pointed to a strange-looking house surrounded by overgrown ivy and ornaments. There were two mini gargoyle statues either side of a wooden gate, which joined a wide wooden fence with spikes on top of each panel. The bushes in the front garden concealed the house from public view, making it easy to remember as it stood out visibly from the other houses on that road. I followed behind Danielle as she made her way to the front door, knocking twice and waiting for Kennedy. He soon appeared and invited us in, offering us a seat whilst he rolled a spliff. I felt wary of being in this stranger's house, as he was still a stranger to me, but more so of the fact that he was a drug dealer and I was unsure what to expect whilst in his company. However, he seemed reasonably polite and unthreatening at this point, so I soon relaxed and smoked the spliff with him and Danielle whilst discussing the drugs. He told us he was meeting another drug dealer a few blocks away, but that Danielle and I would have to wait round a corner as our school uniforms would attract attention if police drove past and saw us.

As we walked to a rundown children's park, Kennedy told

us to wait there whilst he went to get the drugs. I didn't feel comfortable handing over our money without being sure he'd return with our drugs, but Danielle trusted him and eventually persuaded me to hand mine over. He made his way down through an alleyway and my eyes followed him until he was out of sight, at which point I asked Danielle, 'Do you think he's coming back?' She replied reassuringly, 'He's not like the others, I trust him.'

However, after twenty minutes I started to worry, as he had still not returned with our drugs. Danielle kept trying to reassure me but I could tell by her facial expressions that she was also having doubts and by the time she tried to call Kennedy, we had already been waiting for over an hour. He didn't answer his phone at first and when he did, he hung up straight away. It was clear what had happened, but I still insisted we wait another twenty minutes. As the second hour passed we were both becoming more and more agitated, because we knew now that we had been robbed of all our money as well as having no drugs. I couldn't bear the thought of going another day without any speed… All that hard work, all those blisters from stripping copper, it had all been for nothing. The pride I felt from making my first legitimate wage, which I'd worked so very hard for, had been ripped away from me by Kennedy and I could not deal with the dark cloud of emotions. I was so angry that all I could do was cry and if I'd had a blade, I would have taken it straight to my wrist.

As we searched the estate for Kennedy, we thought maybe he had gone home with our money so we took a walk back to his house. When we knocked at the door we didn't get an answer, so we kicked it until an older man appeared from inside. It was Kennedy's father, who shouted, 'What the hell are you girls doing? Get away from my house!'

Danielle shoved her foot in between the door and doorframe, jamming it open as she shouted, 'Your son stole our money! We want it back… We know he's in there!'

I was shaking by this point as I was so angry and heated up from arguing, but Kennedy's father insisted he did not know where his son was and told us that if we didn't leave, he would phone the police. I said to Danielle, 'Come on, babe, he's not worth it. We'll get him back later.'

I was still extremely upset but knew the smartest thing to do was to stay calm, as there were other ways of getting Kennedy back if we couldn't get our money. I knew we'd have no chance using our usual methods of regaining control of a drug deal, which was to simply jump the person who owed money and beat them close to death if they could not pay. There was no way this would work with Kennedy as he was well over six feet tall and much stronger and older than Danielle or me, who were merely fifteen-year-old schoolgirls. Something had to be done and I wasn't sure exactly what, but I knew it had to be serious enough to teach him never to mess with us again.

Danielle and I split up after returning to her house and as I walked home, all I could think about was how I was going to get Kennedy back. I hated myself for being so stupid in trusting a drug dealer with my money, but if Danielle hadn't persuaded me, I would never have given it up in the first place. Mum was standing by the front door when I walked in. I was trying to hide my emotions as best I could but she could tell there was something wrong so she asked me if I was OK, then told me to look at her so she could see my eyes properly. I knew she was trying to see if I'd taken drugs, so I snapped aggressively at her, 'I haven't taken anything! Why do you and Dad keep hassling me?!'

She then asked what was wrong, but there was no way I could talk to her about what had happened so I shouted at her, 'You wouldn't understand.'

I knew I had to calm myself down if I wanted to go back out without them worrying, but I was so angry about what had happened with the drugs money that I couldn't hide it. I felt extremely guilty for shouting at Mum and Dad, who were only looking out for their daughter, but they were beginning to uncover my secret, which was my only escape from depression. I was petrified of them finding out about my drug use because I was gradually falling into a hole so deep I knew they couldn't pull me out of it, and the drugs allowed me to escape what I couldn't deal with. I hated lying to Mum and Dad but no matter how bad I felt, I knew I had to keep my guard up if I wanted to escape my depression. I eventually made it up to my bedroom, where I immediately changed out of my school uniform and into a grey tracksuit, then suddenly I imagined something insane… There was a petrol scooter in the garage that I had been given for my fifteenth birthday. I rarely used it but the petrol tank was full and I knew there was a five-litre jerry can filled with petrol inside the garage. I'm going to burn that cunts house down, I thought to myself as the anger inside me slowly started to turn into adrenaline.

As I phoned Danielle to tell her about my psychotic plan, I put a black tracksuit on over my grey one so that I could discard the clothing that would be described to police if anyone saw me. I strapped my breasts to my chest with bandages to make them appear flat, so that any witnesses would think I was male. I wore black gloves to avoid leaving any finger prints, as well as wearing a bandana around my neck to pull over my face. My hoods were enough to hide my hair so I didn't bother wearing a hat, but I knew I could not sneak the jerry can out as it was far too big. Instead, I filled a litre bottle with petrol and packed it into a string bag. It was cold outside so Mum didn't ask why I was wearing so many layers, but she insisted on driving me to Danielle's house so that she knew I wasn't lying to her about where I was going. I think she thought I was going out to buy drugs as I was in such a hurry to leave the house, but nothing she could have said or done would have been enough to stop my actions that night.

As we approached the Totland Estate in the car, I stared blankly out of the window as I played the scene over and over in my head, contemplating what could happen if I went through with setting Kennedy's house on fire. Someone could die… Kennedy might not even be home and I'd be murdering his innocent family… But I didn't care. He had to pay for what he'd done and as I consumed myself in anger, I realized that I was not only angry at Kennedy… I started remembering every bad thing that had ever happened to me; every sexual assault and rape from James and Drew, every lost fight with bullies and depression. Suddenly I felt the anger and pain which had been building up inside me for years, and I knew I had to let it all out. I had to find release and it seemed like the fire would make all the pain go away, so I knew for definite that there was no backing out now.

As Mum pulled up outside Danielle's house, I stepped out of the car and approached Danielle. She appeared nervous as though she was not sure what to expect, wondering whether or not I would actually go through with it. I took a deep breath and told her, 'This is it… Take me to Kennedy's house.'

She walked beside me as we made our way to a field nearby, waiting for sunset so we could hide in the dark. I took my bag off and hid it in a bush so that the petrol was far away from us whilst we smoked, but also to avoid suspicious questions if we were approached by police. I didn't care about getting arrested as I was so depressed from having no drugs that I could barely feel anything anyway, but I knew I had to stay free long enough to torch Kennedy's house. When I thought about the reality of what I was actually doing, I didn't truly believe that anyone would die… I thought that some higher power, greater than us, would protect innocent lives and decide who lived and who didn't, meaning blood would not be on my hands if the situation got out of control. It was up to the angels now.

I knew my insane theory of how 'everyone would be fine' would not convince Danielle or any other friends we saw that night, who would think I was a complete lunatic, so I kept myself to myself and simply waited for darkness to consume the night sky. When darkness eventually fell I was still feeling the adrenaline rush I'd been experiencing all evening and although it felt almost like I'd taken drugs, I saw it as a threat more than a comfort. I was extremely agitated for the entire walk to Kennedy's house and although Danielle had stayed by my side for everything else, she told me she would not walk further than the end of his road. As I walked towards his house alone, giving one last hand signal to Danielle as I walked away, I pulled my hood over my head and my bandana over my face. Taking the bag off my back to retrieve the petrol, I unscrewed the lid before pouring the entire contents of the bottle over Kennedy's garden fence. I had originally intended to pour it through the letterbox but something must have made me regain some sanity, because I knew that pouring the petrol through that letterbox would surely have made me a murderer.

Before I could light the petrol I noticed a neighbour staring out of an upstairs window opposite Kennedy's house, on the phone whilst pointing at me. I knew he was calling the police so without a second thought, I lit a cigarette and threw it at the puddle of petrol below the fence. As the front garden was engulfed in flames, I took a moment to stare up at the sky with my arms out wide. It felt as though all my demons had left my body and were now nothing more than the black smoke that surrounded me, before disappearing into the night sky. I felt such a huge sense of release, for all the pain and abuse I had suffered throughout my entire life. It was finally over, so I thought…

As I lowered my eyes to face the ground I heard sirens, so I ran away from the scene as fast as I could. I bolted through an alleyway and quickly took my black tracksuit off, shoving it into my bag along with my bandana and gloves. I untied my hair and the bandages from around my chest, making sure I looked nothing like the person who had started the fire. I then ran for half a mile down back roads before heading back onto the main road, where I proceeded to meet Danielle. Two police cars drove past and the officers looked straight at me but carried on driving, so I assumed I was in the clear. Now all I had to do was ditch my bag with the clothes I'd worn outside Kennedy's house, along with any other potential evidence I had in my possession. When I met Danielle she asked if the house definitely went up as she couldn't see any smoke, but there was so much adrenaline pumping through my veins that I couldn't look back to the housing estate I'd run away from. I assumed the fire had gone out, which came as a relief, but I still felt satisfied I'd scared whoever was in the house. With no sign of Kennedy or any fire engines, I walked back to Danielle's house through back roads as we shared our thoughts on the night.

'You're fucking mad!' Danielle said, smiling at me in total shock.

We knew we probably wouldn't get our money back, but the fact that I'd taken such serious action showed Danielle how tough I was. I didn't want to be a bad person but I knew other drug dealers would hear about what I'd done, so I hoped that my reputation would be enough to stop anyone robbing us again.

As I sat in Danielle's back garden, I knew I could not walk home as it would be too risky with police driving around. I was covered in petrol and the smell was overwhelming, so I phoned Mum to see if she could pick me up. When she arrived outside Danielle's house she could smell the petrol on me but I told her we'd been joyriding motorbikes in the woods. She notice I had changed clothes but I told her I'd spilt something on my jacket, so was borrowing Danielle's until tomorrow. When we got home it was too late at night for me to wash the clothes from my bag, which I had forgotten to ditch, so I shoved them into a cupboard at the back of my bedroom. The cupboard which was in the eaves spread around the perimeter of the roof as my bedroom was in the loft, so I pushed them right to the back of the cupboard where they could not be seen or smelt from my room. As the hours ticked by I was feeling calmer because I thought the situation was over, but as soon as the adrenaline faded, my depression was back in full swing and I started thinking about suicide. I couldn't bear feeling suicidal and there was nothing I could do about it, except cut my wrists and cry in the hope that the pain would allow me to escape... I hated feeling nothing, as depression tore away every feeling I had left in me, so I induced pain through cutting myself to remind me that I was still alive.

After sleeping for almost two hours, I was woken by a loud knock at the front door. It was the police. I was still in bed when Dad let them in at around 1am, bringing them upstairs and into my bedroom. I suddenly felt scared as I sat up from under my duvet cover, reaching for a t-shirt and tracksuit bottoms that were on the floor beside my bed. I was half naked and felt extremely uncomfortable as the police officers were both male, and I knew they were going to search me.

'Robyn Hennessy?' one of them asked. 'We are arresting you on suspicion of arson with intent to endanger life…'

I froze. Just the word 'life' was enough to tell me this was a serious charge, and I knew by the look on Dad's face that he could not protect me from this. As they began searching my room I was placed in handcuffs, which I resisted and asked, 'Can I at least put a bra on before you take me down the station?'

They said I could get dressed after they'd performed a search but one of them would have to watch me. I sat quietly on my bed as they searched my room, being sure not to look at the cupboard where I'd hidden my clothes from that night. To my great relief they did not find anything, but I still felt embarrassed as they searched my underwear drawer and private diaries, which consisted of broken diet plans and poems about depression. They found a blade I cut myself with but did not confiscate it as it had no relation to the arson charges, but they asked what I used it for and Dad knew straight away.

I saw the sadness in his eyes as he took a look at my arms, which were covered in scars and cuts that I never meant for him to see. Mum and Dad were suffering because of the things Ashleigh and I did, as they couldn't understand why we were so depressed and they felt like it was their fault. That hurt me more than anything because I felt so guilty for all my pain, which was hurting them too, when they'd done nothing but love us our entire lives. I couldn't understand it myself at the time, because I was too young to understand that the sexual abuse years ago could have an effect of what was going on now. Instead I simply thought there was something deeply wrong with me, and maybe I was just a bad person.

After finding nothing relating to the arson in question, the police took the handcuffs off my wrists and told me they were no longer taking me to the station. I was still under arrest but because they had not found anything suspicious, they didn't see much point in taking me to the station for the night. I would have missed school the next day because they would not have interviewed me until the morning, so they cautioned me and arranged to interview me the following day. I was happy about being able to stay home that night but in a way I was also dreading it, because it meant I'd have to explain myself to Dad as soon as the police had gone.

Dad walked downstairs with the police officers and showed them out, locking the door behind them. As he made his way back up the stairs, I counted the steps to see if he was coming back up to my room. Ground to middle floor was fourteen steps where my parents' bedroom was, then another twelve steps up was the top floor with mine and Ashleigh's rooms. As I counted past the fifteenth step, I knew he was walking back to my room to confront me.

'What the fuck have you done?! You better start explaining yourself, girl!'

I tried to lie and say that I didn't have a clue what the police were talking about, but they'd already been told by Kennedy's father that Danielle and I had been arguing with him earlier that day. The police knew the fire had been started over a drugs dispute and Danielle and I were prime suspects because we'd been reported by Kennedy's father, demanding money at his door earlier that day. The police had told my dad this and he wasted no time in telling me he knew, saying 'I know you're on drugs! How stupid are you? You think you're big enough to set a fucking dealer's house on fire? Do you know what they'll do to us now?!'

I was crying by this point. I was always scared when my dad kicked off as I worried he might hit me, even though it was mostly just noise and he'd never laid a finger on me. He carried on shouting, 'You've sent drug dealer's round our fucking house! They'll probably come and set our house on fire now! Do you see what you've fucking done?!'

I was so angry and upset. As tears streamed down my face, I tried to force words out of my mouth but my voice hardly made a sound. I was too afraid to look my dad in the eyes so I simply stared at the ground with my head in my hands as I whispered, 'I'm sorry, Dad… I'm so sorry. He's not even a proper drug dealer, he's just a friend who can get drugs… He doesn't know where I live. Nothing's going to happen to you!'

Dad lowered his voice slightly and was no longer shouting as he sat beside me on my bed, but he still sounded angry as he looked me directly in the eyes and said, 'I'm not worried about me. I'm worried about us, our family... If anything happens because of this, I will never forgive you.'

And with that he left my room, leaving me in tears on my bed. I didn't think twice before reaching for my blade and stabbing it deep into my arm, ripping my skin open as the cuts grew deeper. I carved the words 'sorry dad' on my right arm then carried on ripping dozens of deep cuts into my left arm... It doesn't hurt enough, I thought to myself. I wanted to hurt, to take back the pain I had caused Dad. As I took the blade a final time, I held it diagonally against my skin before pressing as hard and fast as I could to rip open a cut so deep I could not see blood for the first few seconds... I heard the skin rip wide open and as I stared down at my wrist, I realized I'd cut through all the layers of skin, ripped open a vein and had cut so deep that it was blue in the centre which meant it was over 1cm deep. I tried to hold it back together as it desperately needed stitches but there was no way I could go to hospital, so instead I phoned Danielle. I put the phone on loud speaker and placed it beside me on my bed whilst I tried to stop the uncontrollable bleeding from my arm.

As soon as I heard Danielle's voice on the phone I felt safe, knowing that I would not be alone if I died from the bleeding. She answered in a soft voice, asking what was wrong as I never usually phoned her this late for no reason. 'Dani... I've done something stupid... I need your help, please can I come to yours?'

She asked what it was that I'd done but I couldn't answer her. Instead I simply broke down in tears on the phone as she tried to comfort me and asked if I wanted a lift. She got her mum to drive to my house and pick me up, as her parents were both awake, unlike everyone inside my house. I wrapped a towel around my wrist and tied it tight to try and stop the bleeding, before throwing some clothes into a bag and walking out of the front door. I felt so guilty at hurting my family that I knew I could not go back home, at least not for a while. I hated myself for everything I'd done and I couldn't cope with the guilt of being alive anymore. I had to leave.

When Danielle's mum picked me up she seemed tired but was still happy to see me. Danielle threw her arms around me and told me everything was OK now, but she still wanted to know what I'd done that was so stupid. I held my arm up with the towel wrapped tight around it, keeping it held above my heart to slow down the bleeding. When we arrived at Danielle's house she sat me down in the light where she could see my arm, which had bled right through the towel and soaked my jacket. As I slowly pulled back the towel, Danielle gasped in horror as she saw the extent of my wounds. Her mum took one look at it and said, 'You need to go to hospital, right now! Your cut needs stitches.'

I didn't want to go to hospital. If I went to A&E, they'd know I'd been self-harming and Dad had threatened to send me to a mental ward last time he saw this amount of cuts up my arms, so I refused to go. I was scared I'd be sectioned, but more worried about the police knowing where I was if they found evidence against me for the arson. Danielle's mum knew she couldn't talk me into going to hospital, so she brought me a first aid box with some bandage tape and scissors. She cut six thin strips and used them to tape butterfly stitches along my cut. She wiped the blood away with a damp cloth before bandaging up the cuts, then gave me a sling to keep my arm held up. I'd have to ditch the sling before school the next day if I didn't want anyone asking questions, but I was so worried about everything else going on that I hardly even cared.

After smoking a spliff with Danielle's dad, I went upstairs with Danielle and tried to sleep. The bed was warm and comfortable but no amount of blankets could make me fall asleep. I was so upset and ashamed at what I'd done to my family, because whatever happened to them now was my fault, so I knew I couldn't go home. I was too much trouble and destroyed everything I touched... I loved my family too much to let myself near them again and that hurt me more than anything, but I didn't know what else to do. I didn't deserve to be loved anymore.

CHAPTER 20

I'm Not Crazy

The next morning I untied the bandage from my wrist to take a look at my cuts. The one which needed stitches had been held in place with the tape, but the blood had still seeped through and I was worried it had soaked the tape too much to hold the cut together. Danielle's mum offered us breakfast and asked if we were going to school as she wasn't sure what to expect after the night's events, but I told her I still wanted to attend school as I was on my final warning and didn't want to be expelled. In some ways I probably shouldn't have gone to school as I was in no fit mental state to get through the day, but I wanted to gain some form of qualifications after being kicked out of Tomlinscote and it meant a lot to me that I stuck it out.

My head of year was standing at the front gates when I walked in, smoking a cigarette. She called me and Danielle straight over to her as she knew we'd bunked off the day before, but I had no intention of talking to her. She didn't care that I was visibly upset when she spoke to me like I was worthless, telling me I was stupid for bunking off and would need to be dealt with later that day. I couldn't cope with sitting through lessons that day, as I found out less than half an hour

217

into being at school, so I headed over to Danielle's form tutor's office. I didn't have him for any lessons but he had spoken to me before when I'd been upset, and seemed like a teacher I could trust at Fernhill. He knew when Danielle or I were on drugs in school and instead of calling the police or alerting other teachers, he'd simply give us the key to his office and tell us to sit in there until we sobered up. I was crying when I went to see him that morning as I was feeling suicidal and didn't know how to deal with it, so I knocked on his door and he immediately opened it and asked me what was wrong. He wrapped his arms around me, which was unusual for a teacher, but he was different to the others, so I felt comforted as I sat down in his office.

Sam had already told him that Danielle and I had both been arrested the night before, as well as telling him about the cut on my wrist. He also knew I'd run away from home because Mum had phoned the school that morning to ask if anyone had seen me, whilst seeming upset about the whole situation. I thought she was just angry with me as Dad had surely spoken to her, so I felt angry the moment I knew she'd phoned the school. Danielle's teacher eventually had to leave to teach a lesson but he gave me the key for his office and told me to lock myself inside until I felt calm enough to go back to class. Sam and Danielle were going to check on me in between every lesson, but I couldn't take it after two hours so decided to leave. I was so depressed that I just couldn't be around people anymore and I knew Mum was on her way to school, so I wrote a note for Sam as I walked out. The note read 'Sam... *I can't do this anymore, I've had enough. I'll be at that place we talked about, high up in the sky... Tell my family I'm sorry.*'

I knew that committing suicide was selfish, but I was so traumatized by everything that had happened in my life that I'd had enough and was ready to end it. I knew Sam would know I was talking about the abandoned warehouse, as I had told her I'd jump off the roof if life ever got too much for me. I didn't know, however, that the police had turned up at school wanting to speak to Danielle and me, so by the time Sam found the note, there were already police walking up the stairs towards the office, searching for me. Sam was running down the stairs at the exact same moment and as she tried to run past the police, she dropped the note in a panic and could only watch as they read it in disbelief. They immediately knew it was a suicide note and as they rushed back to their cars, Sam and Danielle were called to go to the warehouse with them. Meanwhile, I had already climbed to the roof and was thinking about jumping. I sat with my legs dangling over the edge whilst I drank a bottle of vodka I'd stolen from a shop on the way, staring up at the clouds as I thought about joining them.

As I stood up and took one final look to the ground, my entire life flashed before my eyes. I thought about the rape, the fire and my depression, along with every other reason to jump... But then I thought about the people I'd be leaving behind, what it would mean for them if I jumped. I thought about my parents and brothers, what they'd have to go through if they lost me. The reason for jumping was so that I was no longer a burden on them, but I knew I'd put them through an even worse hell by ending my own life. I thought about my older sister and wondered about the conversation she'd be left facing when her new-born son was all grown up, how she'd have to tell him he'd had another auntie who was too selfish to face life. Then I thought about my twin sister, and knew that she could not cope without me... How could I be so selfish, after everything we'd been through together? I wanted to jump so bad because the pain was surreal and I just wanted it to end, but I knew I couldn't burden my family with the pain I'd leave behind. No one would be able to handle that.

After crying at the pitiful sight of my pathetic life, I threw the bottle off the roof instead of myself and slowly made my way back down the ladder. I saw the police cars rushing to the scene with sirens blaring but I managed to flea before they saw me, not realizing that both Danielle and Sam were in the cars. I was extremely drunk by this point and although I was worried about returning home, I barely thought twice before walking there. I don't remember much apart from arguing when I entered the house, but my older sister Callie was downstairs and noticed I was drunk. She didn't know the full extent to which Dad and I had been arguing, but she knew I'd been in trouble with the police and wanted to find out why. After realizing I was not going to open my mouth she tried to joke around with me, asking about girl stuff and boys. She went on to ask in a sarcastic voice, 'What's the furthest you've been with a boy? Did he touch your minky?'

I snapped back in anger as tears filled my eyes, 'He fucking raped me…'

I then pushed past her and stumbled up the stairs to my bedroom as fast as I could, barricading my door before collapsing on my bed and rocking myself to sleep. Mum eventually found out and asked if this was true, as Danielle's mum had also told her prior to this after I'd mentioned it whilst drunk at Danielle's house. I was still slightly drunk when I let Mum into my room as she asked, 'Is this true, Robyn? Who did this?'

I told her it was Drew and James and that it went on for years. I told her that Ashleigh was abused too, until the age of eleven like me. Mum had tears in her eyes and I felt guilty for telling her as I knew it greatly upset her. She looked at me along with Dad, who had also entered my room by this point, and said, 'This explains everything… You don't have to fight us anymore…'

I didn't understand how this solved anything. How could something that happened so long ago mean anything significant now? Dad told me that Drew had always seemed afraid of him even when we were kids, and now he understood why. Mum and Dad told me that the dates added up because the year of the rape was the year my behaviour started spiralling downhill, getting me into trouble at school and with the police. They understood that my depression was caused by this, and maybe the reason I'd started drinking and taking drugs was to deal with the sexual abuse that happened all those years ago. They then told me that it was not my fault and they just wished I'd told them sooner so they could have stopped it or done something about it, but I was too young to know it was abuse at the time and I felt like it was all my fault. I hated myself for the sexual abuse because it made me dirty and disgusting, but Mum and Dad thought everything would change now that they knew the truth.

I wish I could say that my life changed positively there and then, but sadly it didn't. Mum and Dad felt guilty for not being able to stop what had happened and I felt guilty for everything I'd put them through. I was still depressed so I continued to take harder drugs, and that caused more arguments than ever before. Dad would pressure me into talking to the police about the sexual abuse and I knew he was only trying to help, but I was not ready to talk about it so I continued to argue with him more than ever. Being home was like treading on eggshells 24/7, so I preferred to stay out and take drugs on the Totland Estate. When I was feeling suicidal I'd start arguments at home to provoke a reaction from Mum and Dad so that they'd tell me to leave, then I'd run away to Danielle's house and spend days taking drugs. If I was high on anything harder than cocaine I couldn't even be seen at Danielle's house, so I'd roam the streets all night, high on drugs by myself. Danielle stuck by my side all the time, but as the weeks went by, I noticed her acting strange whenever we were high or drunk. She would constantly look at me with tears in her eyes and say, 'Robyn… I've done something bad… I'm so sorry, you shouldn't be my friend.'

I thought she was talking about her depression, which was maybe causing her to feel like she didn't deserve any friends, so I stuck by her side and we continued to stay as close as we'd always been. One evening I had a knock at the door from the police, who arrested me on further evidence in the arson investigation. Danielle and I had both been interviewed already and I told the police that Danielle had waited for me at the end of the road when I poured the petrol over Kennedy's fence, as she was my friend and I did not want to get her into trouble. I told them truthfully that she had introduced me to Kennedy and that half of the money was hers, but it seemed she did not tell the same story in her interview. The police searched my house a second time and found the bag full of petrol-soaked clothes, including my shoes, which had left a footprint in the petrol on the ground. I thought maybe a witness had described my clothes and bag, which was how the police came to find out what I'd been wearing.

At the second interview I made no attempt to defend myself, but Mum was sitting through the interview with me and explained that I was angry because I'd worked hard for the money Kennedy stole. She, along with my solicitor, agreed that it was best I use the rape as a sob story, to show the courts that I was not an arsonist but simply a child who was abused and attempted to start the fire for release. Because the fire had gone out by itself, the damage caused to the fence was minimal and I was told to say that I was not intending to endanger lives, but merely wanted to cause my money's worth of damage to Kennedy's house. The police eventually dropped the charge from 'arson with intent to endanger life' to 'attempted arson', but I was still facing a two-year prison sentence if the judge was harsh at court.

Months went by and I was continually brought to the station for more interviews, which caused me more worry each time. I continued to socialize with Danielle and we went on to find other dealers, so continued to use cocaine and speed. We also tried magic mushrooms, MDMA and crack, along with countless varieties of alcohol and prescription drugs. When the court date finally arrived I was bailed to reappear on a later date because the judge needed more time to decide on the verdict.

Ashleigh was extremely depressed at this time as she was petrified of the fact that I could go to prison, because she didn't think she could cope with being home if I was not there. She told me she'd commit suicide if I went to prison and I believed her but knew I could do nothing to stop it, and that hurt me more than the fear of going to prison. I hated being home because I could not face the sight of my loved ones slowly dying around me, and Dad had just been told that his mother had terminal cancer. On top of this, Ashleigh was struggling with gender identity and her sexuality, which I thought was only because of what had happened to us regarding the sexual abuse. My family had always been acceptant of sexuality and had told us from a very young age that if any of us turned out gay, they would still love us the same and just cared that we were happy. However it was still a difficult time for Ashleigh because she was struggling to accept it herself.

I was also confused about my sexuality because I was petrified of men after what happened to me all those years ago, but I later found out that I was not interested in women either so it put me in a very confused place. Ashleigh and I would argue and I hated that more than any other arguments at home, because we were so close that we took all our anger out on each other. I was expelled from Fernhill for my behaviour and drug-use, which left me too young for work, but too messed up for school. I was angry at Mum for signing papers to say that I was being home schooled, when everyone involved knew I wasn't and it was only to pull me out of education without a fight. Fernhill came under Hampshire borough but I lived in Frimley, which came under Surrey, so both councils argued over whose problem I was until I eventually became no one's problem. I was livid because it seemed as though the entire world was against me, whilst every choice I made turned out to be the wrong one.

When the second court date arrived I found it strange that only I had been bailed to appear and not Danielle, as we were both in this together. It was only when I read the papers which showed everything that had been said in both Danielle's interviews and mine that I started to realize what had happened. Mum held the interview records first before saying to me, 'I think you should read this, Robyn.'

I saw Danielle's name printed on a sheet of paper which almost looked like a drama script, with her lines in one colour and the police in another. I read the first few lines, which said *'when asked about the night in question, Danielle said: I did not know Kennedy until Robyn introduced me to him. I did not want to buy cocaine but Robyn seemed desperate for drugs. Robyn set the house on fire and it was all her idea, not mine. I had nothing to do with it...'*

I went on to read that Danielle had described every item of clothing I was wearing, down to the logo printed on my bag. I felt physically sick as I realized what she had done. How could she betray me like this? After everything we had been through... I felt as though a knife had stabbed me in the stomach, ripping through my organs as it surfaced through my back. I had to leave the courtroom... I needed to run, I needed to get away from it all... I couldn't even breathe. As I ran out of the waiting room, I barely made it outside before almost crying. I wanted to burst into tears but I was surrounded by hardened criminals and knew I wouldn't stand a chance in prison if anyone saw me crying. Instead I stood outside smoking as I flicked through the contact list on my phone, wondering whether or not to call Danielle. What would I even say to her? How can you make up after that? I was so overwhelmed with emotions that I didn't even know where to start if I phoned her, so I put my phone back in my pocket and started walking back inside.

Mum could see how upset I was but deep down I thought she would probably be happy now, as Danielle's actions would mean I'd have to stop hanging out with her for sure. Mum and Dad had tried to stop us seeing each other countless times since I'd started taking drugs, but that was the very reason I couldn't leave her. I was torn between keeping a back-stabbing friend so that I could have my precious drugs, and giving up the drugs alongside Danielle so that I could have my family back. I pondered on this thought all day and when was finally called into the courtroom, I couldn't even concentrate on my case. Luckily I had a lawyer speaking for me, but I still struggled to take in anything that was going on. Occasionally the judge would ask me a few questions and I knew how important it was that I backed myself up, but the stress of Danielle's actions had disabled my mind from focusing on anything else. Mum tried to defend me as she listened to the judge comparing my case with much more serious retaliation crimes, such as a house fire started by a twelve-year-old back in the nineties which killed four people, and other fires started by children who became murderers.

Mum pleaded with the judge, 'But this case is nothing *like* any of the fires you've referred to... The incidents you're describing caused murders, when my daughter didn't even succeed in setting the house on fire. She only wanted to cause her stolen money's worth of damage, not death! She's not a psychopath!'

The judge and police involved knew that I hadn't murdered anyone, but it was the extent to which I'd planned the arson that made it so serious. I'd brought the petrol out from my house, roamed the streets with it until dark and then wore two layers of different-coloured clothes to avoid matching the police description. I'd worn gloves to hide my fingerprints as well as covering my hair so as not to leave any DNA at the scene, which caused the judge to think that if I'd murdered anyone I would have tried to discard their bodies too. Because of this, everyone involved thought I was capable of committing murder in the future and therefore wanted to lock me up regardless of how trivial the situation was. I was terrified of this because I didn't want to go down the criminal route, which would waste my life from the moment I went to prison, but with everyone having the same opinion of me I began to wonder if I really could kill someone. I didn't want to think about it as I didn't want to believe it, but when everyone expected bad behaviour from me they would usually get it.

The trial went on for what felt like hours, then finally a decision was made by the judge. As I stood up inside my glass box, I watched Mum cry as the judge began to speak. I felt so guilty for the pain I was causing Mum and it felt worse knowing that if I did go to prison, the court security would take me away and I would be unable to comfort her. However, as the judge began to speak, I let out a huge sigh of relief as I learned I would only receive a nine-month referral order. This meant I was required to attend regular meetings with a support officer from the Youth Offending Team, who would work with me for the duration of the court order. When we left the courtroom, Mum and Dad told me everything would be OK now and I'd never have to see Danielle again. I didn't want to see that back-stabbing bitch, but I wasn't ready to let go of the drugs she provided, which left me struggling to make my decision about confronting her.

CHAPTER 21

Snitches Get Stitches

On the whole, I was deeply traumatized and upset by being betrayed so harshly by Danielle. I couldn't understand what would possess someone to act so coldly towards their friends, but then I remembered how I'd struggled to make friends my entire life and so it was probably destined to happen. I was angry beyond words, and we had always said that snitches got stitches, but I needed my drugs more than I needed revenge so I foolishly stayed friends with Danielle.

There was an awkward silence when I entered Danielle's house after telling Mum I was going to see other friends on the Totland Estate. Her mum and dad were sitting at the table smoking whilst Danielle greeted me at the back door. Danielle's mum spoke first, asking how court went as I sat down beside Danielle. 'You didn't get sent down then?'

I smiled politely and replied, 'No, I got off with a referral order.'

As I continued to speak, Danielle asked if there was anything else I wanted to tell them. I took a deep breath and said nervously, 'I read what you said in your interview. I want you to know that I am upset, but you're still my friend and I understand why you did it...'

Danielle interrupted me before I finished speaking, as guilt consumed her face. 'I'm sorry, Robyn! I was scared... I didn't know what to say. I'd never been arrested before! I don't think I deserve you as a friend after this...'

I looked her in the eyes and told her it was OK, but I needed her more than anyone because she had been there for me through so much. She hugged me and apologized again and again, but I told her she didn't need to worry as I would still be there for her and I forgave her. Inside I knew that our friendship was worthless beyond this point, as her parents couldn't even understand why I was still there, but I burst into tears and told them that I didn't want to lose Danielle. I think they admired me for forgiving her, but at the same time they must have known I was using her for something as I'd be stupid to stay friends with her after what she had done. I vowed never to trust her again, or anyone for that matter, even if I spent more time with her than my own family. It's like the old saying goes, 'Keep your friends close but your enemies closer.'

It was almost 9pm by now and I wasted no time in following through on the real reason I'd gone back there, which was to get drugs. I told Danielle that we should celebrate me not going to prison, so she soon scraped up some money from around the house and we were on our way to buy drugs. Her parents bought us a bottle of cider each and we smoked weed whilst we walked to meet a cocaine dealer, before bumping him and running off with his goods like Kennedy had done to us. He didn't have much money but we still managed to get away with over five grams of coke, so we laughed together as we legged it after beating him and leaving him lying on the floor. I felt guilty for beating him up as he was unable to defend himself due to his small-set frame and weak build, but the drug world was a dangerous place and if you couldn't be a predator, you'd become prey.

After ensuring we were in a safe place, well hidden from police or the dealer we'd bumped, we began to rack up the cocaine ready for snorting.

We snorted half-gram lines on top of smoking bongs and drinking, so it wasn't long before we were completely out of our minds and in no fit state to make rational decisions. Although I couldn't physically see vivid hallucinations when I was high, my imagination became so wild and powerful that I could see almost anything I thought of right in front of me. When I closed my eyes all I could see was beautiful colours and even when I opened them, the colours would still be there when I looked up to the sky. My mind felt at ease and as the happiness took over, all I could think about was how great my life would be if I could stay this high forever. All I wanted was to escape the guilt I felt from being depressed, which by now had reached such a severe extreme that I felt I had no other option than to continue taking drugs. The drugs gave me an escape from the things I was not ready to deal with, providing a comfort which I used more and more often. I knew that someday I'd have to go back to reality and face my problems properly, but for now I was happy hiding out in 'La-La land' with my drugs.

After snorting almost two grams each, we decided to take a walk around the estates surrounding Totland. I was so high I could barely walk but we continued to roam the streets until the early hours of the morning, by which point we had run out of drugs. We must have passed out while it was still dark because when we woke up it was daylight and we were still outside, lying on the street in wet clothes. We were still high as we walked back to Danielle's, at which point I phoned Mum to see if she could pick me up. I knew I couldn't walk home without being stopped by police in the state I was in, but I needed to go home so that I could shower, change clothes and sleep. Mum didn't know I was with Danielle as I had kept my secret about staying friends with her, so I asked to be picked up from the park a little further down the road from Danielle's. I felt bad for lying to Mum and Dad about giving up Danielle's friendship after what she had done, but there was no way I could give up my only way of getting hold of drugs.

When Mum picked me up I tried to squint my eyes so that they wouldn't appear so big from all the drugs, but she wasn't stupid and knew I'd taken something. She didn't question me about it as it only led to arguments because this happened so often now, but I could tell from her eyes that she was angry and upset. Nights like the previous one seemed to happen more and more often and over the next few months, I continued to take drugs and drink heavily every time I was with Danielle. I would lie to Mum if she gave me a lift by asking to be dropped off at the park, from which I would walk straight to Danielle's house. It was hard to hide how I really felt about her as there was no trust left within our friendship at all, but I kept my mouth shut so that I could use her like I'd planned. When I was high this proved extremely difficult as I was brutally honest when intoxicated, but I knew how important it was that I stayed friends with her as the drugs were my only escape from my own mind.

My YOT worker from the 'youth offending team' had arranged a doctor's appointment at the request of Mum and Dad, to provide me with counselling therapy for my depression. They wanted to talk about the sexual abuse but I was not ready for that, so I refused counselling altogether and opted for drug treatment instead. They put me on Prozac, and though it began to have an effect after a few weeks, the first week was nothing but severe side effects. I had been arguing with Dad after coming home from Danielle's and sleeping all day as he knew I was taking drugs, so he grounded me and stopped me seeing all of my friends from Totland. He knew the side-effects of the Prozac were causing me nausea and vomiting but he was still aggressively harsh to me and demanded that I dag holes in the garden all day as a punishment. I physically couldn't do it and after digging for almost an hour whilst vomiting and crying, I threw down the shovel and told him to 'fuck off'. He shouted at me and said that no daughter of his was going to sit around the house doing nothing all day, but he couldn't seem to understand that I was depressed and physically exhausted from the side-effects of Prozac so couldn't work. I told him I was too young for work anyway and that if Mum hadn't signed the papers at school, I'd still be attending some form of education. Therefore it was not my fault

I had nothing to do and it didn't matter how often I drank because I had no reason to get up in the morning.

Dad shouted up the stairs as I ran to my room, still feeling sick and drowsy. I grabbed my runaway bag, which I'd kept pre-packed since I ran away so often, before making my way downstairs in tears ready to leave. Dad shouted with pure hatred in his eyes, 'So you're just going to fuck off like you usually do then? You're just a stupid child, can't deal with anything like a fucking adult.'

I ran out the front door, shouting and swearing back at him as I began the four-mile walk to Danielle's house. I walked into a shop down the road, picked up a crate of beer and threw a tenner onto the counter. I knew I wouldn't get served as the shop owner knew I was underage, so I snapped at him as I walked out, 'There's more than enough money there, I've had a fucking shit day and I'm taking these so don't even think about chasing after me.'

He looked scared, which was what I wanted, as the last thing I needed was a stupid shop owner starting a fight, so although he knew I was underage he didn't call the police as I'd left enough money to pay for the beer. I downed the first can in one go before opening up the second can and lighting a cigarette. I stared blankly ahead as I pulled my hood down and over my face, covering up the mess I'd made by crying. A police car pulled up and tried to stop me for drinking but I managed to run away fast enough to reach an alleyway and hop over a fence, at which point they decided I was not worth the chase. I then stuck to back roads as much as I could for the rest of the walk to Danielle's, where I felt safe as I was away from police and close to drugs. Her mum asked if I was OK or needed a place to stay as I told her I'd been kicked out again, before explaining to her how my dad had treated me whilst I was feeling sick from taking Prozac. She had taken other anti-depressants in the past so knew exactly what it felt like to be nauseated as a side-effect, so she completely sympathized with me and agreed it was best I stayed there for a few nights.

I didn't have enough money for hard drugs but I still smoked weed and drank with Danielle every day, until I received a phone call from Mum and Dad, who were asking me to come home. They didn't seem angry, but they weren't happy by any means and whenever they acted overly calm it always seemed like it was because they'd run out of emotions to feel. I must have drained them with all my anger from depression but it was something I couldn't stop and could only keep running from, in the hope that one day I'd run away from it. They sometimes used Ashleigh to get at me because when Ashleigh was upset I'd always go back home to try and comfort her, but it was useless as I was the one causing the problems. She would cry and tell me how much she hated what I was doing to Mum and Dad, but I was so angry at them that I couldn't see how I was solely at fault. She called me a druggy and said that I did everything for attention, as well as sarcastically asking 'Are you happy now? Did you upset everyone like you wanted to?'

A few weeks went by with the same arguments, day in, day out. I had stormed out of the house whilst on curfew for drinking so it wasn't long before the police came searching for me. They would knock at my door after 7pm every night to make sure that I was in, but until now they had only came once each night so I assumed it was safe to go out once they'd been and gone. I was off my face on crack, MDMA and cannabis, as well as having drunk almost five bottles of wine. The police found me lying in a ditch with a knife in my pocket and blood on my arms, at which point they arrested me for 'possession of an offensive weapon', 'drunk and disorderly' and 'breach of bail conditions'. I kicked up a bigger fuss than ever before, resisting with all my strength as I lashed out at every single officer who was called to the scene. They eventually had to shock me with a stun-gun, before cuffing my hands behind my back and strapping restraints around my legs, upper arms and torso. I screamed uncontrollably as I smashed my head against the cage inside the police van, which they'd carried me to as I was restrained to the point that I could not walk.

When we arrived at the station I had still not calmed down, so they left me locked inside a three-by-three-foot cage in the back of the van for almost an hour. I was falling around so much because of all the alcohol and drugs that when the police carried me into the station to be booked in, the custody sergeant took one look at me and ordered me to be taken to hospital right away. I don't remember anything else until waking up in a hospital bed in Woking, but I must have been there for at least four hours as it was gone 2am by the time I was taken back to the police station.

I refused to comply and as the hours ticked by, I became more aware of what was happening around me because the drugs were starting to wear off alongside the alcohol. I had barely been inside the police station long enough for them to book me into custody, before kicking off and swinging a fist at an officer. It was a male officer who was trying to hold me against a wall whilst another male searched me, so I felt extremely violated as both their hands ran over my body. I hated being touched, more so by men because of what I'd been through with James and Drew, so I was becoming increasingly angry with the police officers at the station.

Once they'd thrown me into a cell, I was left with just one thin blanket on top of a foam mattress. I was extremely upset as well as coming down from all the upper drugs I'd taken, so it wasn't long before I was banging my head against the wall in an attempt to knock myself unconscious. I already had a black eye from resisting arrest as one of the officers had kicked me in the face whilst I was on the floor, but I didn't care about the pain anymore. I was so full of adrenaline that I hardly felt the pain, so I continued to hurt myself inside my cell. I had a small blade that I kept inside my bra, as it was too small to show up on the metal detector used by police when they searched me. I pulled it out from my bra and began to cut my left arm, ignoring the pre-existing scars, which were still healing. I looked straight up at the camera inside my cell as I screamed and violently stabbed the blade deep into my arms, before smearing the blood all over the walls and camera. I then threw the blade on the floor as I twisted the blanket from my cell bed and wrapped it around my neck. The custody staff then charged into my cell, armed with batons and pepper spray as they knocked me off my feet by hitting my legs twice with batons.

There were now more than twelve police officers, both male and female, taking hold of me from all directions as they cuffed my hands behind my back and jumped on top of me. They then tied restraint belts around my legs, arms and torso, whilst threatening to spray me if I did not stop resisting. I screamed for the entire time as I struggled with all my strength, but there were too many of them holding me down in too many places. I felt male hands tightly gripped around and all up my legs, arms and back, pushing me towards the floor whilst other officers had hold of my ankles, head and neck. One officer held my mouth shut by tightly gripping my jaw from the neck upwards, whilst a medic tried to check my arms. I was bleeding heavily, but because I was deemed a risk to myself, they couldn't bandage my wounds for fear that I'd use the bandages to harm myself. After controlling the bleeding but leaving the wounds open, the medic gave a hand signal to the police who then left my cell almost as quickly as they had entered it.

They left the restraints and cuffs on my body as I was seen as too much of a risk to be left unrestrained, so I struggled and tried to get out of the restraints until I eventually gave up and simply cried. The restraints were hurting me now because I'd struggled so much that my skin had begun to swell wherever it was touching them, and they were now too tight for the swelling, which quickly became bruising. The bruise on my eye had grown and now covered half of my face, but no bruises on my body were as bad as the swelling on my hands. My wrists had swollen significantly where I'd resisted handcuffs countless times throughout the night and I thought my knuckles might be broken, due to the extent of the bruising I'd suffered after punching the ground. I ended up crying on the floor for over an hour, at which point a police officer opened the hatch in my cell door and asked sarcastically, 'Have you calmed down yet? We want to get those restraints off just as much as you do.'

I stared into space before slowly answering him and asking, 'Yes, I've calmed down now... Can I please have a blanket? I'm so cold.'

He unlocked the door before entering and kneeling down to untie the restraints from around my body, whilst radioing for another officer to bring me a blanket. As a female officer arrived with my blanket, I told her I needed the toilet desperately. There was no toilet inside my cell and I was severely claustrophobic, which was the real reason why I wanted to walk around the station, but I knew she'd have to take me out so I continued to pretend I was desperate for the toilet. As she began to lead me out of my cell, another officer stayed close behind me. I wasn't hand cuffed but I was surrounded by police inside a police station so I knew there was no point in trying to kick up a fuss or run off... Until I saw a man walk through the exit which led to the public entrance of the police station. The door was locked and needed a swipe card to open it, but I knew I had a good chance of escaping if I ran through it when someone had opened it.

I kept a close eye on the door and as soon as I'd been to the toilet, I saw my chance and made a break for it. From walking calmly, I suddenly jerked sideways and started sprinting towards the door which was around twenty feet away. I skimmed past two officers whilst others jumped out at me from all directions, after the police women who'd taken me to the toilet pressed the red emergency alarm. Once that alarm signalled, every single officer in the station stopped what they were doing and immediately chased after me. I thought I was going to make it but suddenly the custody sergeant jumped out of nowhere and threw himself on top of me. He was six-foot-six and much bigger-built than me so I had no chance against him, but I still carried on struggling with everything I had. I was forced onto my front as eight male officers pinned me down, taking no chances wasting female officers on me as they would not be strong enough to restrain me. I shouted, 'Get the fuck off me you fucking pigs!' though I knew they would only hold me tighter.

I was still resisting and struggling to breathe as my heart was beating so rapidly, when one officer who was standing placed his boot directly over my head. His heavy foot pressed down on my temple, causing me so much pain that I was unable to breathe and completely stopped moving. When he released the pressure, I was able to start resisting again, so he continue to stand on my temple until I eventually stopped moving when he took it off my head. I was petrified by this point because I knew they were not allowed to do this, so what else were they going to do that was not allowed? My head hurt so much that I started blacking out, but I was still semi-conscious when they restrained me once more and carried me back to my cell. Everything went blurry and I kept blacking out, but I still remember screaming as they stuck a plastic bag over my head and began taking my clothes off. All I could think about was the rape and how much worse this felt, as there were eight males instead of just one. I screamed as tears streamed down my face, 'Please stop! Please… Don't blindfold me! Someone fucking help!'

No one listened, they only carried on tearing the clothes off my bruised and swollen body. I made one last petrified cry for help as they took off the remaining items of clothing, which were merely my underpants and bra. They then forced me into a suicide suit and pushed me to make sure I stayed on the ground as they ran out, leaving me crying on the floor. I think the bag over my head was to disturb my breathing, so that I wouldn't have the energy to resist so much as I'd be struggling to breathe. I hated how they'd shown me I was worthless, as they ripped away the last bit of dignity I had left, which was the clothes covering my naked body. I was now extremely cold as I was not even allowed a blanket, but I was so bruised and beaten that I blacked out and fell in and out of consciousness for the remainder of the night anyway. I was in the least pain when I stayed still, so I lay down on the floor until around 6am when the night shift was over and a team of new police officers were in charge. Even if I had wanted to move, I was in too much pain and decided it was not worth the energy.

As I began to hear footsteps of heavy police boots, I looked up towards the hatch on my cell door, which soon opened as I was greeted by a police officer who had just started his shift. He smiled at me as he asked if I'd like my clothes back, to which I replied, 'Yes please. Can I have a blanket too? I'm freezing...'

He handed me my underwear, top and tracksuit bottoms, but refused to give me my hoodie. However, I was happy enough with underwear, top and trousers which he gave me, so I thanked him and waited for my blanket. I felt so much calmer for having my clothes back but I was still extremely embarrassed and ashamed that so many people had seen my naked body, so I pledged from that moment that I would start losing weight and never be that fat again. If this happened again, but after I'd lost weight, I wouldn't give a fuck who saw my body as I wouldn't be ashamed of it, so I decided to starve myself from that day forwards.

Mum came to pick me up after I was interviewed about my arrests, but just the sight of her brought back all the feeling from the last time I saw her which was when I stormed out of the house mid-argument. She asked me calmly and pleadingly, 'Why do you keep doing this to yourself, Robyn? What happened to our sweet little girl?'

I was so upset at her words because they made me feel guilty, for hurting her and not turning out the way she'd planned. I hated myself for hurting everyone around me, but I was so depressed that I couldn't stop it. I didn't want to cry so I turned my tears to anger instead, storming out of the visitors' room and attempting to run back to my cell. Mum cried as she watched the custody staff restrain me, helpless to stop them hurting her baby. I cried because I was at fault for upsetting Mum, but I couldn't face up to the guilt I felt so it came as a relief when I was taken back to my cell. I wanted to comfort Mum but she was told to go home, as the police had decided I was not mentally fit to be released until the following day or later... I was distraught.

CHAPTER 22

Stupid Little Girl

I was furious with the police for not letting me go home, but looking back now I know I would have attempted suicide if I had been released feeling the way I did. I was taken to hospital for an x-ray of both my hands since my knuckles were swollen, but I felt embarrassed walking around the hospital in handcuffs because everyone who looked at me must have thought I was a serious criminal. A stranger in the waiting room cheered me up slightly as he saw me attempt to run off after slipping out of my handcuffs, shouting 'Go on girl!' before offering me a cigarette as the police grabbed hold of both my arms. They allowed me to take it and said I could smoke it when we were back at the station, so I thanked the man and behaved for the rest of the trip, as I knew the police could refuse to let me smoke as a punishment.

I think the hospital trip did me good because I was able to leave the station for an hour and although I was cuffed and surrounded by police for the entire time, it felt good to breathe some fresh air. When we arrived back at the station, I sat outside in handcuffs as I smoked my cigarette before being taken back inside to my cell. I was offered a microwave meal and a can of cola but all I really wanted was a shower, so I asked for a drink of water whilst I waited for a female officer to take me. There was twelve other people being detained in police cells and there was limited time for officers to staff the showers, so the custody staff asked every other female who'd been arrested if they wanted a shower, so that we all went at the same time. I didn't like this idea as I was ashamed and embarrassed at how fat my body was, but I'd already been seen naked by almost all the staff in the police station so the thought of a few more people seeing me didn't bother me too much. When I got to the showers, it was a small, box-like room with six shower heads. The water was cold and the floor was dirty, but it was better than sitting in dirty clothes for another night.

There were three female police officers and one male standing further back so that he couldn't see us properly, but was close enough to help if any of us kicked off. There were two other women showering with me, one around thirty years old and another around fifty. We faced the wall as the police officers told us what clothes to take off, one item by one as they watched us to make sure we weren't hiding anything. Eventually we were all standing naked under the shower heads, before the police officers pressed a button on the wall that released the water. I was crying as I kept my face pointed at the floor, totally embarrassed and traumatized by the event. I was in a lot of pain because I hadn't eaten since the day before I was arrested, as well as being dehydrated and covered in swelling and bruises. The older woman was showering next to me and noticed I was crying, so she leant over and said in a motherly voice, 'Don't worry babe, there's no need to be upset. Don't let them get to you!'

I thanked her as she continued to comfort me, telling me that she would have given me a hug if we weren't so naked. She cheered me up then asked my name, before telling me hers, as we became friends. When we finished showering, the officers handed me some prison clothes, which were ill-fitting and ugly but clean, which was all I wanted. I was walked back to my cell where I was given two blankets for the night, which went faster than the previous night as I had calmed down and was in comfortable clothes. I was still cold, as I had not eaten for days so my body temperature had dropped, but I was warm enough to sleep when I curled myself up in the foetal position so that's exactly what I did.

The next morning, the transfer van arrived to take me to court around 10am. Now that I was sober, I had been exercising in my cell to pass the time. The custody sergeant unlocked my cell door after cuffing my hands through the hatch, before taking hold of me by one arm as another officer held the other. They walked me to the front desk where I was asked a few medical questions before going to court, so they could assess whether or not I was mentally fit to be released that day. They put me in a small holding cell by the back entrance of the police station whilst they waited for the transfer van, explaining to me what would happen when I got to court. The van soon showed up and I was walked to a cell within the van that was no bigger than a toilet cubicle and had no windows or outside light coming in. There was a hatch in the door which was locked as soon as I was inside, before the officers escorting me took my hands out of the cuffs through the hatch.

I felt as though I was being treated like a hardened criminal, because I was unable to count the number of procedures put in place to stop me escaping. There was no seat belt inside the cell so I struggled not to fall over throughout the journey, which was fast, as there were sirens on this van. I hadn't had a real look at what the outside of the transfer van was like, but we soon arrived at court and I was able to see what I'd travelled in... Once we'd driven through a twenty-feet-tall entrance gate with barbed wire on the top, I was taken out of the van after being cuffed through the hatch on my cell door. The transfer van was white with no windows past the driver's seat, with red writing on the back which read 'WARNING! PRISON TRANSFER VAN. KEEP BACK.'

Two officers held me from either side as they handed me over to the court security, who walked me inside to yet another cell. This cell was nicer than the police station cells, but I still felt claustrophobic and was becoming increasingly nervous about court as I was told that if I broke the law after the arson charge, I could go to prison for not sticking to my referral order.

I was eventually brought up the stairs from the holding cells and escorted to the courtroom, at which point I was placed in a glass box opposite Mum and Dad. They had driven out to support me in court, along with Ashleigh, who was waiting with them. I felt ashamed that I'd brought them there, as I did every time I stood trial in court, but I felt comforted to see Ashleigh as I had missed her all that time I'd been locked away. I was charged with all three offences I'd been arrested for, which resulted in a three-month curfew on an electronic tag plus three months added to my referral order. I was angry with this outcome as I hadn't caused anybody any harm and thought I'd already been punished enough at the police station, but I didn't argue as I was just happy to be released from police custody.

Ashleigh asked if I'd read the letters they wrote for me that Mum had left at the police station, but I was confused as to what letters she was talking about as I hadn't received any. Apparently, my entire family at home had written me a letter each as asked by Mum and Dad, who thought it would help me see right from wrong whilst I was in the station. Mum handed me the letters as the police had given them back to her at court, but after reading just half of one I was so upset and angry that I threw it onto the floor. We were now in the car and on our way home, so I couldn't walk away from Mum and Dad, who had known this would probably start an argument. The letters were full of pleas from Mum and Dad, who wrote things such as 'We know you're still in there somewhere, please change your life before it's too late.'

I was angry because I was not ready to accept how bad my problems had become, so instead of taking in what was written I tried to ignore the letters and focus on getting my next fix. It was 8pm by the time we got home and as I had to wait for the tag company to come round and attach the tag to my leg, I knew I would not be able to go out that night. However, I knew it would only be one more day until I could go back to Totland and see all my friends along with my drugs, so I went about my usual routine whilst settling back into being home. I had only been locked up for a few days but I'd spent most of the past weeks out with friends, so it seemed strange being home for a whole night. I couldn't wait to change out of the clothes I'd been given at the police station, so I switched the shower on before heading back to my bedroom and stripping down to my underwear as I waited for the water to heat up.

Mum walked into my bedroom whilst I stood almost naked, covered in bruises and cuts. She took one look at my body and gasped in shock, asking, 'What have they done to you? You look like the victim from the child abuse advert!'

I didn't want her to see me because I knew it would upset her, but she just stood there, staring at my body. My legs were covered in bruises the size of oranges, which ran all the way from my feet up to my pelvis. There were bruises on my hips, stomach, arms and chest, but none as big as the hand-print bruise on my back. My knuckles and hands were almost completely black with bruises and the swelling on my wrists was still yet to go down. My arms were covered in deep cuts and my neck had red marks on it from strangling myself back at the police station, but no swelling was as bad as the lump on the side of my head from where the police officer had stood on it. Mum asked me if I was OK or if I wanted to go to the police about this, as they shouldn't have given me the amount of bruises I had. I told her there was no point as they'd simply say they were using 'reasonable force' to detain me, but Dad was the real reason I didn't take action. He had drummed it into my head that I was merely a child who no one would take seriously or care about, especially the police, who would see me as a waste of time and space. This was mainly said only in arguments, but the words stayed with me and I had lost all confidence in standing up for myself and my rights. Dad had also led me to believe that being an adult only meant realizing 'no one cares or gives a fuck' about you, so I finally felt like an adult, as I had learned never to ask for help.

The following day I was in a meeting with my YOT worker, who came to my house. She tried to talk me into reporting what had happened with the police, particularly the incident where they had stripped me naked by force, as they were not legally allowed to do that because of my age. Though I was angry about the way I had been treated, I knew they would not believe a fifteen-year-old alcoholic over the police so I told my YOT worker that I didn't see any point in taking action. She was still concerned because I'd been stripped naked by male officers, as well as having one of them deliberately stand on my head, but I was used to being abused and thought it was normal, so I simply got on with it like every other bad situation in my life.

The following weeks went by fast as I seemed to drink them away and although I spent most of the daytime with Danielle on the Totland Estate, I usually ended up drinking alone in my bedroom once it reached 7pm. I hated being on tag because I couldn't go out at night, but I still managed to buy drugs now and then as I'd send Ashleigh out to meet Danielle. Ashleigh would return late and smoke weed with me, but I could never buy any real hard drugs as I'd have to share them with her, and I couldn't afford to pay for two addictions. The first time she tried cocaine was in her own bedroom, as I'd been caught red-handed when she walked in and saw me racking up. I didn't want to share at first because I knew it was dangerous and although she was less than a minute younger than me, she was still my baby sister and I didn't want to hurt her. She acted as if we were ten years old again, fighting over Ritalin, as she looked me straight in the eyes and said, 'Give me some or I'm telling Mum!'

I tried to talk her out of it but it seemed there was no way out now, so I racked up two lines and showed her how to snort it. Her line was smaller than mine since I'd paid a lot of money for it and had a much higher tolerance than her, but she still asked for more as she couldn't see what the big fuss was about… Until she sniffed her line. I passed the snort to her and as she brought it to her nose, I told her, 'You'll have to push it up further than that if you want to get high. Let me show you…'

I then stood close to her and put a finger from her other hand on the side of her nose which didn't have the snort, before telling her to face away from the lines and breathe out as far as she could. I then told her to breathe in really fast through the snort, as I directed it across one line on the table. Her eyes were closed as she was not used to it, which also meant she had not expected the tingling sensation in the back of her throat. As she tried to cough, I placed my hand over her mouth and told her to look upwards as it would stop her coughing, but that she shouldn't cough because all the cocaine she'd sniffed would go straight out of her mouth. Her eyes watered a little but she was OK. I then snorted my line and told her to gag back and swallow the coke when I did, so before long we were feeling the euphoric effects.

I was already used to the cocaine, but because Ashleigh had never done it before, she felt the same rush I had felt the first time I took an upper drug. She looked at me and we both laughed as we collapsed on her bed, smiling as we enjoyed the buzz and started listening to music. Music had always sounded truly wonderful when I was high, and Ashleigh was now experiencing this feeling for the first time. When I asked her how she felt, all she could say was, 'I... I don't know how to explain it but... Everything's amazing now... My depression's completely gone!'

I laughed as it was funny seeing her in such a state from just one line, but at the same time I was constantly checking on her as I did with anyone who was with me and trying a different drug for the first time. Ashleigh was my sister and although I hated the guilt from providing her with drugs, I thought it was only fair she got to feel the happiness I felt at least once. I wanted to remind her what it was like, not to be depressed, and it seemed that the only way I could do that was to let her try cocaine.

We rarely did that together again as I did not want to get Ashleigh hooked like I was, but the few times we did it were lots of fun and we were able to spend quality time together, which was something we'd longed for since we were kids... Everything was different now because I spent most of my days on the Totland Estate taking drugs with Danielle, whilst Ashleigh stayed inside and dealt with all the drama I left at home.

Mum and Dad would blame each other for the way Ashleigh and I both acted, as they'd approach my drug use in different ways, Mum trying to stay calm whilst Dad got angry and upset. Neither of them knew for definite that I was taking drugs as I'd never admit it unless I was caught, but they knew I was wasting my life away and that it was slowly ripping the entire family apart. I think Mum and Dad preferred me when I was on tag because they knew I couldn't go out past 7pm, so there was much less chance of me taking drugs, but I'd still drink inside the house and that affected my youngest brother a lot because he was only ten years old and should never have had to see me in the state I was usually in. I'd lie on the sofa after arguing with Mum and Dad because I was drunk and my emotions all came out, so I'd sometimes end up telling him my depressing outlook on life, which was 'Don't try to do anything or be anyone, because everyone will just rip it away from you.'

He was also usually around when Mum or Dad would approach me whilst I cried, asking me, 'What happened to you Robyn? Why do you hate yourself so much?'

I felt bad about exposing my youngest brother, Jed, to the depressing side of life, because he was not old enough to have to think about it, but in a way it brought us closer as siblings since he'd always come straight to me with things that he couldn't tell Mum or Dad. I remember taking him out for the day with my friends to an abandoned house, as he'd had a shitty birthday because his friends had ditched him and were bullying him. I made him stand outside the shop as we stole spray paint on the way, making sure that if we were caught then he wouldn't be in any trouble. I introduced him to some of my other friends who acted extra nice towards him and I know he had fun spray painting and setting fire to the house (accidently) with us. I know it was the wrong sort of fun to be introducing him to, but the happiness in his eyes made me feel proud to be his older sister. At the end of the day when we were walking home, he looked at me and said, 'Thanks for today, Robyn, this was the best day ever!'

I found that most of my siblings came to me with their problems before approaching Mum or Dad, as they felt I acted so rebellious that maybe I knew the answers to their problems, which they couldn't tell Mum or Dad for fear of being in trouble. I was still on tag the day I took Jed out to cause havoc, but I'd managed to see some of my friends, including Danielle, before I went home. I didn't like being home in the evenings because I felt uncomfortable around Mum and Dad, as I was treading on eggshells constantly, so I spent most of my time alone in my bedroom, which never helped my depression. I ended up overdosing on my Prozac, which I was taking for depression, as it made me feel more suicidal than ever before, but my YOT worker found out because I was acting strange in our meeting, and she called for an ambulance as soon as she knew.

They wired my tag up to the hospital, which meant I couldn't leave when all I wanted to do was go home. If I absconded from hospital, my tag alarm would go off as it did at home if I was out past 7pm and I would go to prison as I was on my final warning with the courts. Dad didn't bother visiting me and Mum only stayed for a short while, so I was left crying once again in a hospital bed. When I got out of hospital, it was only a few weeks until my sixteenth birthday, but my excitement was almost non-existent because although I would have lots of friends round my house, Danielle couldn't be there because Mum and Dad didn't know I still saw her. On top of that, I couldn't do any drugs, and all I wanted was a nice gram of coke, but I was left with alcohol and cannabis, which only made me gain weight. My bulimia was extremely bad at this time because I was drinking so heavily and would binge on anything I fancied at night, as I'd be inside the house when I was hungry from alcohol. When I was outside drinking, there would be no food around so by the time I sobered up or got home, I would no longer be hungry.

Mum was in a bad way at this time because she'd had a horse-riding accident just after my birthday, where she broke two vertebrae' in her back as well as fracturing both sides of her pelvis and one knee. She'd done amazingly well with her weight loss and had lost over 110kg (238lb), so was finally able to ride a horse for the first time in years. It was so awful the day she had her accident because she'd been dreaming of horse-riding for so long whilst working so hard to lose weight, only to be thrown off by an ill-trained horse at a riding stable. I remember the tears filling my eyes as Dad put down the phone and told me, 'Mum's had a horse-riding accident... She's just been air lifted to hospital...'

I froze in shock for a moment before asking, 'Is she going to be alright?'

Dad replied, 'I don't know... The doctors won't tell us anything, it's probably best we just get over there.'

I could barely speak because I was terrified at the thought of losing Mum, but I knew I had to stay strong for the rest of the family. It was around 2pm so Jake, Jed and Ashleigh were still at school. Callie had moved out by this point but she was still called by the hospital who informed her of the situation. When we arrived, Mum was lying in a bed with a head splint strapped to her head and neck, keeping it in position, as they suspected a spinal injury. There was still grass and mud in her hair, which was all tangled up, and she looked terrified, but was trying to put a brave face on for me and Dad. I felt tears filling my eyes but I quickly hid them away and forced myself not to cry, so that Mum wouldn't worry. I hugged her gently because I was scared of hurting her, as I didn't know how many broken bones she had. I could tell it was bad as she was not moving and was very drugged up on painkillers, so I kissed her on the forehead before leaving Dad with her and walking home to look after my siblings who'd be arriving home from school shortly.

I was scared, but didn't let Jake or Jed know, as I explained to them briefly what had happened, but that Mum seemed OK. I told Ashleigh the truth, that the doctors didn't know if Mum would be paralysed from the neck down or not, at which point we both started crying. I told her it would be OK and Mum would be home soon, but I knew deep down that I was terrified of what could happen to Mum. I cooked dinner and did all the housework whilst Dad was in the hospital with Mum, running the house and playing Mum whilst she wasn't home. I enjoyed this, because although it was for a scary reason, it felt good to know that

I was helping my family and Dad was grateful for how mature I acted when they really needed me. Dad eventually came home in the evening and drove Ashleigh and the boys to the hospital to visit Mum, to see that she was OK and to tell Mum they loved her. I stayed home because I was on tag, which upset me because I lost out on seeing Mum.

I felt extremely sorry for Dad after Mum's accident because he was already grieving for his mother who was slowly dying of cancer, but now he was also faced with the thought of losing Mum. I felt guilty about Nan because although it was out of my control, she knew about what the rape and drug incidents that had led to me being in trouble with the police. Both my parents had relatives of some sort who'd been to prison or were there now, so the reality of what could happen to me was stressing everyone out. I felt guilty for smoking because Dad's parents both smoked ridiculous amounts throughout their entire lives and now Nan had terminal cancer as a result. Because of this, I thought it was extremely disrespectful towards Nan for me to continue to smoke, but I was addicted and so depressed all the time that I couldn't help it.

CHAPTER 23

Her Majesty's Prison

When Mum came home after almost a week, she spent two weeks bedbound in a bed which Dad had set up in the front room. There was a wheelchair to get her from the bed to the toilet and Dad became her twenty-four-hour carer. Dad was also running the house most of the time as I was bad at cooking and my brothers refused to tidy up after themselves, so he became easily aggravated and irritable. I kept my distance from him most of the time but would try to help out as much as I could, so we stayed close even though my depression was driving me further and further away from my entire family.

Mid-November my tag was taken off and I was finally free to go out at night, but this caused a lot of stress for Mum and Dad as they were constantly worrying about what I got up to on the Totland Estate. They knew the estate was rough and the people I was hanging out with probably weren't the best of influences, but I denied taking drugs any time I was questioned and continued to do as I pleased. One night I was round at Danielle's house and told her about the morphine my mum had been given for her back after the accident, and that since she was almost fully recovered, I had thought it would be OK for me to take it as long as she didn't need it. It was Danielle's idea originally but when she saw the state I was in after drinking the entire 600ml bottle, she told me there was no way she would try it. It tasted like a mix between Calpol and vodka, with the effects being similar to heroin… I felt as high as if I'd smoked a whole bag of weed, but at the same time my heart was racing fast as though I'd taken cocaine. My eyes were so big they were bulging out of my skull but at the same time I couldn't open them, unlike my mouth, which I couldn't close. My body felt paralysed but at the same time I wanted to keep moving because I was experiencing an extreme adrenaline rush, which quickly turned to sickness as I started vomiting. I made it to the end of Danielle's back garden before I puked up, but I still felt too ill to clean it up.

Danielle's mum took one look at me and asked if I was OK, before suggesting I slept on their sofa until I was sober enough to go home. She was used to seeing Danielle and me overdose many times on cannabis, but this was new and she knew I'd taken something stronger. I openly informed her about the morphine I'd taken, so she knew how to look after me, since different drugs produce different side-effects with overdose. I no longer enjoyed the buzz and wanted it to end, but I knew from experience that the only thing I could do was wait it out. I hadn't eaten for two days as I'd been out with Danielle, so that made the effects worse, as the morphine was the only thing inside my stomach. Looking back now I probably should have gone to hospital, but I was unaware at the time of how dangerous overdoses were.

After sobering up enough to walk home, I said goodnight to Danielle and her parents before making my way home. It was late when I walked through the front door and Dad was still up, watching TV on his own. He immediately started shouting at me, asking where I'd been and why I hadn't called home. He was angry at me because my YOT worker had been to the house searching for me, as I was supposed to attend a meeting with her. She'd told Dad to tell me that I was down to start a group counselling course at a women's prison in Woking, which started the next day, and my attendance was compulsory. I hated having to abide by stupid rules on my court order, but I knew if I didn't then I'd end up going to prison, which was far worse than silly little meetings. I was actually looking forward to the counselling course as I thought it would be interesting to meet some inmates and hear their stories, so I apologized to dad before heading up to bed and falling asleep.

My YOT worker had arranged for a taxi to take me to HMP in Woking, directly from my house. I did my make-up and hair before packing a small bag with cigarettes and my phone. I knew we probably wouldn't be allowed to bring cigarettes into the prison, but I wanted to test the metal detectors to see if a lighter would show up or not, as I could sneak a cigarette in if I had a lighter too. When I arrived at the prison I was greeted by six other girls who were on the course because they'd been in trouble like me, so we soon became friends as we understandably had a lot in common. The prison was a large building with white walls and thirty-foot fences with barbed wire on top, covering the perimeter to stop inmates escaping. The entrance gates were black metal bars, which appeared intimidating to outsiders, so I couldn't imagine how scary it would feel for inmates arriving for the first time.

Two prison officers greeted us at the gates, which they opened with a thick, metal key, before walking us towards a second set of gates once the first ones had been locked. Through the second gates we were directed to the entrance reception, where we were searched one by one before walking through a metal detector. My lighter was hidden in my bra but I kept my cigarettes inside my bag, which I openly admitted, so that if I was caught bringing in a lighter I could simply say that I forgot to take it out of my bra. The alarm didn't go off, but I was searched a second time because the sniffer dog took a suspicious interest in my shoes. The shoes I was wearing had never been used to hide drugs, but I had worn them around the house, which was always filled with dogs as Mum had started a doggy day-care business. Of course the usual excuse for anyone being sniffed out by a dog was that they had a dog of their own, so the officers didn't believe me until they'd searched my shoes themselves.

We walked through the prison gardens to a shed-like room, which was where the prisoners taking part in the course were waiting. They were sitting in a circle of chairs with a space between each inmate, where the other girls and I would sit. I smiled politely as we shook each other's hand one by one, before sitting back down. The instructors of the course asked us to introduce ourselves and say why we were there, before playing some team games to get us all used to each other. The first game we played was 'Guess the Crime', in which point we were asked to guess what crimes each inmate was in prison for. This proved fairly fun as the youths like me didn't want to be rude or judgemental, but at the same time wanted to guess correctly. Most of the crimes we guessed were petty, such as shoplifting, which we wrote on a card we had each been handed. When the inmates held their own cards up with the crimes they were really in there for, it was somewhat shocking, as all but one of them were in for murder. One of the girls who had been put on the course like me said to the inmates, 'But you don't look like murderers,' to which the inmates replied, 'How can you tell what a murderer looks like?'

I was stunned... All of these inmates were pretty, young and appeared so normal, unlike the crazy psychopath you'd expect a murderer to look like. I knew these women were dangerous people, but I couldn't help but feel sorry for them, thinking they must have had some awful things happen to them to cause them to murder someone. As we got to know each other more and more over the next few sessions, which were once a week, we learned the stories of these women who were locked up for such horrific crimes. One of the inmates, who was called Katy, had been locked up for stabbing a neighbour during an argument that started over a parking space. The knife had gone straight through his heart and killed him almost instantly. When hearing the story of the crime on its own, Katy definitely sounded like a psychopath. However, when she told me her life story, I felt so awful for the things she had gone through that I just wanted to hug her tight and tell her everything would be OK.

She told me about her childhood, which was full of abuse and neglect by her mother, who eventually chose an abusive boyfriend over her daughter. So, at only six years of age, Katy went to live with her father, who never showed her any love. She started taking drugs when she was nine, and at fourteen years old painted her entire bedroom black. Her dad went ballistic and when she came out as transsexual less than a week later, he put her into care, so she ran away to London. She then met a drug dealer who sold her into sex trafficking, before kidnapping her aged sixteen and taking her to his home country of Barbados. He beat her in front of his family, who didn't speak English, then raped her at gunpoint before forcing her to keep the baby. She was eventually allowed back to the UK but was forced to live with him, being abused on a daily basis whilst she tried to bring up her son.

She gave birth to a second child three years later, who sadly died of cancer aged just five. The drug dealer, who was now her husband, had been beating her and threatening her with a knife when a neighbour parked outside her house. She had nothing left, nothing of her own except the small parking space outside her house. When the neighbour refused to move his car, she ran inside and picked up a kitchen knife... Without warning, she stabbed him in the heart and let out a huge scream as she mentally released all the pain that had built up inside her. She didn't want to take an innocent life but she knew it was him or her, and she felt she had no other way to release the pain she suffered as a result of the abuse.

After being convicted and locked up for murder, she was forced to put her son into care. He eventually committed suicide aged thirteen by hanging himself on a shower curtain in a foster home. Katy was not allowed to attend his funeral and now lives with the guilt of her son's death, which hurt her more than any other pain she'd suffered in her short life. As I made my way around the room, speaking to the rest of the inmates, it seemed they had all had terrible lives full of abuse and neglect. One inmate had been raped by her stepfather whilst her mother protected her sisters in a separate room, allowing her to be raped and beaten from the age of five.

Some of them had been gang-raped and most of them had been abused, and it seemed the only real difference between us was that my parents were not at fault for my abuse. I was angry about what Drew and James had got away with, but they were not in my life now, which meant I took it out on my parents by taking drugs and getting angry with them. I got arrested so I'd have someone to fight, whilst I cried alone at the end of it all. The more I thought about it, the more I had in common with these women, which was why their stories really hit home, because they'd had much worse lives than mine although at the same time our lives were very similar. When I'd started the house fire over Kennedy and the drugs, I was searching for release from all the pain I'd suffered through years of abuse.

The murders these women had committed were of innocent lives, but the fact that all of them were searching for release meant that the small arguments which resulted in each murder could well have well been mine. The only difference between my crime and theirs was that mine didn't actually kill anyone, so I felt relieved to know how lucky I was to still be free. However, at the same time it made me feel guilty, because these women would never get a second chance like I had, and for the first time, I truly wanted to change, as I felt I needed to turn my life around out of respect for them.

It was sad saying goodbye on the last counselling session at the prison because I'd met some truly inspirational people and I knew we'd never see each other again. I brought in a Christmas card for each of them and felt touched when I received the card they'd written for me, which had so much writing inside that it covered the entire card. There was a small message written from each inmate, who wished me luck for the future as they thought I deserved to be happy. One of the messages read, 'Dear Robyn, it was great meeting you and a privilege getting to know you. I hope one day you'll be able to see all the amazing things others see in you and I wish you all the best for the future. Good luck, I'll never forget you! Love from Katy.'

I cried as we said our final goodbyes and walked out of the prison. I went home to my family and didn't touch drugs until after Christmas, as I truly wanted to turn myself around before New Year, but that was when everything changed... After seeing the lives lived by the women inside prison, I honestly didn't want to end up like them. However, temptation got the better of me and on Boxing Day that year, I was back at Totland Estate with Danielle, who introduced me to yet another new drug.

CHAPTER 24

Meth

After walking from Danielle's house to an empty field behind some trees, Danielle pulled out a small bag of yellowish-white crystal shards. She took a CD case from her bag and tipped some of the shards out, before crushing them with a bank card and some paper. She then pointed to the powder she had crushed and said, 'This is Meth… It's not been around for long but it's amazing and you have to try it!'

I watched her face twitch as she snorted her first line, struggling not to gag as it tasted so foul. I snorted the line she'd racked up for me and gagged it back to swallow it as fast as I could, as it tasted worse than anything I had ever imagined. Within seconds I started feeling a rush, which felt like a mix between cocaine and ecstasy. Danielle then pulled out a second bag of Meth, which she handed to me, and said, 'Merry Christmas, Robyn.'

I was amazed at how fast the rush kicked in, but also at how long it lasted. I knew it was wrong to accept the gift she'd given me, but as soon as the Meth kicked in I forgot all about wanting to change, as all I could think about was how great I felt. I felt an intense love for those around me, as if I would take a bullet for any stranger who stood next to me. My eyes began to shake uncontrollably and I was unable to focus on anything as my vision became blurry. My heart was beating wildly fast as though I'd taken speed, which also meant I was unable to stop moving. After an hour of talking non-stop nonsense, we snorted another line each before heading out for a walk around the estate. We then continued to spend the night how we usually would when we'd taken drugs, except I still intended to arrive home on time as it was Christmas and I didn't want to upset Mum or Dad.

After walking around all evening, high on Meth, I said goodbye to Danielle and the rest of my friends before heading home around 10pm. We had finished Danielle's bag of Meth but there was still over a gram left of mine, so I continued to rack up lines which I snorted alone throughout my walk home. I stayed in the shadows, using every bush or fenced-off area as a hiding place to snort Meth. By the time I arrived home I was completely out of it but I still knew I could not be seen by anyone, so I snuck past Dad, who was still awake downstairs, as I ran straight up to my bedroom.

I opened my window, which was directly above my bed, before switching a fan on beside the open window to let the cold air into my room. I was sweating heavily as my heart was beating faster than any drug had ever made it beat before, but that still did not deter me from racking up more lines in my bedroom as soon as I was certain everyone else in the house was asleep. I opened a CD case from my bedroom drawer and threw away the inside casing and CD, leaving only a clear, plastic case, which I would use to rack up on before storing all of my drug paraphernalia inside it.

I sat on the side of my bed, and poured out some of the Meth, which I then crushed and separated into lines ready to snort. As I checked one last time to make sure everyone was asleep, I closed my eyes and held my breath to ensure I heard any sound that might indicate someone was awake. All I heard was silence, so I lowered my face down to the CD case and began to snort. My nose hurt because I'd been snorting since I'd been out with Danielle, hours ago, so I pushed the rolled up ten pound note as far up my nose as it would go to avoid the Meth coming into contact with the rest of my nostril, which was burning. I snorted one line as fast as I could, before pushing the snort up my other nostril and snorting a second line. I knew I had to gag it back and swallow it before I'd feel the rush, but doing so would inevitably wake someone up with the noise.

Suddenly I looked up at my window, which was still wide open... I thought that if I stuck my head out of it, no sound I made would be heard inside the house and so I began to make my way towards it. I stood up on top of my bed and leant right out of the window, holding onto the frame to stop me slipping on the roof tiles, which were wet from melted ice. I closed my eyes and brought my hands up to my face in an upwards arrow shape, before placing them over my nose and blocking my nostrils. I gagged back as far as I could, before swallowing the foulest-tasting drug I'd ever swallowed. As with every line I snorted that night, I fought not to vomit and managed to swallow every bit of Meth that didn't end up directly in my brain from my nose. I was too intoxicated by 3am to lie still in my bed, so I started pacing around my bedroom whilst listening to music with headphones. I wanted to sit on the edge of my window as I was effectively on the roof, which was the coldest place at night, but I almost fell out of it because I was too high to balance. My feet made too much noise walking around the laminate floor when I climbed back inside so I wore socks and walked heel to toe, so that I didn't make a sound.

I eventually ran out of Meth around 4am, which felt awful because I was hitting a come-down but couldn't sleep, so I lay in bed crying until I was sober enough to fall asleep. The next day I went back out to Totland to meet Danielle, who had bought more Meth. We ended up snorting Meth every single day for two weeks, sharing one to four grams between the two of us. We hung out with a large group of friends who also started taking Meth and we'd roam the streets all night getting out of our minds, chipping in five or ten pounds each to buy as much Meth as we could. If I couldn't sneak out past Mum and Dad on the lie that I was sleeping at someone else's house, I'd simply take Meth home and snort it all night alone in my bedroom. When I was allowed out, I would meet straight up with Danielle, who'd take me to meet different dealers to see who we could get the best deal from.

We stopped taking it so much during the week once our friends had gone back to college and work after the Christmas holiday, but we still met up with everyone at the weekends and would party on Meth, cannabis and alcohol. I started searching for a job as I needed money to buy Meth, but it was difficult because I was not of legal age to work as I was technically supposed to be in school for another year. I eventually found a leaflet distribution job which only paid thirty pounds per day, but that meant I could make over two hundred pounds in a week if I worked every day.

When I started the job in January, I was unaware of just how hard walking all day was. I'd end up with blisters on my feet from walking five to seven hours every day, but I soon got used to it and it was worth it to buy a huge bag of Meth at the end of the week. I didn't see my drug use as an addiction at that point because I was only using it some weekends, but by late February I was using it almost every single weekend and I began to lose track of how much I was taking.

Mum and Dad had started to guess something was up because over those first few months of that year they began to notice changes in me. I became extremely secretive and distant from my family and as soon as I was on first-name terms with Meth dealers myself, I no longer relied on Danielle to get hold of it for me. I'd still hang out with her and many others who I'd became close to on the Totland Estate, but when we were all high on Meth I found it hard to get along with everyone as the drugs would always cause fights. Because I worked for my money, I could always afford two or three times the amount of Meth that my friends could, so they'd become bitchy towards me once I stopped sharing after my first gram or two. My tolerance was becoming much higher than theirs because I always took significantly more Meth than them, so I found it harder to feel a rush, as I no longer felt high from just a few lines. My friends on the other hand would share a few grams between them and that was enough to keep them all out of their minds for an entire night, so they thought I was being selfish when I refused to share more than two grams.

I suppose it started becoming a real problem when my weekends would spill into the week, leaving me unable to get through the day without taking Meth. I would stay out all night, walking through the streets with Danielle and the rest of our friends, before walking to work for 7am the next morning. I would then walk around until 4pm delivering leaflets, only to walk four miles home before heading back out to do the same the next night. As I never ate when I was high, I began to lose weight from all the walking, which my parents noticed as another sign that I was taking drugs.

I also started acting extremely strange as I'd start hallucinating from lack of sleep, which would drive me crazy. When I'd been awake for three days, I'd usually start losing touch with sanity as I began losing the ability to distinguish reality from illusion. I started seeing shadowed figures in the corner of my eyes, as well as hearing insects buzzing around which would terrify me. One night I was hallucinating so vividly that I thought someone was standing on the roof of my house, so I climbed out of my window and onto the roof with a knife. When I got up there I couldn't see anyone but could still hear footsteps, as though someone was standing right behind me. When I eventually climbed back through my window and into my bedroom, all I could see were flies the size of footballs that buzzed constantly as they flew towards me. That hallucination would occur often and although I began to realize it wasn't real, the giant flies would never disappear unless I closed my eyes and forced myself to ignore them.

When I eventually got to sleep after being on Meth for days, Dad would enter my room and shout at me to wake up. He knew I was on some kind of drug as my behaviour and sleeping patterns were so erratic, but without proof he was simply left arguing about it. Now that I could buy drugs without Danielle, I started taking drugs at home more often.

I hated being around people when I was high on Meth anyway, because I couldn't communicate with anyone as my short-term memory would reduce to around three seconds, which made it impossible to say or hear more than five words without completely forgetting what was said. If I tried to talk I would barely get three words out, before I suddenly forgot where I was and what I was doing. I would then repeat that process like a goldfish, for as long as I was high, which left me with no sense of time since I was taking Meth almost every day.

One evening I was sitting at home in my bedroom, waiting for everyone to go to sleep so I could start racking up Meth. I never usually snorted it before 11pm as that's when my family generally went to bed, but for some reason I felt cheeky and began to rack up around 10pm. Mum had come up to the bathroom, which was beside my bedroom, when she walked in on me sitting opposite a CD case with five lines of Meth on top of it. I panicked but knew I had to stay calm, so I quickly came up with a plan to prevent her from seeing the drugs.

As the CD case was on top of a hardback book, I picked up another book the same size and placed it directly on top of the CD case, whilst keeping eye contact with Mum to make sure her eyes looked nowhere else. I then picked up the two books together with the CD case in between them, before moving them to the other side of the room and placing them down on the floor as I sat in front of them. Mum seemed only slightly suspicious because my eyes were big with dilated pupils, but apart from that I went unnoticed and she soon left my room to use the bathroom.

As soon as my door was closed I picked up the book and scraped the Meth back onto the CD case and into five neat lines, which I snorted one after the other before hiding the CD case under my bed. The sound of the bath running was enough to drown out the sound my nose made when I gagged the Meth back to swallow, but I struggled to keep quiet when my nose started bleeding. I rarely had nose bleeds up until this point as I'd constantly switch nostrils when I snorted Meth, but this time I'd been high on the stuff for three full days and nights. This was my fourth night and my nose had become red and swollen, due to the Meth having burnt off the skin inside my nose. I was scared at first as I'd never induced this amount of blood before, but I lay down on my bed and let the blood drip onto my sheets until I stopped bleeding. I was so intoxicated I could barely move as my heart was beating so fast, so I stayed in bed and pretended to be asleep until everyone else was.

I was so high now that no more Meth could physically make me any higher, but I continued to snort lines any time I felt it wearing off. If my nose bled I'd simply push the snort up further than where the blood was coming from, so I'd usually end up tasting my own blood when I gagged it all back. I couldn't close my eyes as the Meth was stopping me from even blinking, so my eyes soon became dry and red. My face was ghostly pale and my eyes already had huge dark circles around them but no matter how obvious it was that I'd taken drugs, I still refused to admit it when Ashleigh caught sight of me. At around five o'clock in the morning, I had woken her up by crying and talking to myself in the bathroom, which was right beside her room. I'd been hallucinating beforehand, lying on my bed, which I thought was no longer inside my room.

When I looked around the room, I thought I was outside with some of my old friends from Frimley. I recognized a field which was part of a children's park, along with friends I remembered from the Ansel Estate. I had run out of drugs by this point and could see my old friends as clearly as if they were standing right next to me, when suddenly they took my drugs and told me it was for my own good. One of them said, 'We're just looking out for you because you're our friend and we don't want you taking drugs. We've thrown them into the lake.'

With that I screamed, demanding they get my drugs back as they had no right to take them. My heart was beating fast with anger, which caused me an adrenaline rush as though I was about to fight. I hit one of my friends in the face, knocking them unconscious on the ground. I then reached down to see if they were OK as I started to panic, thinking I'd murdered them because they were now lying in a pool of blood. As I held the lifeless body in my arms, I closed my eyes and rocked my friend… I suddenly felt a cold shiver rinse through my entire body, as I felt the weight of my friend turn to dust. When I opened my eyes, I was no longer at the park. I began to realize I was kneeling on the floor in my bedroom, cradling a blanket which had been a dead body mere seconds ago. I opened my mouth to scream but no sound came out. Probably just as well I suppose, as it was almost 5am by this point and I remembered I could not make a sound or I'd wake someone up.

I was now petrified, because I didn't know if what was happening now was a hallucination too… How could that not have been real? I felt the weight of my friend's body, dying in my arms as I cried. I'd seen them all face to face and heard their voices when they spoke as they stood right next to me.

My heart was beating so fast I thought I might have a heart attack if I didn't stop moving soon, but I had to run to the bathroom to check if I was really there when I looked into the mirror. I knew I probably wouldn't have a reflection if this was not real, but when I saw my face in the mirror I felt more scared than ever. My pulse rate was too fast to put down in words but I knew I had to stop it somehow, so I lay down on the floor to ensure my heart was only beating at the slowest pace it could to keep me alive. It was then that Ashleigh walked into the bathroom, after waking up from all the noise I'd made whilst I'd been hallucinating. She looked down at my body, which was frozen still as I struggled to breathe. My nose was covered in dry blood, which also covered half of my face, and she asked, 'Robyn? Are you OK?'

Her voice was quiet and croaky as she'd been woken up after being asleep all night, but she didn't seem angry with me. I told her in a shaky voice from all the drugs, 'I'm fine, sorry I woke you up.'

She knew I was not OK, but she'd seen me in this state before so I think she assumed I'd be fine if she went back to bed. I didn't expect her to help me as I knew seeing me in that state would have upset her, but I felt extremely guilty as I listened to see if she cried when she went back to bed. She had school the next day so I didn't bother trying to keep her up, but I wondered if my drug use was affecting her more than she let me know.

When she entered the bathroom a second time, she told me to get up as it was now 7am and she was getting ready for school, which meant Mum and Dad would be waking up soon. I crawled into bed after throwing up bile, feeling sick from all the Meth I'd snorted over the past four days without eating a thing. I drank some water, which was a struggle because my throat was swollen from swallowing Meth, but I knew I was severely dehydrated so had to force it down if I wanted to feel better. I'd barely been asleep for an hour when Dad walked into my room, demanding that I got up and either went to work or did chores around the house. I didn't want to go to work but staying in the house around Mum and Dad would be even worse, so I told him I'd walk to work after having a shower. Dad didn't trust me to walk to work as it was over four miles away and he knew I'd be late, so he offered me a lift and told me to hurry up. When I got into the car we barely spoke, but I could feel the tension between us; he stared straight ahead and didn't bother asking questions.

When I arrived at work I waited until Dad had driven off before walking away down an alleyway, with no intentions other than finding somewhere to sleep. I'd packed my bag with water, cigarettes and a blanket, instead of my work things, as I knew I would not need them. After walking for almost an hour through roads I was unfamiliar with, I made my way through a wooded area before realizing I was near the Totland Estate. There was a small bench hidden behind some houses that backed onto the woods, so I checked to make sure no one was looking before taking my blanket out and proceeding to sleep. There were enough bushes and trees to hide me from public view, so I set an alarm on my phone for 3pm and slept until it woke me up. Any normal person would never have been able to fall asleep where I was, but I had been awake for almost one hundred hours so I was able to fall asleep almost instantly.

When I woke up, I lit a cigarette before putting the blanket back inside my bag and walking to Danielle's house, which wasn't too far away. I had to take the back roads once I was out of the woods as I knew my boss would be driving around this time of day, so I kept my hood up and looked straight ahead as I walked through the estate. When I arrived at Danielle's house I was greeted by her father who was sitting inside smoking weed, whilst shouting to Danielle who was upstairs in her bedroom. She soon came down and asked if I was OK as my face was extremely pale, but I told her I'd been up all night and asleep all day in the woods. She said I should have gone straight to hers as I could have slept in her bed, but I knew her parents would have known I'd been snorting drugs all night. Her mum made me something to eat after testing my blood-sugar levels with her diabetes equipment, which said my blood sugar was almost non-existent.

As I was coming down heavily from all the Meth I'd taken, Danielle was not surprised when I started crying in her bedroom. She hugged me and told me everything would be OK, but we needed to cut down on the Meth. I knew this was the sole reason for my whole world slowly falling apart around me, but the thought of going without it scared me beyond belief. I knew I had to do something about it, but I wasn't ready to quit. Danielle felt the same way I did, so it was nice to have a friend going through the same thing as me, as we could get through it together. We soon agreed that we would lay off the Meth for a while, which meant we could still take it again once we'd been sober for long enough. This comforted both of us because although it was going to be tough quitting the drugs, we knew it wasn't forever and we were just laying off it for a while. This stopped me panicking so much about what I'd do without it, as it wouldn't be too long until I could take it again. I just had to wait a few weeks.

CHAPTER 25

Nothing Changes

After spending the rest of the day with Danielle, I made my way home around 10pm. I hadn't taken any drugs apart from alcohol and weed as they helped me to cope with my come-down, but Mum and Dad saw nothing except a drugged-up waste-of-space daughter when I walked in. Mum started shouting first, asking where I'd been all day as she'd made a trip to my work to see if I was there. Dad was also shouting at me, telling me I looked a complete state and had clearly taken drugs. I started crying as I knew what to expect, since this argument happened so often, except this time I was trying to quit drugs, so felt extremely offended when both of them accused me of taking drugs that day.

I told them to leave me alone as I ran upstairs to my bedroom, but they followed me up and I was finding it increasingly difficult not to react aggressively. Before they made it to my bedroom I managed to keep my door shut for long enough to check a small box which I kept hidden under my bed, containing all my drug paraphernalia. There were also empty drug bags and a few lighters in the box, one of which belonged to my Nan, who was dying of cancer. I kissed the lighter then put it back in the box which I placed under my bed, before standing up and bracing myself for the argument that was about to take place.

Dad stepped towards me as he screamed in my face, 'I don't know what's wrong with you but you need to stop this, right now! I've had enough of everything with you!'

I was so angry and upset when I shouted back whilst packing my things in front of him and Mum sat on my bed and cried. She looked up at me and said, 'You're only starting an argument so that you can go out and take drugs! Why don't you just stop it?'

I pushed past them both and ran down the stairs, before standing outside the front of the house and lighting a cigarette. Dad followed me out and called me over to him, saying he wanted to speak to me. I thought maybe he'd be apologizing, telling me I didn't have to go as we could work things out. However when he grabbed hold of the hoodie that was wrapped around my neck, I knew he was not apologizing. He pointed inside through the front window with his other hand, as he looked me in the eyes and said, 'Your mum's dying in there… That's your fault. Ashleigh's upstairs slitting her wrists again and that's your fault…'

He then looked at me with tears in his eyes as he whispered with pure hatred in his voice, 'I'm going to slash my throat tonight… And that's your fault… Don't you see what you're doing to this family? Fuck off and take your drugs, because you love them more than us!'

I cried as he let go of my hoodie and walked back inside. My tears suddenly turned to anger as I ran down the street, smashing every single fence and car that I saw on my way. No one dared to stop me and someone called the police, but I barely even noticed because of the pain I felt inside of me. I knew I could not go home, but I didn't want to be with Danielle or anyone from the Totland Estate because I knew I'd end up taking drugs. Instead I decided to walk around until I found somewhere to calm down and sleep. I'd been walking on the main road for around twenty minutes when I came across a motorway bridge, which I decided to sit under, as I would be able to throw myself in front of a truck if I saw one drive past.

I reached into my pocket to pull out a fifty-gram pouch of tobacco, but I couldn't smoke any of it because I'd lost my papers, which I needed to roll with. I walked back the way I'd come but there was no sign of them, so I decided to walk to a twenty-four-hour supermarket two miles away. By the time I got there it was raining, but my bag of clothes was watertight as I always packed everything into individual plastic bags, so that if I got wet I would still have dry clothes to change into. I entered the supermarket around midnight, but I was too young to buy tobacco papers, so I reluctantly walked back outside and approached strangers, asking them to go in for me. I was beginning to lose hope after asking more than five people who all refused, but one man took an interest in me and asked what I needed. He was tall and slender, twenty-five years old at most, and spoke with a strong Australian accent. I had asked people politely if they'd go into the shop for me but no one had wanted to help me so far, so I decided to tell him how just how much I needed the tobacco papers. I looked up at him- he was slightly taller than me- as I asked, 'Excuse me sir, can I ask a favour please? It'll only take a minute.'

He stopped walking and asked me what was wrong, so I told him, 'I have nowhere to stay tonight. I have tobacco to get me through the night but I can't smoke it as I haven't any papers and I'm not old enough to buy any. Would you please go into the shop for me and you can keep the change?'

I reached into my pocket and pulled out a two-pound coin, but he refused to take it from me. He seemed shocked about my situation as he asked if there was anywhere I could sleep that night or anyone I could go to, but I told him there was no one. He politely said, 'Keep your money. I'll go into the shop for you. I don't smoke so you'll have to tell me what to buy.'

I explained to him that there was a cigarette counter where he'd have to ask for papers, before pointing it out to him as he walked inside. I was beginning to think he wouldn't return as he took longer than I first expected, but he soon walked out with two packs of tobacco papers, which he handed to me outside the shop. I thanked him before walking away, grateful for this stranger who had acted so kindly towards me. It was 1am by this point and as I had nowhere to go, I sat outside the shop against a brick wall underneath a glass roof that provided shelter from the rain. After smoking a cigarette, I rubbed my hands together and breathed down my hoodie to try and keep warm. It was below freezing temperatures now as the night had set in, so I chain-smoked to try and deal with the cold. I was now sitting behind the supermarket as I'd left the front entrance because I didn't feel safe out in the open, but my quiet spot was soon discovered by staff who had walked out to smoke. A small lady in her late fifties approached me and asked if I was alright, before sitting next to me and offering me a cigarette. I told her I'd had a fight with my parents and I had nowhere to go, when she asked me, 'Would you like a drink? I can get you a cup of tea if you like?'

I cried at the thought of a hot cup of tea because I was so cold and knew I needed something to warm me up. She soon brought out a cup of tea and I thanked her, before heading out for a walk to warm up. It was almost 4am when I left the supermarket, at which point I was so cold I could barely breathe. My legs ached and I was desperate to sleep but I knew if I sat still any longer, I would probably go into hypothermia. I walked to a skatepark nearby and saw a teenager walking out from an alleyway, trying to light a cigarette with a broken lighter. I approached him and asked if he wanted to borrow mine, and then we started talking. He asked me what I was doing out so late and when I told him I was sleeping rough, he asked if I wanted to go back to his friend's house with him. He had been taking Meth with his friends before going to buy some cigarettes, but his friends were also high so probably wouldn't mind if I went back with him. I knew from experience that the reason he was acting so kind was because of the Meth, but that also meant he was genuine when he said he wanted to help me. I didn't want to get back into drugs as I had barely been clean for a day, but the thought of being warm from the drugs appealed to me and I had no choice in the circumstances I was in.

It wasn't too far of a walk and I knew where I was as the house was near Totland, so I followed him inside as he introduced me to his friends. He placed his arm around my shoulder as he held his other arm out towards his friends, who were sitting in a circle in the living room, snorting Meth. 'Hey guys? This is Robyn! I met her at the skatepark and she's got nowhere to stay tonight, so she's staying with us now.'

His friends, who were also high, took a shine to me right away and all came to hug me, before offering me a line of Meth. It sounds strange to outsiders, how strangers can be so accepting and welcoming to a homeless girl they've just met, but that's one of the side effects of drugs. I placed a snort up each nostril before holding them whilst lowering my face down to the kitchen plate where the Meth was racked up, before snorting two lines in one go and proceeding to gag back what I'd snorted. They cheered me on as they'd never seen anyone snort two lines up both nostrils at the same time before, so I immediately gained their respect as all of them were impressed. Although I felt guilty for taking drugs after I'd said I'd quit, it seemed like I had nothing to lose because Mum and Dad thought I was taking drugs anyway. Their argument that night made me think 'fuck it'; as I had nothing left, I might as well do what was expected of me.

The night went on and though I was grateful for the selfless actions of my new friends, I knew I couldn't stay with them. I left around 8am and made my way to Totland, searching for a place to sit and wait until it was late enough in the morning to knock for Danielle. I ended up waiting outside her back garden until I heard the door unlock, at which point I walked through the garden and knocked at the back door. Danielle was asleep but her dad invited me in, before sharing a spliff with me and asking if I knew anything about Danielle taking harder drugs.

I hated lying to her parents as I respected them, but I couldn't let our secret slip, so I told him I had no knowledge about her taking drugs other than cannabis. Danielle eventually woke up but was grounded, which meant she wasn't allowed out and I wasn't allowed to stay longer than a few hours. I told her what had happened and she pleaded with her parents to let me stay the night, but they wouldn't allow it as she was having her own problems. We had both taken Meth since we'd said we wouldn't, but neither of us would admit that we had a problem. This caused arguments between Danielle and her parents just like it did with me and mine, but we stuck together and refused to let it break our friendship.

Early afternoon I was told to leave, as Danielle wasn't supposed to have any friends over at all, so I thanked her parents for letting me stay the few hours I was there. Danielle hugged me and told me to stay safe, and that she would be out in a few days to see me. I tried all of my friends that day, dozens of them, trying to see if I could stay with any of them that night. However, no matter how hard I tried, no one could fix me up a place to stay. It was then that I learnt the harsh reality of real life, that no one cares, because I had all the friends in the world yet not one of them could sort me out a bed for the night. I wasn't even asking for a bed, just a mere six-foot space on the floor would have sufficed, but I gave up and roamed the streets once again to stay warm.

By the time it got dark I was already exhausted, but I knew I had to keep moving if I wanted to stay warm. I smoked the last of my tobacco pouch, which was almost finished, meaning I'd smoked almost fifty grams of tobacco in less than two days. This caused me to develop a chest infection which caused me to cough whilst suffering a severe pain in my chest, but warmth and shelter were my main priorities so I ignored the pain and kept moving.

It had just gone 3am when I decided to get going after sitting down for a short rest. I kept my phone off and only switched it on to check the time, trying to save the battery for as long as I could. I was walking from Farnborough town centre on my way to McDonalds, which was open twenty-four hours a day, when I suddenly felt anxious whilst walking down a large, empty road. It was pitch black outside with not a sound except for my footsteps, when I heard a car driving in the distance. It sounded very far away but I knew it was going fast because of the engine noise it made, so I turned around to check behind me. Sure enough there was a car approaching from a distance, so I turned around to face forwards as I continued walking.

I was approaching a junction which I needed to cross, when suddenly a gust of wind blew the woolly hat off my head. There hadn't been a single gust of wind that night but that particular one was strong enough to pull the hat off my head, which caused me to stop just as I was about to cross the road. As I crouched down to pick up my hat, the car that had been driving in the distance was now feet behind me, swerving in all directions before screeching its brakes and smashing into the metal railings at the side of the road opposite me. It was then I realized that if my hat hadn't blown off, the car would have hit me and I would probably have been killed. I didn't want to go near it but I knew I had to help the driver, as there was no one else around and I couldn't just leave him.

As I walked towards the car, which now had smoke rising out of it, I approached the driver's side and asked, 'Are you alright, mate? Can you hear me?'

I didn't receive an answer, just a few faint moans but no actual words. The driver then became fully unconscious so I ran towards a phone box opposite, calling for help by dialling 999. I told them a car had crashed and a man was lying unconscious in the driver's seat, covered in blood and possibly drunk. I then ran back over to the car, crying by this point as I knew the man was dying. I placed my hand inside the car, trying to untie his seat belt to release him from the wreckage. I tried to get a response from him, asking if he knew where he was and what had happened. I kept trying to reassure him, telling him that the fire brigade and an ambulance were on their way, but no matter how much I spoke he didn't answer… Realizing that he was showing no signs of life, I tried to call for help, but all the surrounding neighbours were asleep.

'Stay with me… Stay with me,' I kept whispering, as if maybe it would keep him alive. I didn't know what to do as I was not first-aid trained and was suffering from extreme sleep deprivation which blurred my senses, but I knew not to pull him out from the car as he could have suffered a spinal injury.

It wasn't long before all three emergency services arrived with their sirens blaring, at which point I fled as I knew I'd be taken home if they caught me. In total shock at what had happened, I looked up to the sky and whispered, 'Thank you...'

I wasn't sure who I was thanking really, but I knew something out there blew the hat off my head to stop me crossing that road. If I hadn't stopped, I would have been dead just like the driver of that car. I didn't know how I was supposed to feel, because I'd been thankful for a life which I'd wanted to end so many times prior to this night. Maybe I had a reason to be here, maybe there was hope in my situation.

I eventually went home late the next day after fainting at a bus stop due to lack of food and sleep. I didn't like arguing with my parents and I just wished that all of it would stop, but I didn't know how to end it. I called Mum with the tiny bit of battery my phone had left, after a stranger who found me unconscious demanded that I called my parents or someone I trusted to pick me up. I felt extremely awkward and uncomfortable getting into the car when Mum arrived, but I knew I had to make up with her and Dad before I lost them for good. I was crying when Mum picked me up and she was upset too, because last night had been the first year anniversary of the death of her online friend Fletcher, who passed away aged seventeen due to Cystic Fibrosis. They had met playing an online video game which Mum spent a lot of time on, but would only go online if he was playing as they became best friends. He lived out in New Zealand and Mum planned for us to go over there and visit him one day, but he died before we ever got the chance. It was then I realized that he must have saved me from the car that night, as he was the only angel who could have been in the sky to save me.

I told Mum what had happened, and though it sounded insane, she believed my story and said it must have been Fletcher who had saved me. I was still angry at Mum and Dad for letting our argument result in me sleeping rough for two days, but I was more upset by the fact that

Mum thought I'd deliberately started the argument so that I could go out and take drugs all night. I was in a lot of pain from my chest infection and asked Mum if I could take some strong painkillers, so as soon as we were home she gave me some Tramadol. I apologized to both Mum and Dad, but there was still lots of tension between us, so I stayed in my room and hardly spoke to anyone at home. Ashleigh, Jake and Jed had all been home whilst I'd been gone and like with anytime I argued with Mum or Dad, they'd heard the whole thing but had locked themselves inside their bedrooms as they tried to ignore what was going on. When I was home they didn't know how to act around me as the drugs made my behaviour unpredictable, so all of my siblings stayed away from me most of the time.

My chest started to hurt again when the Tramadol wore off so I continued to take more, but Mum refused to give me anymore after I'd taken two full packets of 250mg pills. She told me to go to the doctors if my chest was really hurting that bad, but I knew they wouldn't give me any Tramadol and I was beginning to enjoy the buzz. A few days later I decided to search the Totland Estate for Tramadol and sure enough, I found someone who was selling it. I bought two hundred pills for ten pounds and started taking them from the moment I got them, popping ten pills in one go as they were not as strong as the ones I'd been taking from Mum. I was back at work by this point but that still did not stop me taking a full pack of Tramadol as soon as I'd finished delivering my leaflets each day, which became my daily routine for the rest of the week. I'd work until four in the afternoon, delivering a thousand leaflets over six hours, before popping ten Tramadol pills and making my way home to sleep for the remainder of the day. The buzz felt like I was high from smoking weed except I didn't feel hungry, which was a huge bonus for me as I hated taking drugs that made me gain weight.

After almost a week of taking ten or twelve Tramadol pills per day, I was off work so thought I'd get high in my bedroom. I'd slept in until late as the Tramadol made me drowsy through to the next day, but I still thought I'd be OK to take more as soon as I woke up. From 11am I started taking the Tramadol, consuming over thirty pills in three hours. I thought that five of these pills were the same as taking one of the pills mum had given me the previous week, because hers were 250mg and the ones I had were only 50mg. I started to feel weak and dizzy so I soon blacked out and lay down in my bed. Ashleigh came into my room to check on me a few times, as she knew I'd been taking Tramadol and Meth. I always took my anger out on her when I was high or coming down, because I saw her as a threat to my secret. I hated the way drugs made me act out on her, but I acted without thinking when I'd taken Meth and Ashleigh always received the brunt of my violent outbursts. Whenever she left my room after I'd shouted at her, I always felt guilty and cried but I knew my only option was to stay away from her and I think that hurt her more than seeing me on drugs.

Dad came into my room at 3pm, after arguing with Mum about the state I was in. I heard him say to her downstairs, 'Where is she? I'm not letting that druggy cunt sleep all day. I'm going to wake her up right now!'

And with that he marched into my room, switching my light on and opening both of my blinds. He ripped the duvet off my bed and shouted at me to get up, telling me I had to help Mum with her dog walk. Mum's business was thriving at this point and she took the dogs out twice a day in her big blue van, so she shouted at me as she agreed with Dad that I would go on a dog walk with her. I struggled to get up because I was so high from the Tramadol, which was causing my arms and legs to feel like jelly whilst my head felt like a dead weight. I reluctantly dragged myself up and out of bed, before throwing a tracksuit on and making my way downstairs. Mum told me to hurry up as I was taking forever just walking down the stairs, but I physically couldn't walk any faster as the Tramadol was putting my body to sleep. As I crawled down the last step and sat down on the floor, Mum and Dad tried to make me stand up as they thought I was messing around to get out of dog walking. I don't remember what happened next, but my entire family remember it clearly as it was a day that will haunt them for the rest of their lives...

CHAPTER 26

Darkness

I made my way to the van and sat in the passenger seat whilst I waited for mum to pull away from the driveway. Her phone was on the dashboard in front of me and she asked me to pass it to her, but my face was looking down towards the floor and I couldn't speak. I waved my arm around in front of me, trying to grab Mum's phone. She snapped at me, 'Stop being stupid! Robyn… Robyn!'

I suddenly started fitting and Mum ran inside to shout for help. She called Dad whilst panicking at the sight of me, shouting, 'Help! Help! Someone call 999! Robyn's having a seizure!'

My youngest brother Jed, who was eleven years old, called an ambulance whilst Mum screamed and Dad cried. As he carried my lifeless body into the house, my family gathered round and watched in horror as Dad laid me on the floor in the middle of the front room. My eyes were closed and my lips were blue as he tried to resuscitate me, but he couldn't bring me back and it was only when the paramedics arrived that I began showing any signs of life. Minutes passed but for my family it must have felt like hours, before finally I took a breath on my own whilst the paramedics performed CPR. I remember opening my eyes and looking up, only to see my family gathered around me like I'd done something really bad. Dad was out of breath with tears streaming down his face and his hands tightly gripped behind his head, as he looked down at me fearing he was going to lose his child. He was obviously upset and scared but in my confused, semi-conscious state, I simply saw the look on his face as the exact same look I'd seen when we'd argued in the past. This caused me to act completely selfishly, refusing to go in the ambulance as I told everyone that I was going out to see my friends on Totland.

I could barely walk as the ambulance crew lifted me onto a bed inside the ambulance, before asking my family if they knew for certain if I'd taken any drugs. Ashleigh was closest to me as she was my twin, but was now faced with the awful decision of whether or not to tell everyone about my drug addiction. If she told the paramedics I'd taken Meth, Mum and Dad would hurt more than anything as I was slowly killing them inside. If she told them what I was really up to, I'd blame her for opening her mouth, which would cause even more resentment between us. However, if she didn't say anything, I could die and she'd feel guilty for not saving me when she had the chance, so she eventually told the paramedics, 'She's a Meth addict. She hasn't taken it for a few days but she's taken more than thirty Tramadol pills in the last three hours.'

Mum and Dad burst into tears. They were distraught to hear that I'd taken so many drugs, but at the same time they must have felt slightly relieved to know that my secret was out and they could now try to help me. I didn't see any of this, however; all I saw was my sister grassing me up and my parents accusing me of being a drug addict. I was not ready to admit I had a problem, so when I became sober enough to talk about it I simply screamed in anger as I denied there was a problem.

I was sedated for hours after being taken to hospital as they had to give me high doses of other drugs to reverse the effects which Tramadol and Meth had induced. The paramedics thanked my sister for telling them what I'd taken as it was her honesty that saved my life, because the doctors now knew exactly what the problem was and how to save me. I didn't want to lie in a hospital bed and although I was asleep most of the time, whenever I woke up I would throw a raging fit as I pulled wires and drips away from my body before being restrained by doctors and nurses. I attempted to pull the wires away from my chest, which was covered in stickers they used to monitor my heart, as well as pulling out a second drip which had been reattached to my arm after I pulled the first one out. Mum stayed by my side the entire time and I think she forgave me because I was in a confused state, unable to think straight any time I woke up, but it must have hurt her to see me in the state I was in.

When I came round properly, I started to feel an intense cloud of guilt as I began to realize the full extent to which I'd hurt my family. Mum, Dad, all my brothers and sisters, including my older sister's husband and kids, all of them were worrying about losing me. The doctors had told my parents that there was no guarantee I'd survive, as the drugs could still affect my vital organs for days after the overdose. That word also scared Mum and Dad beyond belief because not only did it prove I'd taken drugs, but if I died there was no way of knowing if I'd done it on purpose. The way I was acting inside the hospital would indicate that I had tried to commit suicide, as I was constantly battling with anyone who tried to save me. I wasn't fighting against my life, but I couldn't deal with the guilt I felt for the pain I'd caused Mum and Dad. I also felt extremely guilty for my behaviour towards Ashleigh but I also felt betrayed because she had told everyone my secret. If I'd understood fully that she'd saved my life, I would have thanked her like any decent human being… However, I was so wrapped up in my selfish little head from all the drugs, that all I could think about was getting my next fix so that I didn't have to deal with everything going on around me.

The doctors told me that if I took Meth again I'd probably die, but I couldn't cope with my depression and so that's exactly what I did as soon as I was discharged from hospital. When I arrived home after being in hospital for days, I went to my bedroom and reached under my bed for my black box full of drug paraphernalia. I had also kept the rest of my Tramadol in there, but to my horror, the box was gone. I searched my entire bedroom, tipping everything upside down in search of my drug box, but I couldn't find it anywhere, at which point I realized my lighters were gone too. It had to be Mum and Dad- who else would have taken it? Then I remembered Dad threatening me whilst we were arguing a few days before my seizure, 'You better take anything from your room that you want to keep because I'm throwing it all away.'

I cried. I was so angry and upset because Mum and Dad had invaded my privacy by raiding my bedroom, as well as stealing things which they had no right to take. I ran downstairs, furious with both of them for betraying my trust. I shouted at Dad, 'Where the fuck's my stuff?! I want it back now!'

He shouted back and told me I shouldn't have left it after he'd warned me he was going to throw my things away, which implied that he and Mum had already searched my room before taking my box, which they must have known was there. I cried as I ran to the bin outside, which was filled with rubbish bags as well as my box, which had been smashed up and soaked with rainwater alongside my drug paraphernalia and lighters. I lowered my tone of voice as I said before storming back upstairs to my bedroom, 'Nan gave me that lighter.'

I then cried as I walked back upstairs, trying not to think about anything but leaving. I knew I wasn't getting along with my parents and it wouldn't be long before they kicked me out, but I didn't care as long as I had my drugs. I had to leave that house; I just couldn't take it anymore. I wanted to get some Meth as I knew that was all I needed to cheer me up, so I began contacting different dealers, trying to get hold of my only comfort. Dad eventually walked up to my bedroom with a handful of lighters he had dug out of the bin, one of which was Nan's lighter. I thanked him but felt ever so guilty, as I knew it upset him, since he knew I was only treasuring that lighter because Nan was dying.

I eventually snuck out and bought two grams of Meth but didn't feel like taking it after everything that had happened, as I knew it would hurt Mum and Dad more than ever. Now that they knew I was taking

Meth, they found it harder to deal with me when I was high, as they knew full well I'd taken drugs. At least when they didn't know, there was still that little bit of hope left which would provide an explanation as to why I was acting strangely, without leading them to the conclusion that I was a drug addict. I was becoming more distant from my family, and once my older sister Callie found out about the drugs, she immediately banned me from all contact with my niece and nephew. I was distraught and angry because she had no right to stop me seeing them, as I didn't take Meth when I was around them, so if anything the ban would only make me use more as I didn't have a reason to stay sober.

Ashleigh and I rarely spoke to each other because when we did, we would argue over whose fault it was that the whole family was falling apart. She would constantly call me a 'skanky druggy' and say it was my fault Mum and Dad always argued, because I was the only one taking drugs and it was ruining everything. I hated her at the time but also felt guilty for hating her, because we'd always been best friends and it seemed the drugs were pulling us further and further apart. She angered me when she'd say that I was simply running away each time Dad kicked me out, because she never believed that in the heat of the moment, Dad had in fact kicked me out. She also upset me when she cried and told me to stop taking Meth, but she could barely even look at me now as I was such a mess.

One night I'd been snorting Meth in my bedroom when I dropped the bag of Meth because my hands were so shaky, and Ashleigh walked into my room and saw me attempting to pick up each crystal shard with a magnifying glass and a pair of tweezers. She laughed sarcastically with a disgusted expression on her face as she said, 'And you honestly think you don't have a problem?'

I screamed at her to 'fuck off and leave me alone,' before slamming my door shut behind her and kneeling back down to the floor to pick up the rest of the drugs that I'd dropped. Mum and Dad rarely spoke to me either because I had become ever so secretive around them, but now that my secret was out it was hard for them not to be angry with me. Any time they looked at me, all they saw was what the drugs had done to me and I think they felt guilty somewhere behind all the anger because they'd done their best as parents and look where I was now.

My hair was always greasy because I slept rough a lot and rarely had use of a shower. My lips had teeth marks cut into them from gurning whilst on drugs, which had also made my nostrils huge whilst my eyes were black due to lack of sleep. I looked completely different to the young girl who once lived behind my broken face, so it hurt my entire family to even look me in the eyes. Mum would walk into my work and plead with my boss to pay her instead of me, so that she could ration my money out to ensure I didn't spend it on drugs. My bosses refused, however, and though it meant I could still spend my money on drugs, I felt deeply upset to know how much it was hurting Mum. She would frequently ask me where my money was and if I couldn't show her a huge wad of cash when I'd been paid, she'd demand answers as to where it went, as she knew I was spending it all on Meth. Dad also went ballistic any time I was paid as he knew it was going straight up my nose, so I began spending it as soon as I was paid to make sure Mum and Dad couldn't take it from me first.

I'd stopped hanging out with friends at this point because I no longer needed them to get hold of drugs for me and I was always on a different level to them anyway, because of the sheer amount I'd take. I remembered how back at Christmas, Danielle and I would be high all day off a mere gram between us. Now it would take more than five grams to get me through each day, and I was taking Meth everywhere I went. I'd take it at home when everyone was asleep, at work all day whilst I delivered leaflets, and outside at night if I'd been arguing with Mum and Dad or if I'd simply gone out to see Danielle. Mum and Dad were running out of options, and one particular argument caused a bigger fight than ever before…

I was upstairs in my bedroom after arriving home from work on a Friday, which Mum and Dad knew was when I'd been paid. I was high on drugs when they asked me, 'Where's your money? We're going to look after it from now on. We don't want you wasting your life away with drugs anymore, so we're helping you out. Give us your money.'

I refused. I told them I was quitting and didn't need their help, though that was simply a lie to get them off my case so that I could buy drugs. My money was hidden inside the bra I was wearing and I knew they wouldn't touch me, so no matter how aggressive Mum and Dad both got I kept my cool. Dad tipped my bedroom upside down, emptying out all my cupboards and drawers in search of my cash. I laughed at them. How pathetic were they to think they could stop me taking drugs? I needed Meth for my only way out of depression and although I knew deep down that I needed to stop one day, that day was not today, and so I persisted in hiding my money. Dad grabbed me by the throat and pinned me against the wall, shouting, 'Where is it? Where is it?!'

Mum was crying, shouting at him to stop, but although his hands were tensed, he was not actually applying any pressure to my neck. I still felt threatened, however, and after losing my temper and screaming back at them, I ran out of the house past Dad, who tried everything in his power to stop me. I walked straight to Danielle's house where I met up with my old friends before buying Meth, which we shared between us as we began our night out like old times. There were over twenty of us and we'd spend the night together, partying at one of the boys' houses because his mum worked night shifts, which meant we could take drugs inside his house until she finished work at 5am. When it reached that time, we'd walk to McDonalds in pairs, to make sure we didn't attract any police attention. I'd stopped getting arrested so much by this point as I always had so many drugs on me that I knew I had to behave myself or I'd be accused of dealing, so it was merely my drug addiction that kept me away from the police.

We usually had our individual pairs within our group, and we would walk in these pairs when we were trying to lie low. We tried to stay in 'boy/girl' pairs as much as we could, so that when the police drove past they'd only see what they thought was a young couple walking back from a party. I was always paired with a boy named Jack, who held my hand as we talked continuously for the entire walk to wherever it was that we were going. He'd try to kiss me and ask if he could be my boyfriend, but I wasn't ready for any relationship or even one-night stand at sixteen because I'd never even had a boyfriend due to the sexual abuse I'd suffered as a child. Any time Jack came close, it brought back flashbacks of being in the park with James and Drew and although Jack meant no harm, I had to tell him to stop. When I was high on Meth we would spend the night together and he didn't seem to mind that I wasn't ready for sex, so he stuck by my side and told me he really liked me and just wanted to keep me happy.

One night I was at a house party on the Totland Estate where there were seven of us and four people had already got laid, so in our high and drunken states we thought it would be funny to make it six out of seven. I wasn't being peer-pressured in a physical way, but I did feel some form of psychological peer pressure pushing me to sleep with Jack. I'd never believed at first that anyone could like me in a sexual way, because all my life I'd heard nothing but hurtful comments about my body and how ugly I was. On top of this I still dressed like a boy and was sleeping rough most of the time as I argued with Mum and Dad so much, so I never made an effort with my hair or make-up. Danielle was at the party and had slept with her boyfriend, who was eight years older than her, and a girl named Jess slept with another boy at the party. They had all done it inside the house whilst we were there but I didn't want my first time to be in front of everyone, so I agreed to walk back to Jack's house with him at around 4am.

We snuck past his parents, who were asleep, as we made our way to his bedroom. I hadn't felt scared up until this point but when we got to his bed, I simply didn't know what to do. I was too uncomfortable with my body to let anyone see it, but I knew Jack cared about me and I wanted to make him happy. We stripped off and I downed half a bottle of vodka, which was beside his bed, in the hope that it would cheer me up or make the night go faster. In the end we were unable to do it properly, as he didn't know what he was doing either and I ended up lying there in pain, bleeding. I told myself in my head, 'Just wait it out. It'll be over soon.' Sure enough, it was over, so we got dressed and made our way back to the party. Jack told me he loved me and that I did amazing, so I gave him a few compliments back as you do when you're unsure of what to say. When we got to the party I ran to the bathroom and racked up three lines by myself, as I cleaned myself up before crying in a corner. All I could think about was James and Drew, how much it hurt when they forced me to do things, and how pathetic I was for not even being able to love someone who loved me. All I saw was flashbacks and I wanted to escape them so I chose the only way out I knew, which was to snort all the Meth I had as I tried to get higher than ever.

I went home the next morning and didn't go out for a few days. I still took Meth but it was alone in my bedroom and as soon as it became too risky to take it at home, I started taking it out on the street by myself. I would sit in the graveyard and talk to the angel statue when I was hallucinating, whilst I sat on a small wooden bench beside it. There were water taps around the graveyard which people used to water flowers on the graves, but I used them to wash myself in the morning before I left to go either to work or home. Sometimes I'd spend days there, falling further away from reality than ever before. I felt comforted when I spoke to the angel statue because although I knew it was made of stone and would never answer me back, it almost became a close friend because I'd seen so much death in my short life. The drugs killed everyone inside and even though we were alive in our bodies, we weren't really living at all. The Meth had killed me inside along with all my friends, who I only saw as a last resort if I had nowhere else to go. I felt more of a connection when I spoke to the dead than when I tried to connect with the living, because the dead were at peace and all I saw from the lives around me were anger and pain.

One night I'd been arguing with Mum and Dad but this time was different when they told me to 'fuck off and never come back', as I think they meant it. Mum cried as she told me she didn't know what else to do, and Dad gave me an ultimatum... I could either quit drugs and abide by their rules or it was time to leave and make my own mistakes. I wasn't ready to quit the drugs, nor had I even accepted that I had an addiction, so I left home after a final argument with Dad. Ashleigh didn't believe me when I went upstairs to pack my things. She shouted at me, 'You're not kicked out, you're just running away like you always do! I hate you! You're so selfish... You don't even care about what you've done to me because you're too busy taking Meth to care about anyone else but yourself!'

She changed her tone once we'd both cried in our separate rooms for a while, as she walked into my room and closed the door... 'Please don't go... Promise me you'll come back home in a few days?'

I told her I would go home after I'd finished the Meth I had left, as I began to want to quit. I told her I was sorry but I needed to have a few days to think things over whilst I had my final bag of drugs, which I needed to keep me sane. I couldn't deal with the guilt of being home and Dad honestly had kicked me out, so I hugged her and kissed her goodnight before walking out of the front door.

CHAPTER 27

Lost

With nowhere else to go, I made my way to the Totland Estate. Danielle had been hiding away as she'd been trying to quit Meth after the fights it had caused with her parents, but she'd left without saying goodbye and was refusing to speak to any of us. I knocked for Danielle's friend Chantelle, who I didn't particularly like, but being inside her house was much better than roaming the streets all day. We talked about Danielle, agreeing that it was good she was quitting the Meth but unfair how she had abandoned us all. There had been times when I'd been laying off the Meth for a while, but I'd still made an effort to meet up with my friends and would even sit with them whilst they were taking Meth. I suppose Danielle never had the willpower to be able to sit in a room full of drugs and not take anything, but it didn't mean she couldn't speak to us. I felt hurt because I was one of her closest friends and she'd simply blocked me out like everyone else, but I was pleased to know that I wasn't the only person she was ignoring.

Chantelle's mum had already taken in a homeless child before and it hadn't worked out, so she refused to let me stay the night. Chantelle would only let me take Meth inside her house if I gave her some, so I shared half a gram with her before making my way outside to find a quiet place to get high by myself. Mum drove round the estate a few times to look for me but since she only knew her way to Danielle's house and the park, she didn't have a clue where to look so eventually stopped searching. I slept in Totland Park that night and although Dad had kicked me out, Mum still worried about me and phoned to make sure I had a place to stay. I told her I was staying with a girl named Jess who was in the group of friends I hung out with on the Totland Estate, but I never saw her as a friend. I think she saw me as a threat to her friendship with Danielle because Danielle and I were a lot closer than the two of them were, so she frequently started arguments and we usually ended up fighting. I didn't like lying to Mum about having a safe place to stay but I didn't want her worrying about me, and I felt I could not go home after everything that had happened.

A security guard came out from the flats beside the park as their CCTV cameras had captured me sleeping on the bench, but as I wasn't causing any trouble he allowed me to stay there and offered to charge my phone inside the security office. I asked him to wake me at 6am if I was still asleep as I needed to walk to work for seven, so he returned with my phone, which was fully charged by the time I left for work. I managed to steal some food from a shop but it was not enough to suffice for the day, so I smoked what I could get off strangers until I was able to buy more Meth that night. My boss heard about my situation and asked if I wanted to leave without working that day, but I told him I needed the money and would work just as hard as everyone else. I hated working when I was sleeping rough because it was difficult to get just one full hour of sleep, so my body would usually tell me it'd had enough before I had finished work.

When the security guard noticed me sleeping in the park for the second night in a row, he told me he was sorry but I would have to find somewhere else the next night. I was desperate to find somewhere to stay and I knew I could not turn to anyone I'd previously called a friend, so I decided to phone the housing association to see if they could provide me with shelter. They told me that because I was only sixteen, the only thing they could legally do was call the police to pick me up if my parents had reported me missing, as they had no spaces in any bedsits nearby. However, no such thing was reported as my parents had kicked me out, so I was told to phone back another day to see if they had any spaces then.

I was angry at the world because no matter how hard I tried and how many people I turned to, not one of them would help me. I knew I would have to sleep rough another night, so I decided to walk to Camberley, which was a few miles away. There was a leisure centre in Camberley which had showers available for public use, so I stole a towel from a clothing store before making my way to the leisure centre. The warm water felt so good on my cold, dry skin, which had not felt the warmth of an inside building for days. People stared at me when I walked in but I didn't care. I simply pulled my hood over my face and did what I went in there for, which was to have a shower, before leaving and heading back to Farnborough.

When I arrived on the Totland Estate I was truly exhausted, so I made sure my first priority was finding somewhere dry to sleep. Apartment stairwells were dry and dark, but people would walk through them during the night and I didn't feel safe. The park and woods were both secluded at night but if it rained I'd get soaked, so I started searching for any abandoned buildings I could sneak into. I hadn't found anywhere by midnight and I was beginning to lose hope, when I noticed a small shed behind a block of flats near Totland. The shed was small with no windows, but the padlock on the door was broken and I was able to sneak inside. When I flicked my lighter so that I could see inside, I saw two large bins at the back of the shed. There was a six-by-two-foot space on the floor which I thought would be perfect for me to sleep on, before I opened up the bins in search of anything I might find useful.

One of the bins was full of black bags of general waste and it smelled horrific so I closed the lid without searching through it, but the other bin was a recycling bin which had cardboard boxes filled to the brim.

I pulled out a few flattened boxes, before laying them neatly across the floor to make a bed. I took a spare hoodie out of my bag and used it as a pillow until it became too cold not to wear it, but the bed I'd made was comfortable enough to sleep in. It was only the cold that bothered me, but at least I was dry and safe once I'd barricaded the door from the inside.

As I drifted in and out of sleep, I managed to catch at least three hours sleep before getting up when the sun came up to ensure I was out before anyone caught me. I put everything back the way it was except for the cardboard, which I stashed under a sheet of tarpaulin that I found in the bin, as I planned to return the next night. It was lonely sleeping rough because I'd go days without talking to anyone, but I usually looked such a state that I didn't want to be seen anyway. I hated being alone because it gave me too much time to think about what I'd done and how my life had ended up this way, so I resorted to stealing alcohol if I could not buy Meth. If I was drunk or high, I wouldn't have to think about anything, so my daily mission became getting hold of drugs. One drug dealer paid me to have sex with him, but I ran off with his money before he could force me into anything. I had to watch my back after that as I was gradually making more and more enemies, but I needed to do what I had to if I wanted to survive on the streets.

A few weeks went by and though I managed to stay at a friend's house once or twice, the majority of my nights were spent roaming the streets trying to keep warm. One night it was around 5am and I was sitting against a brick wall beside a road, seeking shelter from a small tree which grew from the other side of the wall and was enough to keep me out of the rain. I was drifting in and out of sleep when suddenly I heard a van screech its brakes on, pulling over right in front of me. It was too dark to see the driver properly but when a hooded figure stepped out of the van, I began to realize it was Mum. She walked closer to me until she was standing right in front of me, telling me I could go home. She then threw her arms around me, hugging me tight once I'd stood up. Her eyes looked like they'd been crying but for some reason had stopped, as she whispered, 'It's OK now, Robyn, you can come home… We love you.'

As I sat back down against the wall to assemble my things, I was mid-sentence when I looked up only to realize that she wasn't there. The van was gone, so was she… It had all been a hallucination. I started to panic… Shaking, with my head in my hands, I cried as I looked around to see if anything else was just a hallucination. I'd felt the warmth of her body against mine when she hugged me tight… I'd heard her voice and seen her face… How could this not have been real?

Not knowing what to do, I backed up against the wall as I kept my eyes open to ensure I saw everything that was going on around me. I'd see a hooded figure in the corner of my eye but when I turned around, there was no one there. I sat and cried until I was out of tears, at which point I lay lifeless on the side of the street. A stranger approached me and asked if I was OK, but I wasn't sure if he was really there either. I didn't answer him and instead simply rocked back and forth on the floor, before realizing he was phoning an ambulance. I didn't know if this was real or not but either way I had to get out of there, so I ran down an alleyway and didn't stop running until I'd found somewhere safe to sit. I didn't want to take anymore Meth but I ran into a dealer who offered me twelve grams for the price of five, so I took it without thinking and spent the entire next day snorting Meth.

By eight o'clock in the evening I was high as a kite so decided to call Danielle, wondering if my friendship really meant anything to her. She didn't answer the phone but when I texted and told her I'd been sleeping rough for weeks, she immediately texted back and said she'd meet me. She didn't know until arriving, however, that I had just over eight grams of Meth left in my possession, so she wasted no time in asking for a line. After hugging me and snorting the gram I shared with her, she told me she was so sorry about my situation and that she would have met me straight away if she'd known I was homeless. She told me that although I was way too high to be seen by her parents, she didn't care what they'd say as she'd take me home with her that night to sleep in a warm bed with clean clothes and food. However, after spending the night getting fucked out of her face with me, her selfish ways got the better of her and it wasn't long before she decided the Meth was worth more than my friendship.

As we roamed the streets late into the evening, I started to feel strange when Danielle led me into a dark alleyway before stopping suddenly. Chantelle was with us at this point and since I was too high on Meth to even know who I was, a mere shove from Danielle was enough to push me down to the ground. I was so high from Meth that I didn't even see what she was doing when she took the bag off my back and started running with it, leaving me lying on the pavement barely conscious. She shouted as she ran off with Chantelle, 'We've got to go, Robyn! We'll see you later.'

I was so high I didn't even know what she'd done until it was too late. Hours later I regained my senses, as I was sobering up when I reached behind me to grab my bag, forgetting that Danielle had taken it. I immediately searched my pockets for my Meth, but that had been in my bag. It then became clear exactly why Danielle had taken it, at which point I realized how utterly vicious she had been. As I let out a violent scream of rage in the pouring rain, I hit my head against a brick wall in anger before falling back down to the ground. I felt sick to my stomach, the exact same way I'd felt when I'd read the papers in court and realized she'd gone behind my back and completely betrayed me. I felt so stupid, so hurt... How could she do this to me? How could I be so stupid?!

I tried to call her with the tiny bit of battery I had left on my phone but she didn't answer. It was gone midnight now and I would have been stupid to go looking for her as she could be anywhere around the estate, high on my drugs. I remember the texts I sent to her as clearly as if it were yesterday, '*Please Danielle... Please tell me this isn't true...*'

I went on to say '*I trusted you! You filthy, back-stabbing bitch... I hope you choke on my fucking Meth!*'

I was getting nowhere, as I knew my drugs were long gone, along with Danielle, who had caused me a worse pain than I'd ever felt. On top of stealing my drugs, she had also stolen every other item my bag was also filled with; all the personal items I left home with, including clothes and photos, as well as a lighter I'd been given as a birthday present. I was so angry for everything she had done, from back-stabbing me twice to getting me into drugs in the first place. I had nothing left and was truly ready to end it, so I made my way to the train station where I prepared to throw myself off the bridge and onto the tracks. Before I got there I decided it would be best to call Mum and Dad, as although they'd be asleep I could at least leave them a voice message to say goodbye and apologize one last time. I thought I owed them, for everything that I'd done because of drugs. To my surprise, Mum was awake and picked up the phone. She asked in a quiet, tired-sounding voice, 'Hello? What do you want?'

I tried to explain what had happened but I was so upset that all I could do was cry and mumble, 'Danielle… She… She took everything… I'm sorry, Mum… I want to quit drugs now, please can I come home?'

She wasn't sure at first and Dad initially said 'no', because I'd chosen drugs over them, but he could tell my apology was genuine and eventually agreed to let me come home. I told them I'd be a couple of hours because I was walking from Farnborough, but they stopped me there and said they'd pick me up as it was late and raining heavily.

I waited by McDonalds, which was a halfway point between Frimley and Farnborough, and Mum and Dad arrived shortly. I couldn't speak because I was so overwhelmed with emotion, but I managed to whisper, 'Thank you… I'm so sorry…' to Mum and Dad as I sat in the car. They wanted to know where I'd been, what I'd been doing and if I truly meant it when I said I was going to quit drugs. However they could see how upset I was, so they left the talking for the next morning and said they simply wanted me to sleep that night. There was an awkward silence in the car with a heavy atmosphere, but I knew this short journey was the first step to regaining control over my life.

When I made it up to my bedroom, I felt extremely strange as I was not used to sleeping in my own bed. I also felt awkward around Mum and Dad as I wasn't sure how to act, because we'd been arguing for so long. I crept into Ashleigh's room and whispered, 'Goodnight Ash, love you,' before heading back to my room and sitting on my bed. I was truly exhausted from everything that had happened over the past few weeks but I was unable to sleep as I was too stressed about Danielle. I was consumed by feelings of anger and hatred towards her, but at the same time I couldn't help feeling the love that Mum and Dad truly showed me that night. After everything I'd put them through, they still allowed me back and gave me a chance to prove myself one last time.

I couldn't begin to explain to them how grateful I was that I had such amazing parents, but at the same time I couldn't help but feel as though the betrayal of Danielle was killing me. I had to get her back, I wanted her dead… But it was then I realized that there was an even better way to get her back, and that was to get clean. Turning my life around would be worth so much more, because I knew it would kill her inside to see me finally find happiness without drugs whilst she continued to rot in the shadows. The meaningless existence I lived whilst on the drugs was a life that she would never escape, so she was the weak one in the end because I would be strong enough to quit drugs despite her pathetic excuse for a friendship. It was time to let go, and although the thought of quitting drugs terrified me, I knew it was the right time and I had to be strong as the rest of my life depended on it.

CHAPTER 28

New Life

When I woke late afternoon, Mum and Dad called me downstairs to speak with them. I felt like I was in a meeting as none of my other brothers and sisters were allowed in the room, but I started to feel calmer once Mum started talking. She wanted to know, alongside Dad, if I meant what I'd said the night before. I was honest with them about Danielle and how I'd stayed friends with her after the arson court case, but that it was only to get hold of drugs, as I couldn't cope with my depression. I explained that I was strong enough now and ready to deal with my problems without taking drugs, so Mum and Dad both hugged me and told me I didn't have to worry anymore. Dad told me that I didn't have to fight alone anymore, as he would be there like he had always been and Mum practically said the same thing. Both of them asked why I hadn't gone to them sooner, about everything from the sexual abuse to the depression, but I didn't know how to answer them. I suppose I felt like I'd let them down or would upset them, but I'd always been the sort of person to bottle things up and fight alone even before I was depressed. There were lots of questions that wanted to be answered but I wasn't ready to talk yet and Mum and Dad understood, so they allowed me my own space. They knew I would go to them when I was ready and would open up to them, but in the meantime we simply worked on rebuilding our relationship as a family.

The first few days were the hardest. I had to tell myself that I was simply laying off the drugs, just to have the comfort of knowing I could take Meth again someday. Deep down I never wanted to go back to drugs and knew I would never take Meth again, but it helped me get through the first few days, which were horrific, as I couldn't stand being sober. I remember walking through the house, not knowing what to do with myself. If I stayed in my bedroom I would cry because any time I closed my eyes, Danielle would be there laughing at me. However I was too depressed to be around anyone, so I found it hard not to think about drugs. After a few days of sobering up, I played my piano for the first time in almost a year. I had forgotten how much joy I got out of playing it and to think, at my lowest point I'd thought about selling it to buy drugs. I'd only played piano once since I'd been hooked on drugs and that was at a church I had gone to when I was sleeping rough. I remembered the look of amazement on the priest's face as he had only asked if I wanted to come in to get out of the rain.

The Meth stopped me being able to enjoy everything that made me who I was. Song writing, friendship, spending time with my sister… The Meth had taken all of that away and it was then that I finally realized just how much I wanted to quit. The gold chain around my neck, which I'd been given for my eleventh birthday and had only taken off if I was forced to whilst under arrest, was nearly sold to buy drugs too. I was so glad that I still had all the things that were precious to me and even though Danielle had taken away my pride, she'd given me my freedom, because if it wasn't for her actions that night, I would never have quit Meth.

As the weeks went by I became closer to my family and was eventually allowed contact with my beautiful niece and nephew. Callie told me how proud she was that I'd quit drugs, and that her children had missed me whilst I'd been away from them. I quit my job and went back to school, studying for basic maths and English qualifications. My family felt happy because they were regaining small pieces of me each day, after the drugs had taken so much of me away. I started to feel happier at home as there were no more arguments about the drugs, but I was still deeply depressed and had to focus my mind on something to take me away from it. Without drugs I barely knew who I was, because I'd been taking them since I was eleven years old, but I now had to deal with the scars they'd left behind. I think the reason I chose the drugs was because it was a twenty-four-hour commitment, which took me away from depression as I had no time left to think about anything else. That made me wonder what else I could do to take me away from my depression for twenty-four hours a day, so I decided to get serious about losing weight.

I'd always suffered with body distortion even as a child, probably from all the weight I had to lose for Judo. I knew I had the potential to get down to the weight I'd always wanted to be, which was 35kg (77lb). I'd never been able to reach that weight when I did Judo all those years ago, so no matter how ridiculous it sounded, that was my ultimate goal from then on. I started working out for six hours every day, whilst trying not to eat at all. The weight dropped off faster than lightning and through searching the internet, I came across something called 'Thinspo'. There was an entire secret online community where girls starved themselves to be thin, referring to themselves as 'Ana' or 'Mia' depending on whether they were anorexic or bulimic. I wasn't looking for an eating disorder, but I must have already had one since half the reason I stayed on drugs for so long was because it made me lose weight. I'd even given up my family to be thin by choosing drugs over them, so I didn't care if these websites would cause something that was already there inside my head.

I typed in 'Thinspo' on Facebook and sure enough, there was a page with over a thousand members. Some of the names were made up with the word 'Ana' beside them, so I searched through their profiles without realizing what I'd let myself in for. I had entered a secret part of Facebook which didn't openly admit to promoting eating disorders, but girls who seemed to have them would meet up online and share experiences and tips for losing weight. Most of the girls starting out with their weight loss were like me, a healthy weight, whilst the people who'd been connected to the online community for some time were extremely underweight. I saw the bones in their photos, which showed nothing but pure elegance and beauty. I wanted to look like them, so I created an 'Ana' account and started adding random people from the Thinspo page.

After just five minutes I'd already made some friends, so I started talking to them about their weight-loss goals and progress. One of the girls mentioned a diet called 'ABC', which stood for 'Anorexic Boot Camp'. I immediately researched this diet and started it there and then, vowing never to quit until I reached my goal weight. Some girls on the online community educated me about BMI, saying that a healthy BMI was between eighteen and twenty-five. I saw a photo of a girl whose BMI was just under thirteen and she looked skeletal, so I calculated what my BMI would be at my goal weight of 77lb. My goal weight would put me at a BMI of just eleven point four, but the girl I spoke to reassured me that anorexics don't usually die unless their BMI goes below nine. That would mean I could look flawlessly skinny, without risking death. All I had to do now was starve until I got there.

Since Mum had been losing weight for years after she'd had a gastric band, there were scales downstairs which mum stored in a kitchen cupboard. I took them out and weighed myself, disgusted at what I saw. Standing in shorts and a strap top, I weighed in at almost 180lb. I knew I'd been heavier than this before as I'd weighed almost 200lb when I'd spent months inside drinking whilst on tag, but I knew I had to start somewhere. When I told my friends on my Ana Facebook account about my weight, they comforted me and told me I just needed to try the ABC diet and repeat it until I was down to a reasonable weight. The diet consisted of fifty days' calorie restriction, each day ranging from zero to five hundred calories, with one eight-hundred-calorie day. The idea behind it was that the eight-hundred-calorie day would spike your metabolism, so that you didn't go into starvation mode from eating so few calories.

After just four weeks I'd already lost over thirty pounds, so it wasn't long before Mum and Dad started asking questions. They would sit with me at dinner to make sure I ate but since I fasted for the rest of the day, it hardly made a difference. Sometimes I wouldn't eat for three days in a row, whilst running on a treadmill and lifting weights every day. I started taking diet pills that I bought off the internet to control my hunger, which would hurt so much that I tried to make sure the muscle pain from training hurt more than the hunger so that maybe I wouldn't feel it. I joined a local gym and would work out for three hours every day, after walking to and from the youth club which was where I studied for my maths and English qualifications. The tutors and youth workers would ask about my weight, saying that if I lost any more there'd be nothing left, but I took it as motivation and continued to starve myself as much as I could. Anorexia was great because it took up all my time and energy, which meant I rarely had time to think about anything else, but in the end it started to make my depression even worse.

I would starve for days and then binge, unable to control my hunger, which would make me feel absolutely awful after eating. I'd feel like my whole life was worthless if I ate and it felt like I walked around with the weight of the entire world on my shoulders. I would walk into the youth club in tears if I'd binged the night before, as I'd feel so depressed I would think about everything that had happened with the drugs as well as hating my body. I didn't tell many people at the youth club about the drugs but they knew I'd been through something, as some days I'd simply sit with my head in my hands, crying. Mum would kick off if I weighed myself downstairs as she could see the weight dropping off me, so refused to let me weigh myself, but I'd simply set an alarm for 6am so I could sneak downstairs and weigh in before she woke up. My YOT worker noticed a change in me but didn't know how to help me as I didn't get along with her very well, but my drugs worker who I got on well with had ended my course of treatment because I was now clean from drugs.

I denied there was a problem as I knew I was still fat and needed to lose more weight, but Mum and Dad weren't used to seeing me looking skinny so they both tried to deter me from losing any more. They would tell me I looked gaunt and too thin, whilst Ashleigh would say I didn't suit that weight and looked better when I was fat. I later found out that she thought I looked great at that weight and had only told me those things because she was jealous, which made me extremely angry after I'd binged for months and regained all the weight I'd lost because of what she'd said. I was so depressed from gaining the weight back that by the time I hit 170lb I was suicidal, but Ashleigh must have been happy as I was once again the fat twin.

The friends I'd made on my Ana Facebook account stuck by me and told me everything would be OK, that I was just having a relapse of bulimia and would soon find the strength to win back Ana. I met one particular friend on there who told me it didn't matter how much I weighed. He was one of the only guys online compared to the thousands of Ana girls like myself, so I took a shine to him immediately as I'd forgotten that this disease could also affect men. When we first started talking, I introduced myself and told him my stats. I messaged to him, *'I am 5ft 9inches tall and I weigh 170lb. My lowest is 145 and my goal is 77. What about you?'*

He stopped me there and told me that he wasn't 'Ana' and was simply searching for friendship, so I continued to talk to him more often as he began to make my depression more bearable. He told me I was pretty and didn't need to look like a skeleton to feel good about myself, so although I continued fighting against my reflection, I found hope in his friendship as he gave me a reason to stay strong. Whenever I was upset I would go straight to him and if he wasn't online, neither was I. We eventually shared skype details and arranged our first video chat, which was nerve-racking but made me feel excited to finally see who I'd been talking to. I'd shared with him my entire life story by this point, because I knew that if he was mean or we didn't get along then I could simply block him and wouldn't have to speak him again. However, no matter how insane I must have seemed, he stayed by my side after listening to my story.

He had originally added me as a friend because my account said that I was sixty years old and he thought it would be interesting to speak to someone with so much life experience, but he soon realized I was only a teenager. He would usually avoid the subject if I asked how old he was, but I didn't care if he was a few years older than me as our friendship was based on more than that. I felt I could truly relate to him with every outlook he had on life and just like me, he didn't bother to keep many friends. I hadn't let myself become friends with anyone except people within the Ana community on Facebook, because I knew I would never trust anyone again after all that had happened with Danielle. I thought, however, that this friendship could go somewhere, so I fought against my trust issues and spent as much time with Chris as I could... That was his name.

Although I was extremely depressed after regaining the weight I'd tried so hard to lose, Chris made everything seem better. He comforted me when I was upset and although he couldn't be there for me in person, I spent more time with him than I did with anyone else in my life. We talked about meeting up one day and although he had a girlfriend, he told me he loved me every single day. I loved him too and although I knew we couldn't be together, it felt reassuring to know that someone out there thought the world of me.

Nan sadly passed away in February of the next year but she died peacefully in her sleep and I felt proud to know that I'd been able to turn my life around whilst she was still alive. Dad felt at peace to know that she'd seen me grow into the person he loved, which was far more than any parent could have ever wished for.

CHAPTER 29

Hope

I was seventeen years old now and although Chris helped me get through a lot, he couldn't stop me having nightmares. Any time I closed my eyes to sleep I would see Danielle and others from the Totland Estate, laughing at me whilst stealing my things and beating me to a pulp. I had nightmares about Dad committing suicide because he couldn't handle the depression and it was all my fault. I dreamt about staying clean, only to run into dealers who forced me to take Meth. When I woke up I would be angry and upset, because it felt good to be high in my dream but I also felt guilty for wanting it. I felt angry towards Danielle and every time I dreamt about her, all the feelings would come straight back to me and it was as if it was happening all over again. I knew I had to do something about it but I didn't know what, so I wrote a hit list in the hope that it would help me to forget. I could hide it away in my bedroom and it wouldn't matter if I forgot about the pain Danielle had caused, because it was on paper, which meant it no longer needed to build up inside my head as I could come back to it later.

Drew and James were on the hit list below Danielle's name, along with Kennedy and some bullies I remembered from school. I folded the piece of paper up and hid it inside my top drawer, hoping to feel released from all thoughts of their actions. It took time but it eventually worked and my nightmares became fewer and further in between. Almost a year went by and I kept hold of the hit list I'd created, intending to burn it when I was truly ready to let go of all the pain.

I continued to build my friendship with Chris and he became the closest thing I'd ever had to a boyfriend. He taught me to accept what had happened and that I can't change the past, but that the future is a great opportunity to be happy. He taught me to love and although I never truly trusted anyone again after everything that had happened, he stuck by me and I eventually learnt to let people in. I started working as a lifeguard at the leisure centre I'd showered at whilst I'd been homeless, but thankfully no one recognized me as I looked completely different now. Back then my hair had been jet black and I was covered in cuts and bruises with huge black circles under my tired-looking eyes. Now I had blonde hair and looked confident in myself… I'd even go so far as to say I appeared happy.

Ashleigh found her first love in a girl named Laura who started college in September with her. Laura originally recognized Ashleigh because she looked like me and I had met this girl previously at the youth centre. They immediately became friends and eventually fell in love with each other which made me feel happy to know that Ashleigh had finally found herself. Ash had fought through years of abuse from bullies and Drew and James, who she originally thought were the only reason for her turning gay. She knew from meeting Laura however, that a girlfriend was all she had ever wanted and it made me happy to know that she could finally be free from her past and feel happy. Laura had a genetic condition known as Ehlers Danlos Syndrome, which caused her many complications including multiple organ failure, but she never let it get in the way of reaching her dreams and I think she helped Ashleigh reach hers.

I met another friend though my Ana account on Facebook and I helped her fight her demons as much as I could, because she was going through a hard time fighting a drug addiction, which was something I knew about all too well. We video-chatted a few times and we'd drink together, whilst I helped her open up to me about all her problems. She'd been through some horrific things and I'd always be there for her, but one night when she asked me to skype, I couldn't be bothered. I was tired so went to bed, not realizing that she would die that night. She overdosed on drugs and I knew for a fact that if I'd been there and skyped her when she asked, she would never have overdosed because she would have been with me. I never got over the guilt of losing her because I felt at fault for her death, which was caused by nothing other than depression and loneliness. She was twenty-two years old, just a few years older than me, which I suppose hit home because I had come close to her situation many times before. I made a small memorial for her when the first year passed after she died, using candles and a small angel statue I bought to remember her by. I wrote a letter to her saying how much I missed her, as well as apologizing for not being able to save her. I burnt the letter to send it to her and the angel statue now lives in my bedroom.

I only had one real falling out with Chris and that was because I met a boy at work when I got a job as a lifeguard at a leisure centre, but I assumed Chris would understand as he had a girlfriend. I was in love with Chris but knew we could never be together, so I went for the first man who took any interest in me. I knew Chris loved me, but I needed someone who could be with me in person, so started dating a man from work. He was a cleaner from Portugal and was very rude to everyone so not many people liked him, but he was nice to me and I jumped at the chance of having a boyfriend who could physically be there for me. He started off nice but I soon saw what everyone else saw in him and worse, which was that he was a controlling schizophrenic. Because he had grown up in a secluded neighbourhood in Portugal, he had the belief that women were there to do as the men told them. He would emotionally abuse me by holding me against my will and keeping me from talking to any of my friends, including Ashleigh and Chris.

It wasn't long before he pressured me into sex and then refused to stop when I said 'no', but I didn't think it was rape because I hadn't said 'no' until we were almost doing it. I ran straight to the bathroom and cried once it was over, but didn't break up with him because it was the only thing I'd ever known with boys. He also made me so depressed that I thought I couldn't turn to anyone else, so I stayed with him because I thought I loved him. He used me for money and sex which he'd pressure me into, but the worst thing about all of it was that he stopped me speaking to Chris. I was working eighteen-hour shifts at the time as I wanted to save up enough money to pay for Mum to have the skin surgery she'd dreamed of after losing all the weight, but my boyfriend had no regard for how sleep-deprived I was and he would refuse to let me sleep at all. I became a full-blown bulimic as the weeks went by and as I thought I'd lost Chris, I had nothing left to live for. My new boyfriend's flatmates were drug dealers so I started taking cocaine and ketamine, which I would only do occasionally but the fact that I was doing it brought me to tears.

I was starving myself and vomiting everything I ate, which would leave me purging up to six times every day. He'd hit me when we argued and I'd hit him back but I always came out with more bruises, so I eventually learnt to accept the fact that this was how my life would continue. I also let my depression get the better of me and stayed with him thinking that he wasn't the problem, since any time I argued with him I would feel guilty, as though it was solely my fault. Everyone at work saw what was going on and tried to help me, but I felt guilty breaking up with him because I still cared about him. I eventually found the courage to end our relationship, and though it had only been three months long, I felt like I was back to square one with turning my life around. He really affected me and it was only when I started speaking to Chris again that I realized my boyfriend had been solely in the wrong for the entire time. Chris eventually forgave me for not speaking to him for almost three months and although I was angry with him for reacting so badly to the fact that I had a boyfriend, it showed me just how much he loved me and made me think that he really wanted me.

I had lost over 30lb from being bulimic but I looked and felt dreadful. I had caused myself an electrolyte imbalance from purging that resulted in me losing all movement in my right foot. However, I eventually became healthier and regained all movement as I filled my body with nutrients so although I was depressed about my weight, I became happier because I felt healthy. After just a few days of being free from my abusive ex, I stopped feeling so depressed and was on the road to recovery. He was later sacked from work and left the country, which meant I never had to see him again, which came as a huge relief because he had caused me so much pain. I researched electrolytes and nutrition, which helped me gain muscle when I started weight training, something that also helped my depression significantly. Lifting weights made me feel like I had a purpose, because the endorphins it released in my brain helped me to overcome my depression. I also felt a buzz from exercising, a rush I hadn't felt since I'd been at Judo all those years ago.

After a year of working hard at my new job, I eventually saved up enough money to fly out to America and meet Chris in person. I had originally wanted to meet him on my eighteenth birthday as his birthday was the day after mine, but my parents were taking a trip to a different state in November and wanted to at least be in the same country when I met Chris. They had spoken to him on video chat and trusted him, but just as a precaution they wanted to be able to come and get me if I got into any trouble. I was scared of flying alone and nervous about meeting Chris for the first time but when he threw his arms around me at the airport, I knew our friendship would last forever. I cried as I was overwhelmed with emotion, in disbelief that I was actually in America and finally in his arms. We spent the week partying and enjoying the beach, spending time together which we had longed for since meeting online more than two years ago. Although we never became anything more than friends, his girlfriend got on with me and I enjoyed every minute I spent out in America.

I cried on the plane home and promised I'd return next year. As soon as I arrived home we video-chatted on skype, which was heart breaking because I missed Chris so much. Meeting him in person was the greatest thing that had ever happened to me, because it felt like finally I'd found a light at the end of the dark tunnel I'd been stuck inside for my entire life. I stayed true to my word and went to see him the next year, after regaining control over my life and recovering from most of my demons. I spent over £2,000 on dentist bills, repairing the damage bulimia had done to my teeth, and although I came close many times, I never purged again. I still self-harmed when I was upset but I never cut myself as badly as I had before. I'd like to say that I never took drugs again but that would be a lie, although I never returned to the Totland Estate, which meant my drug addiction was never as bad as before.

I burnt the hit list I'd written years ago and I was finally free to let go of all the pain I'd held onto for so long, including the sexual abuse, which found its own justice. Drew ended up in prison for something unrelated to what he'd done to Ashleigh and me, but it was still comforting to know that he'd finally pay for what he'd done. Although James was never caught, he stayed away from us and on the rare occasion we bumped into each other, he would turn and walk the other way. On my nineteenth birthday I had been out celebrating with friends from work, who defended me and Ashleigh when he tried to start a fight. I told them what he'd done and word had already spread to all his friends, who stopped speaking to him once they knew the truth.

I never made many more friends as I still have trust issues that stop me letting people get too close, but I got back in touch with Lauren, who I used to hang out with on the Ansel Estate before the drugs took over. She had given birth to a beautiful little boy who eventually became my Godson, a title which I will cherish for the rest of my life. I didn't stay in touch with any other friends who I'd lost because of drugs, but Mr French had stuck by my side since we'd first met at Tomlinscote and alongside Chris, who I truly believe is my soul mate, I realized that the few close friends I had meant more than any amount of fake friends.

My only downfall in my friendship with Chris was wanting more, because I realized that I was completely in love with him and couldn't bear the thought of not being by his side for the rest of my life. When I told him how I felt, he said he was completely in love with me too, but there were simply too many obstacles in the way of us being together. I knew it would be hard, due to the distance and his circumstances regarding his girlfriend, but I was prepared to do anything to be with him. I begged him for weeks, offering option upon option of how we could make it work, but he insisted I stayed in England and moved on. It broke my heart because not only was he the first man I truly loved, but I honestly believed that we were meant for each other. I was not angry at him and I never will be, but the sadness of the whole situation caused me to relapse like never before. I cried so much in the first weeks that I could barely sleep, and when I did, I would wake up in tears after dreaming about him. Mum saw me crying every day and I explained the entire situation to her, but nothing she could say would take the pain away.

I started starving, self-harming and using drugs again, because I thought, why does it matter? Since the only reason I stayed strong enough to fight my demons was because of Chris, but he didn't want me now. I took five grams of MDMA which really messed me up, because it gave me an even bigger serotonin imbalance than I already had, which meant my depression was worse than ever. I'd taken cocaine on a few occasions and it took the pain away for a moment, but when I hit the comedowns I'd always feel worse. A few days before my twentieth birthday, I threw a house party where I took another two grams of MDMA, as well as a gram of cocaine, half an ounce of cannabis and loads of alcohol. Mum was on holiday but dad was home and saw me around 4am, after I accidently woke him up whilst wandering the house, hallucinating. He was so upset when he saw that I'd been snorting drugs again and when I saw the tears roll down his cheeks, I felt the guilt I hadn't felt since my meth addiction. I wanted to cut my wrists just to focus on a different pain but I knew that would upset him even more, so instead I simply went upstairs and lay in my bed until I sobered up.

When I did eventually sober up, my entire body hurt so much that I couldn't even leave my bed for two days, and I was still hallucinating from the MDMA which made it impossible for me to think clearly. I didn't eat for days and I kept fainting any time I stood up for almost a week, but I found the strength to try and make myself better. Dad didn't tell mum about the drugs until she got home from her holiday but I assured both of them that it only happened because I was upset about Chris and that it was the last time I would take drugs. Mum and dad both knew how much I loved Chris and they understood why I took the drugs, although I know it scares them because they worry I'd fall back into the life I lived before, which revolved around nothing except darkness and drugs.

Chris was upset when I told him about my birthday party because I also told him about my entire drug relapse, which dated back months, and it upset him to realize he had not noticed I'd been using right under his nose. He felt bad because he thought it was his fault and although he was the reason I was upset which lead me to taking drugs, it was not his fault because it was my choice to do so. He has since stuck by my side and is helping me to stay away from drugs by pushing me to talk to him when I feel depressed, rather than bottling things up and taking all my anger out on myself. I know I shouldn't take drugs again but the reality of being without them scares me, because it is the only escape I have ever known since I was eleven years old.

The war goes on as I am once again trying to stay clean and am now taking anti-depressants for my depression, but it seems I'm in a hole so deep that I can't find my way out right now. Despite this, I am fighting harder than ever for my happiness because I know I am strong enough and one day I will see a light. Chris let me down when he said he couldn't be with me but he is still my best friend and I will always love him, always. He has apologized for the situation and tries everything to make it better, but until I learn to stop loving him, I will always feel this way.

Ashleigh went on to study nursing whilst I studied fitness, but only as a back-up career since I have recently discovered my love of writing. Ashleigh and I continue to write music and I hope that someday, I will find the confidence to share it with the world. I continue to suffer with body dysmorphia but I try not to let it get the better of me, as I continue to fight for my happiness. I try to look forward to a positive future and although my past makes me who I am, it does not define me and I will never let it break me. I am thankful for everything I have today and if it was not for my family and Chris, I would never have made it this far. Depression is such a lonely illness, so to all those out there suffering, my message is this…

Life is short, so don't waste it and don't be afraid to be someone. We all make mistakes and we all fall down, that's what makes us human. Life is tough but we are strong, that's why we are here. So stand up for your rights and if someone is hurting you, ask for help! The storm may be fierce but it can't last forever, so keep fighting for your happiness because one day, you will see that you were never really worthless....